PSYCHOLOGICAL PRACTICES WITH THE PHYSICALLY DISABLED

Psychological Practices with the Physically Disabled

EDITED BY

JAMES F. GARRETT AND EDNA S. LEVINE

NEW YORK AND LONDON

COLUMBIA UNIVERSITY PRESS

First printing 1962
Second printing 1965

Library of Congress Catalog Card Number: 62-9708

Manufactured in the United States of America

FOREWORD

ONE of the most important social developments during the last two decades has been the increased public and professional recognition given to rehabilitation of the physically handicapped.

Our public program of vocational rehabilitation started in 1920. It had its genesis in World War I when rehabilitation services were established for disabled World War I veterans. During the period 1920 to 1945, however, the program was extremely limited in scope with only about 250,000 disabled persons being rehabilitated into employment.

Services were limited to vocational training "around the disability" with no provision for medical rehabilitation to eliminate or alleviate the disability. Until 1943 it was a program in which funds for support were as meagre as the program concept.

Preliminary estimates for the fiscal year ended June 30, 1961, are that our public program for the sixth consecutive year established a new record with about 92,500 disabled men and women rehabilitated into employment and another 197,000 receiving services at the year's end.

The growth of rehabilitation, however, cannot be measured solely by the number of persons served. Equally important is the scope and quality of the services which they receive.

One of the major developments in rehabilitation during World War II and the postwar period has been the utilization of the team approach in which the various disciplines—medicine, psychology, sociology, and economics—are brought together through the medium of a group of professionally trained persons who focus their skills and abilities on the individual as a whole in terms of his total environment and his total problems.

There is probably no better example of Gestaltism than in the rehabilitation team, for the full force of the contributions of each of the disciplines on the rehabilitation team can be brought to bear only in their relationships to each other.

In accordance with these newer concepts of "total" care of the patient, medicine has been turning more and more, particularly in rehabilitation, to the psychologist for an assessment of emotional abilities, disabilities, and potentialities of the disabled individual and for assistance in developing programs of activity in which such psychological problems will be solved. It is true that the importance of psychosocial services and the psychologist as an integral part of the rehabilitation team is still new and that many psychologists' tools must be redesigned and reevaluated in terms of these new uses.

Similarly, our techniques of integrating the contributions of the psychologist into the total rehabilitation team effort need study and refinement. The success that has been achieved thus far, however, with currently available psychological tools and relatively crude techniques of integration are indicative of the far greater results that will come in the future with continued research and experience.

Basic to this new development of the "team" concept of rehabilitation is our changing concept of disability. As the Task Force on the Handicapped of the Office of Defense Mobilization pointed out in its extremely significant report in early 1952, "When physical standards were drawn up during the first and second decades of this century, they were influenced by the 'anatomical' concept of medicine which was then in sway. Competence was measured in terms of anatomical perfection. A man was either fit or unfit for work, depending on whether or not he was anatomically whole. It was all or none. A man could do the whole job or none of it. He was disabled for all work if he was disabled for part of it."

With the development of the physiological or functional concept of medicine and the specialization and subdivision of jobs into their components, the report states, the "perfect anatomical specimen" concept of man is no longer valid in determining suitability for employment.

An excellent example of this newer concept is found in the preliminary report of a study being undertaken at the Institute of Physical Medicine and Rehabilitation, New York University Medical Center, with the aid of a grant from the Office of Vocational Rehabilitation of the United States Department of Health, Education, and Welfare. In this survey of former patients with quadraplegia, it was found that 33.6 percent were working in competitive employment or were self-employed and another 34.9 percent were working in home-bound, part-time or live-in jobs.

With the "anatomical" concept of medicine gradually being replaced by this newer "functional" concept, the role of psychology in the rehabilitation process becomes increasingly important. The more experience we have the more we recognize that it is frequently not the physical disability per se that limits the disabled person functionally but rather his psychological reaction to his disability.

There is little doubt that psychology's role in rehabilitation has grown in all dimensions within the last twenty years and, as new knowledge becomes available through research, these dimensions will continue to increase and the contributions of psychology to rehabilitation will increase in direct ratio.

It is fitting that the editors of this publication should have assigned themselves this important task, for both have long been recognized as two of the leaders in psychology who have been singularly important contributors to the new dimensions which psychology has achieved in rehabilitation and in its contribution to the rehabilitation process.

HOWARD A. RUSK, M.D.

Institute of Physical Medicine and Rehabilitation
New York University Medical Center
August, 1961

PREFACE

MANY YEARS AGO, Sir William Osler stated that tuberculosis was a social problem with medical aspects. In a very recent survey, Guttman came to the same conclusion concerning paraplegia. Yet, although recognition of the social aspects of physical disability is a matter of record, comparatively little attention has been paid the scientific study of the role of personal adjustment in the total life situation of the physically disabled. That efforts are only now being directed along this line is evidenced by the growing body of literature on the subject.

The present volume represents one such effort. It is based on the psychological premise that, in order to understand the organization of behavior, it is necessary to understand the practical reality as well as distinctive features of the influences to which an individual is exposed through life. Severe physical disability is here thought of as giving rise to a complex ramification of life influences, and, to understand the life situation of the physically disabled, it is essential that the nature and significance of these special influences be understood. Thus, a major aim of this book is to clarify some of the important relationships between physical deficit and personal adjustment. Psychologists in particular are reminded that man neither lives nor develops in a vacuum, and that "the proper subject of psychological examining is . . . a-person-as-a-whole-interacting-with-the-environment-through-time-and-space."[1] The person-environment constellation is the basic frame of reference throughout this volume.

[1] F. C. Thorne, *Principles of Psychological Examining* (Brandon, Vt., Journal of Clinical Psychology, 1955), p. 42.

In this frame, no attempt has been made to solve such issues as the mind-body controversy, e.g., does the psyche predispose the soma to type of disease or disability, or does soma affect the psyche? Emphasis is placed rather on common problems distinctive to the respective disabilities discussed, and on the variety of personal reactions to these problems. One conclusion that becomes self-evident from a study of the various chapters is that nowhere is there a pat one-to-one relation between disease entity and type of personal adjustment, e.g., the "cardiac personality," the "typical hemiplegic response," or the "organic adjustment pattern." It is also interesting to note the body of common problems and reactions that run through all the disabilities. And, finally, a point of great significance that emerges is the degree to which successful rehabilitation can be hampered by such factors of practical reality as sociocultural milieu and attitudes, and family solidarity and support.

As context for understanding the severely disabled individual, the authors have sketched some of the special "disability" influences and problems in terms of (1) medical-physical aspects; (2) psychological implications both in regard to the individual as well as to family, community, and sociocultural and vocational milieu; (3) special considerations in psychological appraisal, management, and in rehabilitation; and (4) suggestions for research as well as for improvement in psychological management and rehabilitation. As will be evident, this scheme of presentation has not been followed slavishly—nor could it be. Each chapter reflects the individuality of its distinguished author as well as of the disability under consideration.

Obviously in a volume of this type many more disability groups or groupings could have been included. However, considerations of space made selection necessary, and the disabilities discussed here were roughly chosen on the basis of (1) incidence in the population; (2) difficulty in psychological appraisal; (3) difficulty in vocational rehabilitation; and/or (4) available related literature on the subject of psychological practice. An effort has also been made to present new areas of investigation that have not appeared in collected form previously; and to update "older" areas where significant new work is being accomplished. It is hoped that this blending will stimulate increased interest among rehabilitation workers of all disciplines—psychologists, social workers, physicians, counselors, and therapists of all types—in the personal adjustment of the disabled they serve.

February, 1962

JAMES F. GARRETT
EDNA S. LEVINE

CONTENTS

Foreword, *by Howard A. Rusk*	v
Preface	ix
Amputation, *by Sidney Fishman*	1
Arthritis and Rheumatism, *by Morton A. Seidenfeld*	51
Cardiovascular Disability, *by Frederick A. Whitehouse*	85
Hemiplegia, *by Leonard Diller*	125
Cerebral Palsy, *by Robert M. Allen*	159
The Language Disorders, *by Joseph M. Wepman*	197
Cancer, *by Beatrix Cobb*	231
Facial Disfigurement, *by Richard Madan*	261
Auditory Disability, *by Edna S. Levine*	279
Visual Disability, *by Nathaniel J. Raskin*	341
Deaf-Blindness, *by Jacob Rothschild*	376
Severe Chronic Illness, *by Franklin C. Shontz*	410
Abbreviations Used in References	447
Index	451

PSYCHOLOGICAL PRACTICES

WITH THE

PHYSICALLY DISABLED

AMPUTATION

by SIDNEY FISHMAN

AMPUTATION is a disability that may affect child, adult, or aging individual, occurring, as it does, at any time during the life span. The youngest chronological occurrence is in the infant born a congenital amputee, with an incomplete extremity or extremities; the oldest in the very elderly individual whose limb is amputated in an effort to add additional months or years to his life. The factors that influence the care and treatment of a child born with a missing limb are considerably different from those that affect the management of an adult with an amputation suffered as the result of an automobile accident or of an elderly man who has had an amputation in his later years because of diabetes. The problems of amputation depend to a considerable degree on the individual's chronological age and are specifically related to the psychological and physical attributes characteristic of that age group (Fishman, 1958, b).

As a prerequisite to an understanding of the psychological aspects of amputation, an appreciation of the physical problems faced by amputees is necessary. Therefore, a brief review of pertinent etiological and medical factors is indicated.

ETIOLOGY AND INCIDENCE. A consideration of the incidence and etiology of amputations is perhaps best approached

Sidney Fishman, Ph.D., is Senior Research Scientist serving as director of Prosthetics-Orthotics Research and Education at the New York University College of Engineering and Post-Graduate Medical School, and also Adjunct Professor of Psychology at Fairleigh-Dickinson University, Rutherford, New Jersey.

in terms of three broad age groups: (*a*) the juvenile group (birth to adolescence); (*b*) the adult group (adolescence to fifty-five years); (*c*) the geriatric group (age fifty-six upward). Of course, these age categories are quite arbitrary since amputee problems are not completely separated on the basis of the groupings indicated. The fluctuating relationship among a person's physiological development, psychological level, and chronological age is always a complicating factor. One eight-year-old may be comparable in physical and psychological maturity to another twelve-year-old. One person may be as old at the age of sixty as another is at seventy. Consequently these age categories are usable only as guides.

A graphic indication of the increase of the numbers of amputees with age is presented in Figure 1. Contributing to these sta-

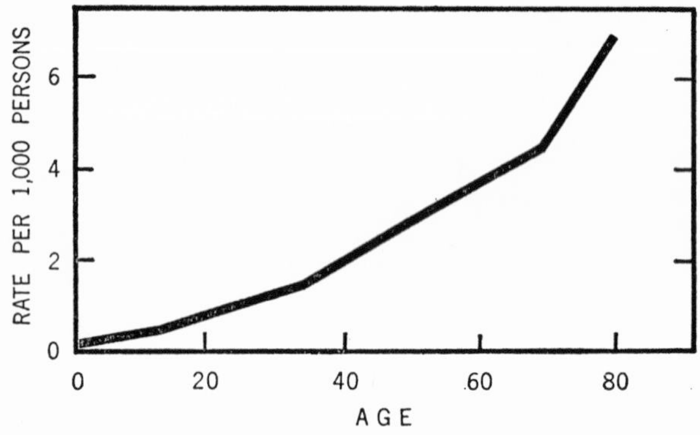

FIGURE 1. *Incidence of Major Amputations*

tistics are the three major types of amputation: (*a*) congenital —involving no surgery except occasionally when stump revisions are indicated; (*b*) traumatic—resulting from injuries and accidents and usually requiring surgical revisions of the stump; and (*c*) elective—involving surgical removal to ameliorate conditions due to disease.

It is interesting to note from Table 1 that the large incidence of upper extremity amputations occurs among younger people

TABLE 1. *Etiology and Incidence of Major Amputations*

Category	*Estimated * Incidence*	*Etiology*
Juvenile (Birth to 16 years)	25,000 About equal numbers of males and females Bilateral and multiple amputees together make up about 15 percent of the group while the remaining 85 percent are unilateral. More than twice as many upper extremity as lower extremity amputees	In child amputees up to 4 or 5 years of age practically all are congenital of unknown cause. From ages 6 to 16, approximately 75 percent of the amputees are congenital. This latter age group begins to be affected by injuries and there are also a very few surgical removals due to disease.
Adult (17 to 55 years)	175,000 Approximately 3 times as many male as female amputees Bilateral and multiple amputees are less than 5 percent of the entire group Approximately 3½ times as many lower extremity as upper extremity amputees	The large majority (75 percent) of amputations in this age group are due to injuries (accidents, war, etc.) A significant number are also due to diseases, particularly cancer.
Geriatric (Age 56 upward)	200,000 No breakdown available	Practically all new amputations in this age category are due to disease (diabetes and cardiovascular conditions). Large numbers of patients whose limbs were amputated during their younger years also require treatment.
All ages	400,000	

* Estimates based on a liberal extrapolation of data from the United States Public Health Survey, the Office of Vocational Rehabilitation, the Veterans Administration, and selected state crippled children's commissions.

and that, as age increases, the incidence of lower extremity amputations becomes predominant. This trend is due to the fact that congenital and traumatic amputations which affect younger people are frequently of the upper extremity, whereas the elective amputations of the lower extremity associated with disease are far more common in the older age groups.

Among the physical attributes affecting the treatment and functional rehabilitation potential of an amputee, the "site of amputation" is fundamental. This "site" refers to the specific location of the amputation on the extremity(-ies) that determines the effective length, strength, and mobility of the stump. For example, the possibilities of ambulation through the use of a prosthetic appliance are considerably greater for an individual who has lost a limb well below the knee as compared to another individual who has lost a leg just below the hip. Consequently, amputations are frequently categorized in relation to the amount of physical loss which is sustained. As a rule, it is quite difficult to communicate with professional rehabilitation workers concerning amputees without some understanding of and reference to these amputation types. Figure 2 presents the more usual sites of upper and lower extremity amputations (Berger, 1958).

All of the upper extremity amputation types occurring between the wrist disarticulation and elbow disarticulation are referred to as below-elbow amputations since they have similar functional characteristics. All of the amputation types between the elbow disarticulation and shoulder disarticulation are referred to as above-elbow amputations. For the lower extremity amputee, all of the individuals with amputations between the Syme's and knee disarticulation sites are known collectively as below-knee amputees, while all those with amputations between the knee disarticulation and the hip disarticulation sites are referred to as above-knee amputees. Consequently, amputees are commonly alluded to in the following terms:

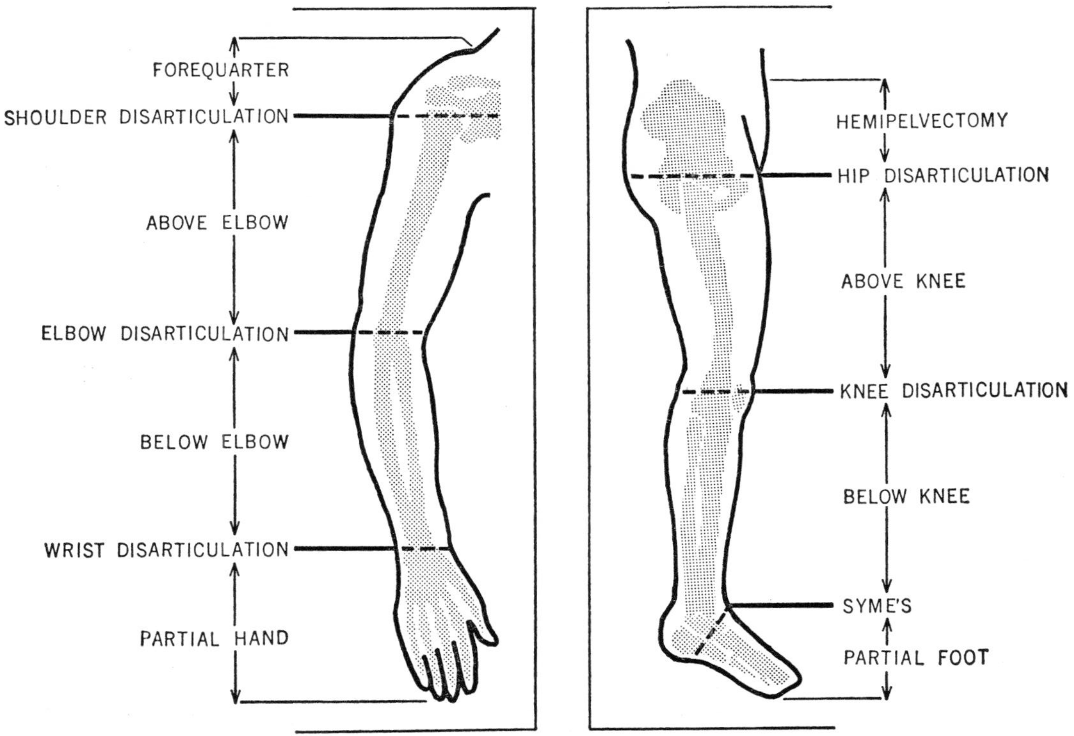

FIGURE 2. *Left: Upper Extremity Amputations; Right: Lower Extremity Amputations*

Upper Extremity	*Lower Extremity*
Partial Hand	Partial Foot
Wrist Disarticulation	Syme's
Below-Elbow	Below-Knee
Elbow Disarticulation	Knee Disarticulation
Above-Elbow	Above-Knee
Shoulder Disarticulation	Hip Disarticulation
Forequarter	Hemipelvectomy

Depending upon the number of extremities that are affected, amputees are further described as unilateral (one arm or leg affected), bilateral (two arms or two legs affected), double (one leg and one arm affected) or multiple (more than two extremities affected).

It is well beyond the scope of this discussion to deal in any detail with the return of physical function possible for various types of amputees through prosthetic replacement. It is sufficient to point out that the amount of physical function potentially restorable to the unilateral amputee is primarily related to the number of normal joints that have been lost and the individual's overall physical condition. In general, as the number of joints lost in a leg (ankle, knee, hip) or arm (wrist, elbow, shoulder) increases, the extent of functional restoration possible decreases significantly. Of course, as the number of limbs amputated increases, functional potential decreases drastically.

It is important to note that among amputees as a group there is no direct relationship between the extent of the physical loss and the patient's psychological difficulties. These difficulties are more dependent upon the personality attributes of the individual than the type of amputation. Therefore, one individual with a "limited" physical loss may present far greater adjustment problems than another with a "major" loss (Fishman, 1950).

MEDICAL CARE OF THE AMPUTEE. With the exception of congenital losses, the treatment of practically all amputees begins with surgical procedures and is followed by a program of postoperative care involving definitive medical treatment of the amputation wound and conditioning of the stump and other segments of the amputee's body. This period of postoperative and preprosthetic care and recovery varies in length but is usually completed within two to three months after the surgery. At this time sufficient healing has taken place to proceed with prosthetic restoration. The prescription, fabrication, fitting of an artificial limb, and the training of an individual to utilize the device usually adds another one to three months to the period of immediate medical treatment.

Consequently, it is not at all unusual that six or more months elapse between the loss of the extremity and the time that the individual is able to wear a prosthesis routinely. It should be noted that the amputee's experiences during the interval have considerable bearing on his ultimate physical and psychological adjustment. When the individual has learned to utilize his first artificial appliance (arm or leg), he has then completed the initial step in the treatment of his condition. Although this is the most crucial step to be sure, it is only the first (Fishman, Berger, and Springer, 1957).

Once beyond the period of initial surgery and postoperative care, the primary chronic medical problem of the amputee is concerned with maintaining a continuing adjustment between the patient's physiological condition (weight, muscle strength and tone, skin condition, and so forth) and the prosthetic device he wears. It is therefore necessary to modify and/or replace the artificial limb from time to time because of wear and tear on the appliance, and because of physiological and psychological changes taking place in the patient.

The chronic medical difficulties that result from amputation surgery and continuous prosthetic wear are as follows: (1) *contractures* (shortening of muscle) of specific stump muscles, which limit the stump strength and the range of motion available to control and propel the artificial limb; (2) *neuromata* (small tumors where nerve tissues are severed) *and scar tissue*, which sometime cause chronic discomfort and pain to the amputee; (3) *excessive perspiration* due to the encasement of the stump tissues in the impermeable, nonventilated socket of the prosthesis; (4) *skin irritations*, which are due to pressure and rubbing of the rigid socket of the prosthetic device on tissues of the stump; (5) *circulatory deficiencies* in the stump, where the amputation was prompted by gangrenous conditions due to inadequate blood circulation exclusively in the lower extremities. Such cardiovascular difficulties, which are progressive, require continuous medical care of the stump and the remaining leg.

These five problems are far more serious for the lower extremity than the upper extremity amputee because of the repetitious weight-bearing function performed by the lower extremity prosthesis. Furthermore, these problems become more severe as the patient approaches old age. As a consequence, many medical specialists consider it desirable to follow up their amputee patients frequently on a scheduled basis, regardless of apparent need.

The medical-physical aspects of amputation may, therefore, be summarized as follows: The definitive treatment ordinarily begins with surgery, which is followed by postoperative care, leading to preprosthetic conditioning of the body tissues. There follows the prescription, fabrication, and fitting of a prosthetic device, which is in turn followed by a period of prosthetic training. Upon completion of this step, the individual is ready for vocational training or retraining. However, there are a number of chronic medical problems that continue indefinitely, and these difficulties require intermittent medical and prosthetic care throughout the individual's lifetime.

Because of the variety of rehabilitation services required by the amputee, the "clinic team" concept has achieved widespread acceptance in the management of patients with this disability. Basically the amputation clinic consists of a specialist in orthopedic surgery or physical medicine as chief, a physical or occupational therapist, and a prosthetist. Rehabilitation counselors, psychologists, social case workers, and administrative personnel often augment this basic group depending on the needs of the situation. In a recent study 359 adult male amputees who had been provided with medical prosthetic care through 75 amputation clinics throughout the country were queried concerning their reactions to the experience. Of the amputees responding, 94 percent considered it the best way to receive prosthetic care. Compared to much less enthusiastic reactions concerning other methods, the desirability of treatment through the amputation clinic was clear-cut (Springer, 1958).

The primary purpose of the clinic team, then, is to provide a proper integration of the medical, surgical, therapeutic, prosthetic, and psychosocial services required so that a coordinated pattern of treatment is provided and necessary frequent communication and mutual education of the various specialists are facilitated.

PSYCHOLOGICAL IMPLICATIONS. In the preceding discussion we have reviewed the variations in age, etiology, and physical considerations. Our attention now is directed to the behavioral reactions of the amputee that are prompted by amputation. An analysis of the psychological aspects of the amputation problem suggests that it is best explored along three channels.

The first is concerned with the experiences and reality problems that impinge on the individual as a result of amputation.

The second deals with the variety of ways in which amputees react to these stimuli: the types of behavior displayed and the patients' introspections concerning their disability. Of particular concern are the amputees' attitudes toward the use of a prosthesis as a means of restoring maximum physical function.

The third is concerned with an identification of those psychodynamic processes that may clarify the relationships between the objective experiences associated with amputation and the resulting behavioral responses.

THE AMPUTATION EXPERIENCE. In considering the context of amputee experiences, let us examine first the reality problems that are engendered by the disability. A number of rather specific physical, psychological, and social problems of a unique nature develop because of the permanency, finality, and irrevocability of the loss associated with amputation. Furthermore, these physical and psychosocial problems must be considered in relation to one another because of their intimate and complex interactions. Lastly, the significance of the problems associated with amputation, prosthetic wear, and personal readjustment deserves detailed consideration.

Physical Capacities: Functional Limitations. Although the psychological satisfactions concomitant with physical activity have not been thoroughly studied, it seems obvious that there is an inborn drive to use one's physical resources. This is evidenced by the baby's unlearned determination to walk, crawl, and manipulate objects. The child's and adult's spontaneous participation in a variety of physical activities is a further example of this need. Although we have some difficulty in defining precisely the nature of this drive for physical activity, it is perfectly clear that there are significant psychological needs and satisfactions associated with it and that, with amputation, these gratifications become limited.

In addition to the pleasures evolving directly from the use of one's physical faculties, as in walking, dancing or swimming, there are other satisfactions that are achieved only through the use of prehensile or ambulatory function as a necessary intervening step. In this latter instance, the pleasures do not grow as much out of the physical activity itself as from the results of its application, as in climbing to the balcony of a theater, holding a drink, or picnicking in a desirable but somewhat inaccessible place.

In approaching physical tasks, both for the direct satisfactions involved and for the related pleasures, the alternatives open to the amputee are (*a*) to avoid performing the task, (*b*) to compensate for his loss by the greater use of the remaining extremities, or (*c*) to perform the function by utilizing an artificial replacement for the missing member. Depending on the task and on the situation with which he is confronted, an amputee is likely to utilize all three alternatives as solutions at various times. But no matter which course the amputee chooses, his need to perform a wide variety of physical acts without restriction, limitation, or special consideration can be only partially satisfied (Kay and Peizer, 1958).

It is important to note that in general the lower extremity prosthesis replaces the lost extremity much more adequately than the upper extremity prosthesis. This is a consequence of the fact that ambulation is essentially a repetitive, cyclic activity taking place primarily in two planes, and can be duplicated by use of an artificial leg with relative effectiveness. Upper extremity function is considerably more varied and complex and almost always involves motion in three planes, which makes the problem of duplication very much more difficult. Because of these facts, it is somewhat fortuitous that arm amputations occur most frequently in younger people who normally have the greater physical and psychological adaptability necessary to learn the use of an upper extremity prosthesis.

Physical Capacities: Functional Failures. The use of a prosthetic appliance inevitably implies a certain amount of failure in physical function as an outgrowth of three facts, which are beyond the conscious control of the amputee. Bearing in mind that the prosthesis is a simple machine, (*a*) any inadequacy in the design or construction of its parts and/or fitting to the amputee can cause a failure in function; (*b*) unless the artificial limb is perfectly controlled by the amputee, it again will fail to provide proper function; (*c*) the new amputee has not developed a sufficient level of neuromuscular coordination to maintain consistent control of the limb.

In view of these considerations, the amputee, especially the new wearer, must anticipate a reasonable number of instances when he will fail during ambulation by falling down or will fail in the simple act of prehension by having something drop from his artificial hand. These failures of essentially elementary human functions are a source of concern and embarrassment for the individual because of the social and physical consequences. Even when the individual becomes expert in the use of the artificial appliance, the occasional possibility of failure exists. Depending upon the individual's need for presenting an appearance of perfection to his peers and himself, this anxiety concerning public failure tends to inhibit the person's use of the appliance.

Comfort: Pain related to Prosthetic Wear. An additional difficulty in adjustment stems from the individual's need to be as free from pain and tension as possible so as to maximize comfort. It is not ordinarily realized that prostheses are inherently uncomfortable appendages and even the most skillfully made cannot be considered completely comfortable and therefore cannot be taken for granted by the wearer. What we have come to regard as a comfortable prosthesis is simply one that offers a minimum and tolerable degree of discomfort.

In fitting a prosthetic device for the lower extremity amputee, tissues and muscles are performing atypical functions, primarily weight-bearing. Until the tissues become acclimated, desensitized, and/or calloused to these new functions, considerable discomfort is the rule. Even after prolonged periods of prosthetic usage, the desensitization is not complete, and some discomfort continues. An additional physiological complication is that most areas on the stump have markedly lower pain thresholds than corresponding areas on the opposite limb.

Although the problem of weight-bearing does not exist with upper extremity amputees, the remaining musculature is still subjected to unusual stresses, and, for both lower and upper extremity amputees, the body tissues are encased in relatively rigid, impermeable materials (wood or plastic) that interfere with normal ventilation and cause irritation and discomfort owing to heat and perspiration.

Comfort: Phantom Sensation and Pain. A second type of discomfort stems from the phenomena of phantom sensation and pain. Especially during the immediate postoperative period, amputees almost universally continue to sense the existence of the distal segments of the lost extremity as if it were still part of the body. In a large percentage of cases, this phantom sensation is initially a painful one, in that the body part is experienced to be in a cramped or unnatural position. In time the painful aspects of the phantom sensation tend to disappear in most cases; however, the presence of the phantom remains indefinitely in varying stages of clarity. In some few instances, especially among older amputees, the phantom remains permanently painful and presents a considerable problem (Feinstein, Luce, and Langton, 1954). At best, phantom sensation is a moderately distracting stimulus and, at worst, tends to be quite painful and troublesome.

Comfort: Fatigue. Although research has not given us final, reliable data concerning the amount of energy expended in typical tasks by various types of amputees as compared to normals, preliminary studies tell us that these differences are significant. For example, an above-knee amputee performing a given ambulatory task expends considerably more energy than does his nonhandicapped counterpart (Bard and Ralston, 1959). Since the amputee is called upon to expend more energy, it is necessary for him to divert effort that once went to other activities and apply it toward his disability. As a result, he is likely to experience fatigue more rapidly than the nonhandicapped person. Both phenomena (continuous expenditure of effort and the early experience of fatigue) tend to interfere with the individual's motivation to participate in activities that are part of the rehabilitation process.

Another part of this problem is concerned with the fact that certain aspects of the operation of prosthetic devices are *not* automatic. In other words, the amputee needs to pay variable but continuous attention to the activation, control, and use of his prosthesis. This requirement for increased attention may be viewed as making demands on the psychological resources of the patient. It serves to divert his attention from other matters and focus it on obtaining satisfactory ambulation or prehension. Although we cannot translate these demands into terms of physical energy and fatigue, their role as an additional and continuing drain on the amputee's resources is apparent.

Appearance: Visual Considerations. The word cosmesis, which pertains to adornment, beautification, or decoration, is widely used in the field of prosthetic restoration as a synonym for problems associated with one's visible appearance. This cosmetic problem is greater for upper extremity amputees of both sexes and for female lower extremity amputees, since in both instances the extremity is not normally covered by clothing (Cattell, Dembo, Koppel, Tane-Baskin, and Weinstock, 1949). Because of our mode of dress, it is a lesser problem for the male lower extremity amputee and for very young children whose state of psychosexual development makes for less concern over matters of personal appearance. With the advent of adolescence this situation changes dramatically, and cosmetic considerations become of urgent importance.

Obviously, when one suffers an amputation, his appearance is changed, both in his own eyes and in the eyes of others. Since the values associated with appearance are important, when members of our society do not meet these standards, they suffer a loss of group acceptance. Since the need to be accepted is great, both intra- and interpersonal problems develop.

Appearance: Auditory Considerations. Although the primary cosmetic problem for the amputee is the adequacy of his visual appearance, there are also problems connected with the noise-producing characteristics of the conventional prosthetic device. Since the prospect of being conspicuous by reason of some inadequacy in one's make-up is a threatening one, the matter of adapting to a substitute extremity that produces noise becomes a cause for concern.

An artificial limb being a simple machine may have a variety of low-level sounds associated with its operation. Some amputees are concerned with noise caused by air escaping around the brim of the socket or in the articulation of the prosthetic knee or ankle. Others are sensitive to the atypical sound of the prosthetic foot hitting the floor in certain situations. Upper extremity amputees may react to the noise associated with the prosthetic elbow locking in position or the terminal device closing on an object. Although these noises are of a very low intensity level and go unnoticed by most people with whom the amputee associates, a significant percentage of the amputees are aware of these sounds and tend to project this awareness to others. Since cosmetic values, both visual and auditory, are threatened by amputation and attendant prosthetic restoration, another area of adjustment is disturbed.

Vocational and Economic Factors. Any interference in an individual's ability to earn his way in competitive society is psychologically threatening. Our understanding of this problem, as it affects amputees, may be aided by considering the "socioeconomic scale," which, in a general way, categorizes people in terms of the social status accorded them. In general, an individual's position on the scale is intimately tied in with his occupational pursuits. The occupations that are accorded the highest status on this scale are professional, managerial, and executive in nature, whereas the unskilled labor categories represent the lowest. It is to be noted that the duties of the professional, managerial, and executive group are primarily dependent upon intellect and personality (ability to think, speak, write, persuade, or make decisions), whereas those in the unskilled group are primarily dependent on manual resources (carry, push, pull, walk, stack, or load).

When people in the former group suffer an amputation, there are probably no significant threats based on economic considerations at all. With the exception of a small group in the performing and fine arts and certain professions, the ability of this group to pursue their occupations is essentially unaffected, as are their positions as wage earners. The only special economic problems faced by this group are the medical and prosthetic expenses associated with this chronic disability. On the other hand, those who earn their livelihood primarily by the performance of physical activities involving the use of arms and legs and who do not have intellectual and personal resources for training in other fields suffer a very severe economic handicap as a result of amputation. They are no longer able to compete with their full-bodied peers.

The empirical fact is that the large majority of unemployed and marginally employable amputees come from this low socioeconomic group. Unless selective placement is introduced or special arrangements are made on the job, these people remain unemployable. Hence for this significant segment of the amputee population, the social need to be economically self-sufficient is threatened.

As one might anticipate, there is a marked decrease in the numbers of amputees—particularly upper extremity amputees—who are employed in agriculture, skilled and semiskilled and unskilled occupations (Berger, 1958). Although similar shifts are to be found in employment data concerning lower extremity amputees, they are not quite so severe, since a lower extremity amputation is less limiting for most occupations than is an upper extremity one.

Social Considerations. Perhaps the single most important psychological prerequisite for a well-adjusted productive life is the respect and the status that one receives from his associates and peers. Over and above the physical amenities of existence, the satisfactions received from the regard and affection of people close to one (friends, family, coworkers) are all important. With regard to the amputee, this status is threatened, and the possibility of loss of acceptance by one's peers becomes very real. The amputee is not ordinarily obliged to guess how others feel about him. He can—except in the case of the congenital amputee—simply reflect upon what he thought about other handicapped people before he himself was amputated. These attitudes, which he held toward other disabled people, are now directed toward the self.

It is likely that early in these reflections, the word "cripple" comes to the amputee's mind along with its various connotations of inadequacy, charity, shame, punishment, and guilt. Obviously, when an individual views himself or feels that he is being viewed by others in these terms, he considers himself an object for lessened respect and will react to this changed status accordingly. Since these attitudes are not at all likely to enhance the self-concept, but rather devalue it, the patient may be expected to undertake defenses against these attacks on his integrity (Dembo, Leviton, and Wright, 1956).

Social prejudices with regard to the disabled have long been reflected in our literature with such villainous characters as Captain Hook, Captain Ahab, Long John Silver, and others being identified as amputees. These characterizations tend to continue unsatisfactory attitudes toward the handicapped by reason of their influence on youngsters during their formative years. It is, of course, true that very significant educational programs have been attempting to change social attitudes toward the handicapped and teach that the loss of an extremity does not automatically devalue a person. However, attitudes toward the disabled that have been centuries in the making are not easily changed in a short period regardless of the intensity of the effort. For the time being, we must face the reality that significant loss of social status accompanies amputation and that the human need to retain self-respect and the respect of one's associates is seriously threatened.

It would be most helpful to be able to formulate a general statement concerning which of the above problem areas are most significant. If this were possible, emphasis and attention could be paid to the more important of the patient's problems and less attention to the others. However, it is not possible to make this generalization, since different problems emerge as significant for different patients, depending upon their personal system of values. Also, the process of prosthetic rehabilitation involves a series of compromises, and, although the treatment serves to reduce a number of the amputee's problems, it does not completely resolve any one of them. In the reduction of certain problems, new ones are sometimes introduced or old ones aggravated. Hence in treating the amputee, one must evaluate the interactions among all of these problems and proceed accordingly.

The reader has, of course, noted the great emphasis accorded matters relating to the wear and utilization of a prosthesis. This emphasis is a direct consequence of the central role of the prosthesis in the personal and vocational rehabilitation of the amputee. The utilization of the prosthesis is the first evidence of the individual's capacity and desire to reenter productive society. As such its acceptance and use is frequently a very reliable prognostic index of the effectiveness of the entire rehabilitation effort.

AMPUTEE BEHAVIOR. In turning to the second question of how the amputee reacts to the problems engendered by amputation two subquestions arise: What are the typical behavioral consequences of amputation? What are the individual's introspections, attitudes, opinions, and feelings?

Behavior during Hospitalization. Let us first consider the amputee's behavior in the relatively immediate postoperative period. During World War II several studies were made of amputees during their period of hospitalization. One study (Wittkower, 1947) noted expressions of depression, resentment, anxiety, defiance, cheerfulness, resignation, and indifference as the dominant behavioral reactions. A second study (Randall, Ewalt, and Blair, 1945) noted shame, self-pity, worry about family, depression, anxiety, feelings of good fortune, and no significant emotional responses among the group. A third study (Hughes and White, 1946) concluded that amputees retained their normal personality reactions. All three investigations found a number of patients who adjusted relatively easily to the loss of a limb whereas others adjusted with great difficulty.

A final study (Ladieu, Hanfmann, and Dembo, 1947) concerned itself with the attitudes of amputees and other orthopedically disabled toward receiving help from nondisabled individuals. Unfortunately, with the conclusion of World War II, there have been no further systematic reports of the immediate postoperative behavior of any sizable groups of amputee patients. These studies, as well as more recent clinical experience in civilian hospitals, have all suggested that, after the immediate trauma associated with the amputation subsides, there is an intensification of the individual's emotional reactions during the first few weeks or months postoperatively. It is at this time that overt emotional reactions to amputation are strongest.

Long Term Behavior. After the immediate traumatic psychological effects of amputation surgery and its realization have passed, as the individual begins to make his adjustment to the experiences associated with amputation, the behavior of almost all amputees falls well within the limits of what may be called "normal." There is apparently no special, definable neurotic or psychotic process involved in the long-term adjustment. It is not surprising, therefore, that a wide variety of amputee behavior is reported by various investigators, since the overt behavorial pattern of amputees reflects the complete spectrum of adjustment and occasionally the predispositions and biases of the observer as well.

Nevertheless, although there are no significant differences in overt behavior as compared with the nondisabled, amputees do express unique attitudes, opinions, and feelings concerning their disability and the recurrent stresses which they are called upon to face.

In an attitude questionnaire administered to some 359 adult upper-extremity male amputees of long standing, an attempt was made to study nine personality variables: (1) acceptance of loss, (2) identification with the disabled, (3) appraisal of functional adequacy, (4) independence, (5) sensitivity, (6) appraisal of acceptance by others, (7) sociability, (8) frustration and (9) optimism (Fishman, 1958, c; Siller and Silverman, 1958). The predominant findings suggested that, no matter which aspect of personality was studied, the subjects tried to maintain feelings of bodily integrity and adequacy by denying many of the personal, vocational, and social consequences of amputations. They attempted to deemphasize physical difficulties, rejected notions of abnormality, and set their cosmetic and functional desires in line with those of normal people. These findings, however, must be interpreted in the light of the amputee's strong need for unprejudiced recognition from the nondisabled. In order to gain this recognition, the amputees obviously responded in a manner that only partially represented their true feelings. Therefore, it is clear that these data more nearly reflect how the amputee feels he should be regarded than how he actually regards himself.

In another investigation (Fishman, 1949), utilizing the clinical interview as the major investigative tool to study 48 lower-extremity veteran male amputees of long standing, it was possible to establish a higher degree of rapport than through questionnaires. An analysis of the interview protocols indicated a considerably higher number of negative self-references than positive self-references, revealing a relatively nonaccepting set of attitudes toward their disability. The major types of overt behavior that were associated with these expressions of negative self-concept were: (1) hostility, (2) dependency, (3) timidity, (4) superficial self-confidence, (5) unstable motivation, (6) rationalization of situations, and (7) compulsivity. The types of behavior that were associated with positive self-concept were: (1) self-assured, confident behavior, (2) stable motivation, (3) gregariousness, (4) no expressed hostility and (5) positive attitudes toward the artificial limb.

Although there were demonstrable differences in the kinds of behavior that accompanied negative and positive references toward the self, in some instances the same or a similar self-concept was the motivating factor behind markedly different reactions. In one nonaccepting person, hostile, aggressive behavior may arise whereas, in another, nonacceptance is expressed through timid, hesitant, or depressed behavior. Rejection of amputee status may, in one instance, produce hostility toward the prosthetic device or toward rehabilitation personnel, whereas, in other instances, attention-getting behavior or complete withdrawal is the result of the same rejecting attitude. The evidence clearly indicates that different types of behavior may evolve from similar self-perceptions depending on the particular personality.

Behavior related to Prosthetic Wear. Probably the next most significant event in an individual's life after the fact of the amputation per se is the receipt and subsequent utilization of a prosthetic device. The individual's acceptance or nonacceptance, use or nonuse of the device and the associated attitudes are pivotal influences on his later life. In view of the emphasis placed on prosthetic wear, it is important to consider if there are any definable psychological consequences associated with such wear. Specifically, are the attitudes or behavior of the amputee altered in any significant way by virtue of wearing a prosthetic device, or does the device simply provide increased physical function?

As a part of the study of upper-extremity amputees referred to previously (Fishman, 1958, c; Siller and Silverman, 1958), 359 subjects were evaluated psychologically prior to being exposed to systematic prosthetic treatment and were then reevaluated some months after the completion of such treatment. The data led to the conclusion that with the active use of an appropriate prosthetic device the subjects experienced (*a*) a decrease in expressed feelings of sensitivity and frustration; (*b*) an increase in feelings of social adequacy; (*c*) a generally greater acceptance of their disabled situation; (*d*) greater self-reliance; (*e*) a greater feeling of effectiveness and functional independence; (*f*) greater security and self-acceptance; (*g*) less shyness and more adaptable behavior. One may question whether the amputee actually fully experienced these positive changes or whether they were in part expounding an expected "cultural norm" toward prosthetic restoration.

On the basis of the data available from this study, it is not possible to answer this question with any finality although one may reason that both considerations contributed to the amputee's opinions. However, when the clinically reported attitudes and reactions of the overwhelming percentage of amputees who consistently wear prosthetic devices are considered, there is indeed strong evidence that there are meaningful psychological advantages associated with prosthetic wear.

Similar values for prosthetic wear were identified among a group of 159 juvenile amputees (Fishman and Peizer, 1958). In this instance prosthetic wear increased the scope of the children's activities and display of independent behavior. This was accompanied by an observable improvement in the emotional stability, school adjustment, social confidence, and the quality of the self-references made by members of this group. Except for one survey (Chapman, Palmer, Bell, and Buckley, 1959) describing the activity patterns of older amputees, there have been no comparable studies to shed light on the psychological effects of prosthetic wear on the geriatric patient.

Although the large majority of amputees profit both functionally and psychologically from prosthetic wear, there is a significant number who apparently do not. In the study of upper extremity amputees referred to above, efforts were made to determine the reasons for unsatisfactory prosthetic adjustment and the following points evolved: (*a*) As a rule very little information concerning prostheses is available to new amputees early in the rehabilitation program, and this deficiency encourages the development of unrealistic expectations concerning prosthetic wear. (*b*) Overly optimistic anticipations concerning the value of prostheses were in most cases modified downward after prosthetic wear and were accompanied by considerable personal disappointment and distress. (*c*) No attempt is ordinarily made to alter pessimistic attitudes toward prosthetic wear prior to fitting.

These findings suggest that a considerable service could be rendered if the amputee would be made aware of the realities of prosthetic wear by appropriate counseling prior to the time of prosthetic fitting and training so as to maximize motivation and minimize disappointments.

In another aspect of this same study it was substantiated that the amputee's post-fitting attitudes and use of the prosthesis is closely related to and may be predicted on the basis of his pre-fitting attitudes. The data indicated that opinions held by the amputee before he had been exposed to prosthetic devices exercise a controlling influence over later prosthetic acceptance, performance, and use. On the basis of these findings, one might conclude that it is not appropriate to provide a prosthetic appliance to an individual until he has developed an attitudinal predisposition to accept its purposes and functions. Should a patient display consistently negative attitudes in this regard, an educational effort would most assuredly be required in an attempt to influence and change the prefitting attitudes.

AMPUTEE PSYCHODYNAMICS. We turn now to the third area of discussion to complete the analysis of the psychological reactions to amputations. In so doing we focus our attention on the psychodynamic processes that act as a bridge between individual experiences and the resulting behavior.

Perception of Disability. In a number of instances, predictions of rehabilitation potential based upon physical considerations prove to be quite inaccurate, overshadowed as they are by the patient's unique perceptions of his disability. In many instances individual perceptions have a greater influence on the rehabilitation process and its result than does the physical extent of the disability. The nature of these perceptions are closely dependent upon the personal meaning of the loss to the individual (Fishman, 1949) as well as upon the value structure of the individual (Dembo, Leviton, and Wright, 1956). A rather well-known correlary concept is the body image (Bender, 1934; Schilder, 1950), which focuses on the individual's perceptions of his body and physique.

It is most unusual to find a realistic self-concept among new amputees. In most cases, relatively inaccurate and distorted self-perceptions exist since the patient does not normally have access to any considerable experience with the disabled. He does not know what to expect in living as an amputated person, and, in view of the rather significant trauma associated with his loss, he focuses his anxieties on the amputation and considers the disability a more central factor in his future life than is realistic. It is, therefore, probably more correct to say that a person "must learn to live with his perceptions of his disability" rather than "with his disability."

Since the amputee acts in terms of his perceptions and not necessarily reality, the consequences of a highly distorted estimate of his disabled condition are reflected in increased difficulty in accepting the requirements of the rehabilitation process. If steps are not taken to correct these self-perceptions prior to the prescription and fitting of an artificial limb and training in its use, it may be almost impossible to accomplish them at all. When rehabilitation does proceed, it does so haltingly, with great resistance on the part of the patient.

Therefore, we are as much concerned with trying to effect a change in the individual's perceptions as we are in trying to change the realities themselves. This being the case, the treatment of the amputee assumes two foci: (*a*) diminution of physical loss by appropriate medical care, introduction of prosthetic devices as well as prosthetic and vocational training and (*b*) revision of unrealistic ideas and attitudes concerning disability through continuous reeducation. Both these approaches are designed to increase the effectiveness of the patient's functional and psychological resources.

Consequences of Frustration. The manner in which people respond to disaster varies in myriad ways. So do the reactions to amputation. Almost any type of behavioral response can be seen in amputees, in line with the expected frequencies of normal, neurotic, and psychotic behavior in the population as a whole.

The previous discussions have described a number of significant human needs that cannot be completely gratified as a result of the loss of an extremity. We have suggested that these circumstances tend to frustrate the individual and to generate conflict because of permanently unobtainable goals. Furthermore, it has been pointed out that the extent of disturbance is dependent upon the patient's perception of his disability as well as its real limitations. The less accurate a patient's perceptions, the greater the anticipated psychological difficulties.

The emotions aroused within the individual may be fairly specific ones, such as anger or fear, or they may be quite diffused, such as anxiety. Furthermore, as a result of amputation the emotional reactions are almost universally of a negative quality (e.g., anxiety, fear, anger) as distinguished from positive feelings (e.g., love, affection, joy). When strong negative emotions are experienced, they tend to be expressed rather directly through overt behavior whereas less strong and less specific emotions tend to be more easily inhibited and modified. In any event, it is most unlikely that the amputee's strong tensions will be relieved through the expression of any single type of emotional response.

The behavior exhibited by an individual also depends on his previously learned adjustive patterns. In many instances unconscious defense mechanisms come into play, such as projection, displacement, rationalization, regression, somatization, and denial. When these are activated, the overt behavior pattern may be void of or extremely limited in any identifiable emotional reactions (Sargent and Williams, 1958). The reactions of the amputee to frustration and conflict usually include both overt emotional experiences and unconscious defenses; each coming into play on the basis of how the individual perceives and interprets the specific environmental situation as well as the nature, intensity, and variety of the emotions being experienced. This psychodynamic sequence serves as a basis for the often expressed conclusion that adjustment to disability is closely related to the individual's preamputation personality and behavior.

With the recognition of the wide variety of psychodynamic processes and emotions utilized in responding to stress, the need to identify, define, and measure the specific processes used by an individual has become quite important. In a current investigation an effort is being made to study how twelve psychodynamic processes are used by amputees in their adjustment (Weiss, 1960).

The measurement of each of these adjustment techniques is being accomplished through the use of an appropriate psychological test. Several of these tests will be discussed later. The plan calls for the performances on this battery to be correlated with the amputees' observable behavior in the rehabilitation and vocational setting so that the relationship of these psychodynamic processes to amputee adjustment and behavior will be clarified. The twelve variables, all of which have evolved from extensive clinical experience with amputees, are: (1) Sociopathic impulsivity—emotion translated into aggressive action regardless of consequences to others; (2) Emotional or neurotic impulsivity—failure of adaptive repression occurring after an attempt at control; (3) Displacement and paranoid reactions—the discharge of accumulated tensions against objects and innocent bystanders, who become scapegoats; (4) Phobic reactions—irrational reactions evoked by stimuli not intrinsically dangerous; (5) Depression—tensions combined with guilt derived from feelings that amputation is a punishment tending to immobilize the amputee with consequent sadness, helplessness and inadequacy; (6) Encapsulation or constriction—the tendency to surround oneself with many barriers against the outside, supposedly dangerous, environment; (7) Somatization or somatic preoccupation—the experience of tensions being converted or "bound up" in a physical symptom, instead of being experienced directly; (8) Inadequate control of tension; (9) Pessimism—a defense against the environment reflected by verbalization of a limited level of aspiration; (10) Inadequate masculine role identification—poor identification with the masculine role, with resultant passivity and lethargy; (11) Inadequate compensatory ambition—the inability to mobilize additional effort to overcome the physical limitations of amputation and to adjust to the demands of prosthetic wear; (12) Stress intolerance. The preceding psychological processes generally result in limited restorative goals through a diminution of the amputee's motivation to regain his lost functions.

Empirical evidence substantiates the theoretical considerations that the single most important problem facing the rehabilitation worker concerns the ways and means of implementing marginal motivation. Since the rehabilitation process is clearly reeducational in nature—and since it has been appropriately said that no one can teach, only create a situation that is conducive to learning—the question arises as to what techniques will help stimulate and motivate the patient's learning during the rehabilitation process.

SPECIAL CONSIDERATIONS IN PSYCHOLOGICAL APPRAISAL. THE PSYCHOLOGIST'S RESPONSIBILITIES. In the usual rehabilitation setting, there are probably three major functions to be fulfilled by the psychologist in relation to amputees: (*a*) diagnostic, counseling, and therapeutic services; (*b*) advisory and consultative responsibilities; and (*c*) research functions.

Diagnostic and Therapeutic Services. An understanding of the psychodynamic processes that govern an amputee's reactions to his disability is indispensable in developing a rational plan for patient management and in analyzing the difficulties experienced by certain patients. The psychologist is in a unique position to make a major contribution by providing this diagnostic service where required. Such a personality analysis is particularly valuable when it can explain in concrete terms the amputee's responses to his reality problems in the light of his personality characteristics.

Since most amputees present no serious psychopathology, intensive psychotherapy is not ordinarily indicated. Actually, psychotherapeutic assistance is most often sought for patients whose motivation for participation or progress in rehabilitation activities is unsatisfactory. The psychologist is asked to assist these patients who display an inability to respond to the suggestions and stimulation of other rehabilitation workers.

The large majority of patients are in a position to accept and profit from personal and vocational counseling services. On the level of a guidance relationship, the reassurance and clarifying suggestions made by the psychologist in relation to the reality problems that the individual faces are most valuable. A reasonably thorough exploration of the patient's perceptions and attitudes concerning personal, prosthetic, and vocational problems is frequently quite helpful. It must be remembered, however, that there are patients who are capable of working out their psychological readjustments without professional help. For these individuals, medical care is the only rehabilitation service required. On the other hand, for those with serious motivational problems, the prospects for effecting dramatic improvement in behavior or personality are almost negligible.

Consultative Responsibilities. Arising largely from the psychologist's understanding of the patient and ability to evaluate the rehabilitation setting, the consultative or advisory role of the psychologist takes form. This advisory role is primarily concerned with the psychological orientation of the physicians, surgeons, physical and occupational therapists, prosthetists, and rehabilitation counselors who normally have the most intimate and extended contact with amputee patients. There is often insufficient awareness on the part of these professional groups concerning the significant social and psychological problems of the amputee, many of which have been discussed previously. It is the responsibility of the psychologist to heighten the appreciation of the professional personnel to the psychological aspects of adjustment to amputation and in so doing to create a greater sensitivity to the "human" aspects of the treatment process. This is a major contribution of the psychologist.

Research Functions. The third area in which the psychologist is able to make a unique contribution is in research. One of the difficulties in developing insights concerning amputee adjustment through research is the difficulty of obtaining suitably sized groups of amputees with appropriate sampling characteristics so that one may draw valid conclusions from the studies. This problem of sampling, perhaps more than any other, tends to discourage the study of problems associated with amputation. One solution to this problem involves cooperative research efforts among a number of institutions all of which treat similar types of amputee clients. Such groups can join together in formulating studies that would benefit from larger experimental samples and joint planning (Fishman and Peizer, 1958; Fishman, 1958, c). Although the problems of such cooperative research are significant, they can be overcome. The alternative is far less satisfactory, since it results in studies performed on such small, heterogeneous samples as to make for equivocal findings, or, worse still, in very little or no research at all.

A second difficulty in conducting research is that amputee behavior is generally well within the limits of psychological normality. This fact suggests that an investigator must study the elusive differences in personality and emotional functioning that makes one human being behave differently from another when faced with significant stresses. This is indeed a difficult area to explore meaningfully.

In spite of these difficulties, psychologists must continue their efforts to isolate, define, and measure those aspects of personality and those behavioral dynamics that are related to the amputee's ability to be rehabilitated. Although admittedly these variables are difficult to sort out, considerable progress has been made through the contributions of previous researchers. Ultimately, most of these findings must be distilled and simplified for transmission to the nonpsychologically trained personnel who are responsible for amputee care.

PSYCHOLOGICAL INSTRUMENTATION. Let us now turn to the psychological instruments that are used in implementing the clinical, consultative, and research activities of the psychologist.

The Case History. As has been stated, apparently the single most important determining factor that is related to the question of how an individual will adjust to an amputation and subsequent rehabilitation efforts is the individual's preamputation personality and psychosocial background. Individuals who have shown an inability to overcome problems, to display responsible behavior, and to evidence productive effort in their previous vocational, social, and personal lives are likely to display similar failings in facing the problems of amputation. As a matter of fact, because of the threatening nature and intensity of the problems associated with the loss, they tend to do more poorly. As one may expect, the converse is equally true. Consequently, an understanding of the behavior of an individual amputee can be best approached through an adequate history of the individual's vocational, educational, social, and family background.

The Interview. More often than not, however, thoroughgoing case histories are not available and are quite impossible to obtain in certain situations. Consequently, the case history material must be developed through the use of a personal interview. For this reason, a well-conducted, comprehensive interview or series of interviews with the patient is probably the single most useful instrument available to the psychologist. There would seem to be four general criteria that should be met by such an interview.

1. Non-Direction. Guidance and direction in the questioning should be kept to a minimum. Structuring of the interview is indicated only when the amputee is unable to function in a free situation and communication becomes difficult for this reason.

2. Specificity. Within the limits of nondirection it is desirable to explore as many aspects of the individual's personality and attitudes as may be necessary to obtain an adequate picture of his psychological functioning. The specific information provided during the interview provides the clues for matters to be explored more thoroughly. Insofar as the content of the interview is concerned, the following areas seem pertinent: (*a*) per-

sonal, family, social, vocational, and amputation history; (*b*) reactions to amputation on the part of the amputee, family, friends, and job associates; (*c*) anticipated reactions of the amputee toward prosthetic restoration, again taking into account the influences of family, friends, and job associates; (*d*) effects of amputation on the self, as evidenced through introspections concerning personal, social, and vocational activities and plans; (*e*) phantom limb and pain phenomena.

3. Range. Sufficient coverage should take place during the interview so that hypotheses concerning personality formulated about the amputee can be verified or refuted to some minimal extent by different data brought to bear on each hypothesis.

4. Depth. It is desirable to obtain during the interview a maximum of self-revelatory comments concerning the subject's experiences and attitudes. In a single interview or even two, it is obvious that no significant "level of depth" can be obtained. However, the effort should be to shift the level of contact toward the unconscious end of the continuum. This is best accomplished by use of follow-up remarks or questions that refer explicitly to the "feeling" context of the amputee's remarks.

Observation. Often the opportunity for discreet observation of a patient's behavior is not available. However, the amputee may be observed for long periods of time in a variety of interactions by the physical or occupational therapist. He is also in contact for considerable periods with the prosthetist and, to a lesser extent, with the physician. The observations that these professional people make should be extremely useful as a source of hypotheses concerning the amputee's personality functioning and as behavioral verification of the results of psychological interviews and testing.

Psychological Tests. There are apparently no special considerations in utilizing the accepted projective and nonprojective psychological tests of personality as methods of describing and understanding amputee personality. There is no evidence that amputees respond to projective techniques or to personality inventories any differently than do their nondisabled counterparts. Also, there are no indications that performance on these tests require any special or unusual interpretations. Projective devices, such as the Rorschach, Thematic Apperception Test, and Figure Drawing, can yield information concerning certain psychological characteristics that have a bearing on some special aspect of amputee adjustment, but in general they do not provide sufficient information concerning the totality of adjustment to amputation and subsequent rehabilitation.

Tests of intelligence, interests, achievement, and aptitude may also be utilized with amputees without special precautions, so long as tests involving manual manipulation are not given to upper extremity amputees and scored on the basis of published norms. Obviously, the standardization data would not apply in this instance.

A number of specialized measuring instruments have been developed as part of various research programs dealing with the amputee, and several of these instruments have proved to be quite promising. The purpose of these instruments is to provide quantifiable measures concerning the nature of an amputee's adjustment or behavior pattern. These measures cannot be considered "tests" on the basis of complete reliability and validity studies, and they are more properly viewed as scorable inventories or projective devices concerned with amputee attitudes and adjustment. Their prime value relates to the quantifiable information that they provide.

The most unsophisticated approach to this measurement problem involves questionnaires designed to explore the amputee's adjustment pattern on the conscious verbal level. Such instruments are beset by the same weaknesses as any other questionnaires designed to study personality, in that the responses are almost invariably colored by the impression that the patient wishes to present. Nonetheless, it is frequently valuable to have a quantifiable estimate of an individual's behavior even when it is altered by his own conscious and subconscious modifications.

Such a questionnaire, consisting of fifty-seven items, was designed for the study of upper extremity amputees described on page 20 to shed light on nine personality factors. Selected items from this questionnaire are included in Appendix I as an indication of the types of questions asked (Peizer, 1958; Siller and Silverman, 1958).

A somewhat more indirect approach, patterned after the picture frustration technique (Rosenzweig, 1944), involves the use of nine cartoons depicting a series of ambiguous, potentially sensitive social situations. The amputee subject is asked to respond to these situations with the expectation that he will express his attitudes with less inhibition than to direct verbal questioning. This device has been designed primarily to estimate the amputee's security. This concept of security includes (*a*) self-acceptance, defined as the ability to view the amputation without self-pity, exaggeration, or denial and without resorting to maladaptive means of defending self-esteem, and (*b*) reality-facing, defined as the ability to appraise environmental situations as they are. The last three cartoons were also designed to reflect the amputee's sense of independence, which involves his motivations to be self-sufficient and to function with a minimum of assistance. Strivings for independence very likely stem from the individual's feeling of security, and, as such, the two variables are closely related. However, since the desire for independent function is a major factor in the rehabilitation of amputees, this factor is scored separately (Peizer, 1958; Siller and Silverman, 1958). Sample cartoons are presented in Appendix II.

A questionnaire has also been developed in order to explore and quantify amputees' attitudes toward prosthetic devices. Since scores on this instrument have been shown to be significantly related to the individual's willingness to accept and utilize an artificial appliance, its predictive value may be considerable. Further comprehensive validation studies of this instrument are currently under way. A number of typical items from this questionnaire are included in Appendix III.

Several tests which have been developed for other applications have proven particularly valuable in working with the amputee. Among these are the Secord Body Homonym Test (Secord [n.d.]) and the Psychosomatic Experience Blank (Seitz and McFarland, 1938), both of which are measures of somatic preoccupation. Since the evidence indicates that amputees who are overly concerned with their bodily attributes and functions have greater difficulty in adjusting than those who are less somatically preoccupied, these two measures are of considerable diagnostic value.

Another instrument of considerable interest and potential value in studying amputee behavior is the Petrovich Pain Apperception Test (Petrovich, 1957). This scale consists of a series of pictures as in the Thematic Apperception Test, but all depicting situations in which an individual is being subjected to a pain stimulus. The amputee is asked to respond to these pictures so that he may project his attitudes and reactions toward a variety of pain stimuli occurring under various conditions. This measure should be of particular assistance in clarifying the factors affecting the ability to tolerate the discomforts associated with prosthetic wear.

PSYCHOLOGICAL REHABILITATION. Aspects of five important areas of human activity have been described as being frustrated by reason of amputation, namely, physical function, cosmesis, comfort, vocational and economic factors, and social considerations. It is clear that, in order to assist the amputee, these problems, as modified by his perception of them, must be dealt with so as to diminish the frustrations and conflicts involved. These problems cannot be erased. They may be modified or compromised but cannot be negated. The problem of the rehabilitation of the amputee becomes, therefore, one of assisting the patient to incorporate certain limitations into his pattern of life so as to assure minimal interference with the large variety of other important activities of living. Several suggestions for extending assistance follow.

First, the actual processes of physical restoration and personal and vocational counseling as well as job placement assist the individual in partially meeting a number of his needs. When the amputee uses a prosthesis, he does not walk as well as a nonhandicapped individual, but his gait more closely approximates that of the normal than it does when crutches are used. The prosthesis does not look exactly like the normal extremity; however, if properly fabricated, it can meet the requirements of reasonable appearance. The prosthesis will not be completely comfortable but probably can be designed to fit within the pain tolerance limits of the individual. As he learns to utilize and control his prosthesis, the frequency with which it fails him diminishes. Personal counseling assists the amputee to clarify and correct his perceptions, so that he comes to understand the goals of the rehabilitation process—what he may anticipate in the future and what he must learn to live with. By appropriate vocational counseling and placement procedures, the insecurity associated with reemployment can be reduced and he can learn to accept himself and thereby the attitudes of others.

A second significant approach revolves about the ability of the rehabilitation personnel to introduce substitute values and life goals in the place of those held prior to amputation and around the patient's ability to accept these new goals. For example, if the patient's occupation prior to amputation involves considerable use of the affected extremity, one can achieve significant psychological progress by suggesting other occupations that make significantly lesser demands on the extremities and yet hold satisfactions for the patient. As a substitute value or goal is offered and accepted, an important factor in developing frustration and conflict is thereby eliminated.

Thirdly, a problem frequently exists in preparing the patient to be amenable psychologically to the processes of prosthetic restoration and vocational rehabilitation. In the early postoperative stages an amputee may be viewed as undergoing an emotional reaction not dissimilar to those of people who suffer a catastrophe, such as the death of a loved one. In both instances the emotional reactions of the bereaved operate in a somewhat circuitous fashion that must be interrupted at some point if the individual is to recover from the loss and reenter normal life activities. These circumstances dictate the involvement of the amputee patient at the earliest psychologically suitable moment in some purposeful activity that will tend to divert him from a continuing preoccupation with his loss.

In this connection, the prosthetic training procedures fulfill the extremely important function of involving the patient in challenging and important activities. In addition to the obvious primary purpose of prosthetic training—that of teaching one to use the prosthesis—the secondary purpose of requiring physical and mental concentration is significant. It is important to note that ordinarily only the occupational or physical therapist spends sufficient time with the patient to provide continuous and important supervision and stimulation along these lines.

Fourth, a technique that is sometimes helpful in motivating the amputee patient involves placing him in contact with previously rehabilitated amputees. This is a particularly important procedure to be used with those amputees who find it impossible to relate to or identify with the nonamputated professional worker. In fact, he is unable to profit from instruction or reassurance as a result of his attitude that no one who has not lost an extremity can really understand his situation. In these instances, the involvement of suitably readjusted amputees as persons with whom the new patient may identify and from whom he may learn cannot be overestimated. A word of caution must be introduced, however, concerning the qualifications of the amputee to serve as inspiration. An individual of substantial personal adjustment must be used so that the new amputee does not become an outlet for the mentor's problems and anxieties.

Fifth, the continuous expression by rehabilitation personnel of appropriate concern, attention, reassurance, and respect tend to assuage the troublesome emotions being experienced by the patient. Negative destructive emotions simply do not flourish as well in an atmosphere typified by this kind of accepting professional climate.

Lastly, the thought that each patient must be treated in terms of his own value system must be emphasized again. Placing the proper emphasis on each of the amputee's problems is part of the process of diagnosis and prognosis and is a prerequisite for developing a sound management concept.

These several suggestions, though by no means exhaustive of what can be done, should tend to reduce frustration and conflict as well as the strength of negative emotions being experienced by the patient. In turn, the individual's motivation to restore himself as a functioning member of society will tend to increase.

CRITERIA OF SUCCESSFUL REHABILITATION. By what criteria can we gauge the success of the rehabilitation of an amputee? Does the answer lie in the apparent perfect restoration of lost function, or in the ideal cosmetic replacement, or in the most comfortable prosthesis? Partially, success lies in all of these, but it may in some cases exist with a minimum of these accomplishments.

We cannot expect the same standards of performance from patients of dissimilar physical and psychological characteristics. We can accomplish only that which the individual's preamputation physical and psychological potentials permit. It is, therefore, possible to have a more successful result in the rehabilitation effort with people who are capable of less physical function than with those who are capable of more.

In view of this fact, success in rehabilitation may be defined in terms of psychological rather than physical criteria. Rehabilitation may be said to be successful when the amputation and its related considerations are no longer the central adjustment problem for the individual. As the ability to use the prosthesis more automatically or subconsciously increases, as the client's awareness of being physically limited and different becomes less threatening, and as the amputation becomes a minimal source of interference in his familial, vocational, and social activities, the elements of successful rehabilitation have been approached.

APPENDIX I. *Sample Questions from Upper Extremity Amputee Personality Inventory (Selected from Peizer, 1958, pp. 46-49)*

The following pages contain a number of questions and incomplete statements. Each of these questions or statements is followed by several choices. Would you please place a check mark (√) next to the choice which most nearly expresses your way of thinking, your attitude, belief or opinion.

The information you give will be strictly confidential. It will be of great value in helping us to help other amputees. Therefore, please answer these questions as truthfully and accurately as you can.

1. I am self-conscious about my personal appearance.
   ___1. Never
   ___2. Rarely
   ___3. Sometimes
   ___4. Most of the time
   ___5. Almost all of the time
2. Do you feel sorry that you're an amputee?
   ___1. Most of the time
   ___2. Sometimes
   ___3. Rarely
   ___4. Very rarely
   ___5. Never

3. If I were being interviewed for a job I would feel:
 ——1. very self-conscious.
 ——2. considerably self-conscious.
 ——3. slightly self-conscious.
 ——4. slightly self-confident.
 ——5. very self-confident.
4. I forget that I am an amputee:
 ——1. never.
 ——2. rarely.
 ——3. sometimes.
 ——4. most of the time.
 ——5. all of the time.
5. When someone offers to help me, I:
 ——1. refuse to accept under any circumstances.
 ——2. accept only if I can't accomplish what I'm doing without help.
 ——3. accept if it makes the task much easier.
 ——4. accept if it makes the task a little easier.
 ——5. accept even if it doesn't make the task easier.
6. When I know that I am capable of handling a task, I:
 ——1. never accept help.
 ——2. very rarely accept help.
 ——3. rarely accept help.
 ——4. sometimes accept help.
 ——5. frequently accept help.
7. If you were a nonamputee, how would you react to an amputee?
 ——1. I would ignore the fact that the person is an amputee.
 ——2. I would treat him as a normal person who just happens to have lost an arm or hand.
 ——3. I would expect less from him physically.
 ——4. I would be more kind and thoughtful of his feelings.
 ——5. I would know that as an amputee he requires special treatment.
8. As far as I'm concerned, the loss of an arm means that I look:
 ——1. completely unlike most people.
 ——2. very different than most people.
 ——3. different than most people.
 ——4. almost the same as most people.
 ——5. the same as most people.
9. In comparison to the treatment I received before my amputation, people treat me:
 ——1. exactly the same.
 ——2. almost the same.

___3. slightly differently.
___4. somewhat differently.
___5. very differently.

10. Of the things that I could do before the loss of my arm, I can now do:
 ___1. all of them.
 ___2. almost all of them.
 ___3. many of them.
 ___4. few of them.
 ___5. very few of them.
11. When someone stares at my prosthesis, I am:
 ___1. not at all annoyed.
 ___2. very slightly annoyed.
 ___3. slightly annoyed.
 ___4. considerably annoyed.
 ___5. greatly annoyed.
12. While wearing my present prosthesis I meet social situations:
 ___1. with extreme confidence.
 ___2. with considerable confidence.
 ___3. with some confidence.
 ___4. with very little confidence.
 ___5. without any confidence.
13. I think my present prosthesis functions:
 ___1. as well as my lost arm used to.
 ___2. almost as well as my lost arm used to.
 ___3. as well as any prosthesis can.
 ___4. as well as any prosthesis I've worn before.
 ___5. worse than any prosthesis I've worn before.

APPENDIX II. *Sample Items from Prosthetic Reaction Scale (Selected from Peizer, 1958, pp. 51-54)*

INSTRUCTIONS

You are going to see a series of pictures that are planned to show situations which are faced by amputees in everyday life. In each picture, there is John, an amputee, and at least one other person.

Below each picture are a number of statements describing what John as an amputee might say, feel, or do in the situation. Please read the description of the situation given above each picture and the statements that apply below it.

Check *one* statement for each situation that most nearly describes what John might say, feel, or do *if he is wearing a prosthesis as he usually does.*

Here is a sample situation:

John notices two arm amputees getting on the bus.

REMEMBER TO: Read the description of the situation.

Then *check one* of the reactions that most nearly describes what John might say, feel, or do.

Check One

1. See what artificial arms they're wearing and how they use them. ___
2. I'll try not to attract their attention or stare. ___
3. Just smile at each other. ___

Hostess (who knows nothing about the guest):

Check One

1. Thank you. I shall help myself to coffee and cake. ___
2. Thank you. I shall try to manage both, but if not would you mind if I find a small table? ___
3. Thank you. I'll have some coffee. (Cake seems too hard to handle, John thinks to himself.) ___
4. Thank you. Would you mind helping me with the cake? I'll take the coffee. ___
5. Thank you. I'll appreciate it if you would set the coffee and cake down for me. ___
6. No thank you. (I'd like some, but what's the use, John thinks to himself.) ___
7. Thank you. Would you mind helping me? It would be somewhat easier. ___
8. Thank you. I'll try and manage. (John thinks to himself, I'll bet she feels sorry for me.) ___

APPENDIX III. *Prosthetic Expectations Scale*

(*This scale was developed and is being validated by the Amputee Psychology Research Project at the New York University Post-Graduate Medical School.*)

Please answer the questions on the following pages. Choose one of the five possible answers for each question. Your answer should be the one which is *most nearly like your opinion*—

(1) Draw a circle around the number next to your answer.

(2) *Also*, in the space to the left of your answer, place one of the following codes to show *how sure* you are about your answer:

AS You are *Absolutely Sure* and there is no doubt that you are right.

VS You are *Very Sure*, but you might just possibly be wrong.

FS You are *Fairly Sure*, but you might be wrong.

SU You are *Somewhat Unsure.*

VU You are *Very Unsure.*

1. What have you heard or read about artificial legs?

—1. You can do *all things* wearing them which can be done with a normal leg.

—2. You can do *most things* wearing them which can be done with a normal leg.

—3. You can do *some things* wearing them which can be done with a normal leg.

—4. You can do *only a few things* wearing them which can be done with a normal leg.

—5. They are completely useless.

2. How much do you know about artificial legs?

—1. Everything or almost everything

—2. Much or a great deal

—3. An average amount

—4. Very little

—5. Nothing

3. An artificial leg looks like a normal leg:

—1. Completely

—2. Very closely

—3. Closely

—4. Slightly

—5. Very slightly

4. Do you think that an artificial leg will feel:

—1. Very comfortable (no different from a normal leg)

—2. Comfortable (but different from a normal leg)

—3. Slightly uncomfortable
—4. Considerably uncomfortable
—5. Extremely uncomfortable

5. How important is it for you to wear an artificial leg?
—1. Absolutely necessary
—2. Very important
—3. Somewhat important
—4. Generally unimportant
—5. Completely unnecessary

6. In order to use an artificial leg well, I think I would need:
—1. Many days of training
—2. Many hours of training
—3. A few hours of training
—4. A few minutes of training
—5. No training at all

7. To use an artificial leg it takes:
—1. A great deal of effort
—2. Much effort
—3. Some effort
—4. Hardly any effort
—5. No effort at all

8. Do you think that an artificial leg will allow you to get around without any problem?
—1. All of the time
—2. Most of the time
—3. About half the time
—4. Only some of the time
—5. Almost never

9. What have you heard or read about artificial legs?
—1. They are *always as good* as a normal leg
—2. They are as good *most of the time* as a normal leg
—3. They are as good *half of the time* as a normal leg
—4. They are as good *only some of the time* as a normal leg
—5. They are completely useless

10. An artificial leg breaks down:
—1. Nearly every time it is worn
—2. Very often
—3. Sometimes
—4. Rarely
—5. Never or almost never

11. Would a good prosthesis help you to get along:
—1. Much better
—2. Slightly better

___3. About the same
___4. Slightly worse
___5. Much worse

12. Putting on and taking off an artificial leg takes:
___1. A very great deal of effort
___2. Much effort
___3. Some effort
___4. Hardly any effort
___5. No effort at all

13. When I wear an artificial leg people will probably:
___1. Always know that I am an amputee
___2. Usually know that I am an amputee
___3. Sometimes know that I am an amputee
___4. Rarely know that I am an amputee
___5. Never know that I am an amputee

14. Do you think than an artificial leg will allow you to do:
___1. Just about everything you would want to do
___2. Many things you could not do without it
___3. Some things you could not do without it
___4. A few things you could not do without it
___5. Nothing more than you could do without it

15. An artificial leg has:
___1. Many more advantages than disadvantages
___2. More advantages than disadvantages
___3. About the same number of advantages as disadvantages
___4. Slightly fewer advantages than disadvantages
___5. Considerably fewer advantages than disadvantages

REFERENCES

Abt, L. E. 1954. Psychological adjustment of the amputee, in P. Klopsteg and P. D. Wilson, eds., Human limbs and their substitutes. New York, McGraw-Hill, pp. 139–58.

Bard, G., and H. Ralston. 1959. Measurement of energy expenditures during ambulation, with special reference to evaluation of assistant devices. Arch. Phys. Med. 40:415–20.

Barker, R. G. 1948. The social psychology of physical disability. J. Social Issues 4(4):28–38.

Barker, R. G., B. A. Wright, L. Meyerson, and M. R. Gonick. 1953. Adjustment to physical handicap and illness: a survey of the social psychology of physique and disability. Rev. ed. Bul. No. 55. New York, Social Science Research Council.

Bender, L. 1934. Psychoses associated with somatic diseases that distort the body structure. Arch. Neurol. Psychiat. 32:1000–24.

Berger, N. 1958. Studies of the upper-extremity amputee. II: The population (1953–55). Artif. Limbs 5(1):57–72.

Bechtol, C. O. [n.d.] Industrial amputee rehabilitation. Boston, Liberty Mutual Insurance Company of Boston.

Cattell, E., T. Dembo, S. Koppel, E. Tane-Baskin, and S. Weinstock. 1949. Social usefulness of the cosmetic glove. New York, Research Division, College of Engineering, New York University.

Cayley, C. K. 1954. Psychiatric aspects of rehabilitation of the physically handicapped. Amer. J. Psychother. 3:518–39.

Chapman, C. E., H. F. Palmer, D. N. Bell, and A. Buckley. 1959. Follow-up study on a group of older amputee patients. J. Amer. Med. Ass. 170:1396–1402.

Contini, R., and S. Fishman, eds. 1958. Contributions of the physical, biological and psychological sciences in human disability. Ann. N.Y. Acad. Sci. 74:3–4.

Cruickshank, W. M., ed. 1955. Psychology of exceptional children and youth. Englewood Cliffs, N.J., Prentice-Hall.

Dembo, T., G. L. Leviton, and B. A. Wright. 1956. Adjustment to misfortune: a problem of social-psychological rehabilitation. Artif. Limbs 3(2):4–62.

Dollard, J., L. W. Doob, N. E. Miller, O. H. Mowrer, and R. R. Sears. 1939. Frustration and aggression. New Haven, Conn., Yale University Press.

Feinstein, B., Luce, J. C., and Langston, J. N. K. 1954. The influence of phantom limbs, in P. Klopsteg and P. D. Wilson, eds. Human limbs and their substitutes. New York, McGraw-Hill, pp. 74–138.

Fishman, S., 1949. Self-concept and adjustment to leg prosthesis. Unpublished PH.D. dissertation, Columbia University.

—— 1950. Some facts and opinions concerning amputees: a questionnaire survey. New York, Research Division, College of Engineering, New York University.

—— 1954. The principles of artificial-limb evaluation, in P. Klopsteg and P. D. Wilson, eds. Human limbs and their substitutes. New York, McGraw-Hill, pp. 775–93.

—— 1958, a. Studies of the upper extremity amputee. IV: Educative implications. Artif. Limbs 5(1):88–93.

—— 1958, b. Studies of the upper extremity amputee. VIII: Research implications. Artif. Limbs 5(2):117–27.

Fishman, S., ed. 1958, c. Studies of the upper extremity amputee. Artif. Limbs 5(1):4–93, and (2):4–128.

Fishman, S., and N. Berger. 1955. The choice of terminal devices. Artif. Limbs 2(2):66–77.

Fishman, S., N. Berger, and W. Springer. 1957. Management of the above knee amputee. New York, Prosthetics Education, Post-Graduate Medical School, New York University.

Fishman, S., and E. Peizer. 1958. The clinical treatment of juvenile amputees, 1953–56. New York, Research Division, College of Engineering, New York University.

Fishman, S., and staff. 1953. The functional and psychological suitability of an experimental hydraulic prosthesis for above knee amputees. New York, Research Division, College of Engineering, New York University.

Garrett, J. F. 1952, a. Applications of clinical psychology to rehabilitation, in Progress in Clinical Psychology. Vol. I. New York, Grune and Stratton, pp. 443–49.

Garrett, J. F., ed. 1952, b. Psychological aspects of physical disability. Rehabilitation Service Series No. 210. Washington, D.C., Office of Vocational Rehabilitation.

Gellman, W. 1959. Roots of prejudice against the handicapped. J. Rehab. 25(1):4–6.

Haber, W. B. 1955. Effects of loss of limb on sensory functions. J. Psychol. 40:115–23.

Healy, W., A. M. Bowers, and A. F. Bronner. 1930. Structure and meaning of psychoanalysis. New York, Knopf.

Hughes, J., and W. L. White. 1946. Amputee rehabilitation; emotional reactions and adjustments of amputees to their injury. U.S. Naval Medical Bulletin, Mar. 1946 (supp.): 157–63.

Kay, H., and E. Peizer. 1958. Studies of the upper extremity amputee. VI: Prosthetic usefulness and amputee performance. Artif. Limbs 5(2):31–87.

Kessler, H. H. 1953. Rehabilitation of the physically handicapped. Rev. ed. New York, Columbia University Press.

Kransdorf, M., S. Fishman, and W. Lifton. 1950. Study of amputee acceptance of prosthetic devices. J. Phys. Mental Rehab. 4(1): 17–19.

Krech, D., and R. Crutchfield. 1948. Theory and problems of social psychology. New York, McGraw-Hill.

Ladieu, G., E. Hanfmann, and T. Dembo. 1947. Studies in adjustment to visible injuries; evaluation of help by the injured. J. Abnorm. Soc. Psychol. 42(2):169–92.

Landis, C., and M. M. Bolles. 1942. Personality and sexuality of the physically handicapped woman. New York, Paul B. Hoeber.

Lewin, K. 1936. Principles of topological psychology. New York, McGraw-Hill.
Litin, E. M. 1957. Emotional aspects of chronic physical disability. Arch. Phys. Med. 38(3):139–42.
Menninger, W. C. 1949. Emotional adjustments for the handicapped crippled child. 27(4):4–7, 26–28.
Meyerson, L. 1948. Physical disability as a social psychological problem. J. Social Issues 4(4):2–10.
—— 1957. Special disabilities. Ann. Rev. Psychol. 8:437–57.
Murphy, G. 1947. Personality: a biosocial approach to origins and structure. New York, Harper.
Nemiah, J. C. 1957. The psychiatrist and rehabilitation. Arch. Phys. Med. 38(3):143–47.
Peizer, E. 1958. Studies of the upper extremity amputee. I: design and scope. Artif. Limbs. 5(1):4–56.
Petrovich, D. V. 1957. The Pain Apperception Test; a preliminary report. J. Psychol. 44:339–46.
—— 1958. The Pain Apperception Test; psychological correlates of pain perception. J. Clin. Psychol. 14:367–74.
Randall, G. C., J. R. Ewalt, and H. Blair. 1945. Psychiatric reaction to amputation. J. Amer. Med. Ass. 128:645–52.
Rogers, C. R. 1950. Client-centered therapy. New York, Houghton Mifflin.
Rosenzweig, S. 1944. An outline of frustration theory, in J. M. Hunt, ed. Personality and the behavior disorders. New York, Ronald Press. Chap. 11.
Sargent, S. S., and R. C. Williamson. 1958. Social psychology. 2d ed. New York, Ronald Press.
Schilder, P. 1950. The image and appearance of the human body. New York, International Universities Press.
Secord, P. F. [n.d.] Objectification of word association procedures by the use of homonyms. Atlanta, Ga., Emory University.
Secord, P. F., and S. M. Gourard. 1954. Body size and body cathexis. J. Consult. Psychol. 18:3.
Seidenfeld, M. A. 1949. Psychological aspects of medical care. American Lecture Series No. 44. Springfield, Ill., C. C. Thomas.
—— 1952. Applications of clinical psychology to physical handicaps, in Progress in Clinical Psychology. Vol. I. New York, Grune and Stratton, pp. 430–42.
—— 1956. Progress in rehabilitation of the physically handicapped, in Progress in Clinical Psychology. Vol. II. New York, Grune and Stratton, pp. 266–94.

Seitz, C. P., and R. A. McFarland. 1938. Psychosomatic experience inventory. New York, Psychological Corporation.

Shaffer, L. F., and E. A. Shoben, Jr. 1956. The psychology of adjustment. Boston, Houghton Mifflin.

Shelsky, I. 1957. The effect of disability on self-concepts. Unpublished PH.D. dissertation, Columbia University.

Sherif, M., and C. W. Sherif. 1956. Outline of social psychology. Rev. ed. New York, Harper.

Siller, J., and S. Silverman. 1958. Studies of the upper-extremity amputee. VII: Psychological factors. Artif. Limbs 5(2):88–116.

Springer, W. P. 1958. Studies of the upper-extremity amputee. III: The treatment process. Artif. Limbs 5(1):73–87.

U.S. Dept. of Health, Education, and Welfare. 1959. Health statistics: impairments by type, sex, and age. Series B-9. Washington, D.C.

Vineberg, S. E. 1958. Concerning job readiness. J. Rehab. 24(6):9–10, 23.

Weiss, S. 1958. The body image as related to phantom sensation: a hypothetical conceptualization of seemingly isolated findings. Ann. N.Y. Acad. Sci. 74:25–29.

—— 1959. The relationship between personality traits and acceptance of prostheses. Prosthetics Devices Studies, New York University. Paper presented at the American Psychological Association Convention, Cincinnati, Ohio.

—— 1960. The problem of predicting success in prosthetic rehabilitation. Orthopedic and Prosthetic Appliance Journal 14(3):53–61.

White, R. K., B. A. Wright, and T. Dembo. 1948. Studies in adjustment to visible injuries; evaluation of curiosity by the injured. J. Abnorm. Soc. Psychol. 43:13–28.

Wittkower, E. 1947. Rehabilitation of the limbless; a joint surgical and psychological study. Occupational Medicine 3:20–44.

Wright, B. A., ed. 1959. Psychology and rehabilitation. Washington, D.C., American Psychological Association.

—— 1960. Physical disability, a psychological approach. New York, Harper.

Zane, M. D. 1959. Role of personality traits in rehabilitation problems. Arch. Phys. Med. 40:197–202.

Zane, M. D., and M. Lowenthal. 1960. Motivation in rehabilitation of the physically handicapped. Arch. Phys. Med. 41:400–7.

ARTHRITIS AND RHEUMATISM

by MORTON A. SEIDENFELD

AMONG DISEASES known to antiquity few have remained to plague mankind so persistently as have those categorized by the titles of rheumatism and arthritis. Neither of these appellations refers to a specific malady but rather represents all-inclusive a descriptive title for a large group of chronic inflammatory pathological conditions that principally affect the joints, including the bones, connective tissues, muscles, and nerves in varying degrees.

There appears little doubt that animals and the *anlage* of man as we know him were afflicted with a wide variety of inflammatory diseases of bones, joints, and associated tissues, for the remains of these early inhabitants of the earth all reveal extensive destruction and deterioration that resulted in deformity and pain. Arthritis deformans was present in early cave dwellers, in Egyptian mummies, and in the remains of man found in the early Teutonic forests. Although it apparently disappeared for a time as man changed his habitat and his modes of life, it again reappeared among the Incas of Peru and later among the North American Indians in the pre-Columbian period (Garrison, 1929, pp. 51–52). As Sigerist (Sigerist, 1951, pp. 50–53) points out, "The arthritic diseases are today among the most disabling and crippling diseases and paleopathology teaches us that this was the case thousands and millions of years ago."

Morton A. Seidenfeld, Ph.D., is Assistant Chief of the Division of Research Grants and Demonstrations at the Office of Vocational Rehabilitation, U.S. Department of Health, Education, and Welfare.

Regardless of the early origin of disease involving joints and the peripheral elements of mobility in man, it was not until the sixteenth century that the term "rheumatism" was applied to such conditions. This term, derived from the Greek root *rheuma*, arose from the humoral concepts of medicine. The term was based on the belief that arthritis was merely a subdivision of a much broader group of diseases in which excess humoral flow to a given part resulted in a congestion in the involved joint. In modern medical thinking, however, the word rheumatism refers to those diseases of muscle, joint, tendon, bone, or nerve which result in discomfort and/or disability. More precisely, the term is applied to a rather wide spectrum of musculoskeletal disturbances in which pain and stiffness, often accompanied by swelling of joints, muscles, and related supporting tissues, are the predominant syndrome. This is somewhat broader in scope than the term "arthritis," which is more often reserved for those inflammatory processes that affect one or more joints.

Whereas these terms are not semantically identical, they are today used together. Thus, in its periodic reviews The American Rheumatism Association publishes them under the title "Rheumatism and Arthritis." Even more recently the United States Department of Health, Education and Welfare through its Public Health Service has conducted the U.S. National Health Survey in which it sought to gain information on the prevalence of "arthritis and rheumatism" without separating these two disease categories. Following this example, therefore, we have adhered to the policy of considering them as substantially an all-comprehensive group of disabilities with joint, connective tissue, bone, muscle and, possibly, nerve involvement in which pain, stiffness, and swelling are prominent symptoms.

INCIDENCE. On the basis of the report from the U.S. National Health Survey (U.S. National Health Survey, 1960) during the period July, 1957–June, 1959, "an estimated 10,845,000 persons in the United States were reported to have arthritis or rheumatism." This means that out of every 1,000 individuals there are 64 who have some form of these diseases. Among those under twenty-five years of age the frequency is much lower, with only 2 cases per 1,000, whereas among the aging population seventy-five years of age or over the frequency is a startling 286 per 1,000. It is also interesting to note the marked differences in the incidence between men and women. There is almost twice the number of females afflicted as of males.

With approximately 10 percent of the population over age 14 the victim of some form of arthritis or rheumatism (National Health Education Committee, 1959), there is little doubt that these pathological conditions become a serious threat to the social and economic status of many American families. This is further emphasized when we consider that over half of those who are seriously disabled by these conditions are under forty-five years of age (National Health Education Committee, 1959). Even more disturbing is the fact that it has been recently reported by the National Health Survey (U.S. National Health Survey, 1960) that *less than half of those suffering from these diseases are undergoing medical treatment.* The lag in efforts to rehabilitate those so disabled must be considerably greater. Thus, in the fiscal year 1958 the Office of Vocational Rehabilitation reports (U.S. Office of Vocational Rehabilitation, 1959) that it had rehabilitated 2,148 persons disabled from arthritis out of a total load of 74,317 who had been rehabilitated from all disabilities encountered during that year.

The failure to reach and treat large numbers of individuals suffering from some form of arthritis or rheumatism is indeed a most unfortunate social situation. Although there is much that is obscure and even unknown about these conditions, there is little doubt that some forms can be greatly helped and deformity and disability minimized or even prevented by early treatment. It is to be hoped that increasing efforts will be made to accomplish early detection and treatment for all such sufferers.

DEFINITIONS. We have already briefly noted the historical background of rheumatism and arthritis. Some of the more common subdivisions of these broad categories, which we shall consider here because they meet the criterion of producing serious, oftentimes permanent, damage to the tissues that play key roles in mobility of the patient are rheumatoid arthritis, rheumatoid (ankylosing) spondylitis, osteoarthritis, and gout, and a few of the more commonly experienced collagen diseases.

Rheumatoid arthritis is a disease of unknown origin that occurs primarily in temperate climates and has a tendency, it would seem, to be familial (though difficult to trace genetically), often insidious in onset, occurring significantly more often in the female than the male, and with an unpredictable course. It is a systemic disease that affects the entire body, producing such symptoms as fatigue, fever, loss of appetite, and loss of weight, all of which may often constitute the only symptoms that are reported. Sometime later, pain and stiffness in the affected joints occur. These joints on examination are found to have as their pathological elements characteristic inflammation of the synovial membrane with associated effusion of synovial fluid into the joint capsule and resulting swelling. In those instances where the disease is detected at this stage, it is likely that the pathologic process can be reversed and as a result the patient may well be expected to recover without serious residual disturbance of the joint. In general, however, the process continues on to serious progressive damage to the involved joints that may terminate in complete joint destruction. Because of the nature of the pathological processes involved, rheumatoid arthritis is frequently categorized as a "collagen" disease.

Rheumatoid (ankylosing) spondylitis has a number of other

names—Marie-Strümpell disease, spondylitis of adolescence, ankylosing spondylitis, and so forth. This is primarily a disease of the adolescent or young adult years, with much greater frequency of occurrence in the male than the female (in contrast to rheumatoid arthritis) and with a strong familial tendency present. It has at its onset characteristic symptoms of pain occurring intermittently in the lumbosacral area of the back, in the legs, thighs, and buttocks. Characteristically these pains occur even after the patient has had a good night's sleep; he may awaken during the early morning hours with pain in the back and legs, which is relieved when he gets up and walks around. As the disease progresses, the pain becomes persistent and more severe. Further, it tends to extend until most of the back is involved. Like rheumatoid arthritis, this disease is systemic and not a disease of the joints of the spine.

Osteoarthritis is "a disorder of the joint characterized primarily by a wearing out of its components, particularly the cartilage between two bones making up a joint, and the ligamentous and fibrous tissue structures supporting the joint" (Lowman, 1959). In addition to these changes, numerous others occur, including the development of small bony spurs along the joint margins as well as increases in bone density in those areas where the bony surface has been left unprotected owing to changes in the cartilage that formerly covered it. This disease, unlike the two described above, is more often characteristically associated with the middle and later years of life, though it may occur at any age especially with reference to joints that undergo unusually hard usage.

Gout oftentimes thought of as a disease of the wealthy is actually a disease associated with a faulty uric acid metabolism, which as yet is not fully understood. Its manifestations in joint pathology are due to the deposition of urates that form *tophi* and sodium urate deposits in the joint and in tissues surrounding the joint. A high uric acid level is found in the blood, and this may rise to peak level during the acute attack. Such attacks may be severely painful during the acute phase which, in the early stages at least, is likely to be followed by a prompt remission with complete relief of pain and a return of normal joint function. With repeated attacks, however, the disease is likely to become chronic, with multiple joints involved, associated with considerable crippling as well as complications, including nephritis, development of renal calculi, and even cardiovascular impairment.

A sizeable group of diseases associated with the various forms of arthritis and rheumatism have in more recent times been called *diseases of collagen.* These conditions include such serum sickness as rheumatic fever, periarteritis nodosum, rheumatoid arthritis, and numerous other diseases. They have certain characteristics in common, such as a chronic, relapsing and prolonged life course; frequent association of onset and acute exacerbations with stress-producing factors; lack of demonstrability of etiological source; general symptoms of fever, loss of appetite, and weight loss; the presence of serious joint involvements; changes in the nature of mesenchymal tissues; and many others.

These few efforts to define and delimit some of the more characteristic diseases that fall into the category of rheumatism and arthritis are indeed too brief to satisfy any but summary purposes. The serious student of these diseases must, of course, turn to more detailed sources. (See Lowman, 1959; Hollander, 1954; Smyth and others, 1959; Robinson and others, 1956; American Rheumatism Association, 1952.)

CLASSIFICATION. Prominent among the more vexatious problems associated with this collection of pathological conditions is that of classifying them properly. In the 1956 issue of the Rheumatism Review (Robinson and others, 1956) it was pointed out that "the obscure nature of many of the 'rheumatic' disorders continued to make it difficult to produce an entirely satisfactory classification of this group of diseases." By 1959 it was apparent that the same conditions prevailed, and it is called to our attention that in a "careful population survey conducted in Pittsburgh . . . of 327 persons with 'genuine rheumatic complaints' only one in eight fitted a classic description of any of the rheumatic diseases" (Smyth and others, 1959).

In view of this situation and the ready accessability of numerous classification schemes in the literature we mention here only the seven broad categories based upon the classification proposed by the Committee on Nomenclature of La Ligue Internationale contre le Rheumatisme, which Lowman has adapted and reproduced (Lowman, 1959). In his presentation Lowman states: "The majority of cases, however, fall within seven groups: (1) Arthritis due to infection; (2) Arthritis due to rheumatic fever; (3) Rheumatoid arthritis (including rheumatoid spondylitis); (4) Arthritis due to trauma; (5) Arthritis of gout; (6) Degenerative joint disease; (7) Nonarticular rheumatism."

MEDICAL-PHYSICAL ASPECTS. THE NATURE OF PHYSICAL INVOLVEMENT. Some mention has already been made of the nature of physical involvement. Here we shall try to make clear some of the specific characteristics of involvement as they exist in some of the more commonly occurring members of this family of disabilities.

Rheumatoid Arthritis (including rheumatoid [ankylosing] spondylitis). In order that we may understand what happens to the involved joints when rheumatoid arthritis is present, let us look at a diagramatic representation of a normal joint and one in which rheumatoid arthritis is present (see Figure on p. 59).

At the left is a diagram of the essential elements in a normal diarthrosis or true synovial joint. One can see the *epiphyseal cartilage*, the *fibrous capsule*, which is separated from the *syno-*

vial capsule by the normal content of fat lobules that produce numerous folds, recesses, and villi. The two layers of the joint capsule may be separated as described or they may be closely approximated as shown in the diagram leaving the joint cavity relatively free of contents. It is well to keep in mind that the presence of excessive numbers of projections into the joint cavity increases the likelihood of adhesion formation and increases the difficulty of draining pathological fluids from the joint (Lowman, 1959).

At the right is a rough diagramatic representation of some of the gross pathological changes involved in rheumatoid arthritis. Among the earliest manifestations of rheumatoid arthritis is the development of inflammation of the synovial membrane, which becomes swollen and thickened, while the amount of synovial fluid in the joint cavity is greatly increased. As a result of these changes, the joint becomes swollen, tender, and at times somewhat reddened. It is usually less acute and less severe than that which occurs in rheumatic fever, but, unlike rheumatic fever, the condition tends to persist, and, with further changes in the joint, it becomes chronic. Actually these changes within the joint are the result of the development of granulation tissue and the hypertrophy of the synovial membrane, which formerly merely lined the joint and now in its pathological state actually fills the whole joint cavity.

One of the very serious characteristics of the granulation tissue within the joint is its characteristic development as a thin coating called *pannus* which insidiously works its way around the articular cartilage of the joint ultimately causing destruction of its smooth surface with pitting and furrowing that destroys the smooth functioning of the joint surfaces. This destructive process continues in many instances to a point where the granulation tissue is changed to a dense scar tissue which causes a fibrous connection between the bones that are the component members of the joint, thus fixing them, somewhat loosely at first but ulti-

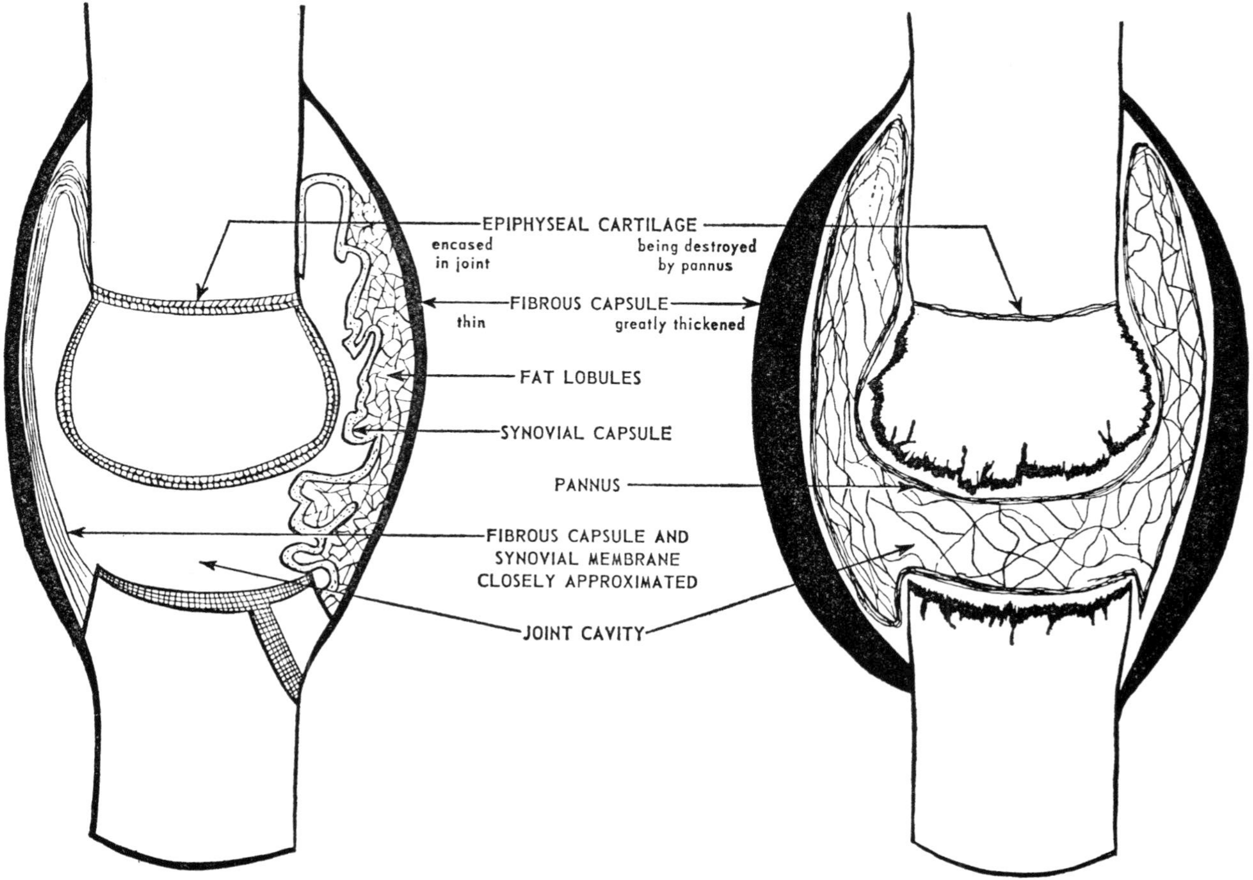

Left: The Normal Joint; Right: The Arthritic Joint

mately in a bony union as the fibrous tissue becomes converted to bone. Thus what was formerly a movable part has been pathologically changed to an immobile structure (Lowman, 1959).

In rheumatoid (ankylosing) spondylitis the changes are much the same, with the exception that the joints involved are in the spine, the junction of the spine with the sacrum (sacroiliac joint) rather than the joints of the extremities. The end result of this disease process is a "bony ankylosis" that may progress to a point where the entire spine is calcified, resulting in a condition that is sometimes called "bamboo spine" because of the degree to which this formerly flexible multijointed structure now resembles a bamboo pole. If the spine happens to become this way in a fairly straight position the patients' problems are minimized since it will not be likely seriously to limit his capacity, but when the spine becomes fused, or when the spine and hip-bone are fused in positions that interfere with the patient sitting or standing under his own power, this, of course, creates very serious incapacitation.

Osteoarthritis. Unlike rheumatoid arthritis, which is a systemic disease, osteoarthritis is a degenerative joint disease that is a result of the "normal physiologic process of joint aging" (Hollander, 1954). In the normal joint the cartilage is smooth and shiny, with a bluish-white translucency. The synovial membranes are pale and smooth. As aging occurs, the joints that undergo hard and persistent usage begin to show signs of wear and tear.

It is the cartilage between the bones of the joint that is most generally involved in osteoarthritis. Changes in the cartilage usually begin in the second decade of life. As the aging process continues into the middle years, the involved cartilage tends to become partially detached and shredded. Later, deep ulcerations of the cartilage may be found, followed by erosion, pitting, and marked fraying of cartilage edges.

As has been pointed out:

In so-called generalized osteoarthritis not all joints equally show signs of degeneration. Those joints that are under maximum stress are apt to show marked changes first. . . . Osteoarthritis is slowly progressive, its rate and development depending on many unknown factors but especially on the amount of trauma being applied to a particular movable part. [Lowman, 1959, p. 57]

Gout. Unlike the above conditions, gout is a metabolic disease in which joints suffer from the deposition of uric acid salts in the soft tissue and from the destruction of bone by the erosion from gouty *tophi.* As gout becomes chronic, damage to cartilage and bone cause severe crippling of the involved joints.

Psychogenic Rheumatism. Although symptomatically similar to the diseases described above, pathology of the joint is not present in psychogenic rheumatism. This condition is not to be confused with the psychological factors that are frequently associated with rheumatoid arthritis in which serious systemic effects, including joint pathology, is definitely present.

MEDICAL TREATMENT. As might be anticipated, treatment for the broad spectrum of diseases categorized as arthritides or rheumatism varies from diversified psychotherapeutic approaches, which will be discussed separately, to a wide range of pharmacologic preparations, physiotherapy, surgery, and orthotic and other self-help devices.

Rheumatoid Arthritis. There are many variations in the treatment regimens established for the alleviation and control of pain and the maintenance of functional capacity.

Rest is of fundamental importance for patients in the active stages of the disease. Since it is a systemic illness, adequate although not absolute bed rest is essential. The maintenance of correct posture while at rest is of the utmost importance. Pain resulting from body movement in bed may be minimized by temporary splinting of the affected joints.

As the patient recovers from the acute phase of his illness, it is considered desirable that he resume a program of physical activity commensurate with his physical capacity. A return to school or to partial to full-time employment is desirable and should be restricted only to the extent that his physician feels necessary. Physiotherapy and exercise are regarded as of the utmost importance in the restoration of normal function to involved joints, for the purpose of maintaining or increasing the strength of the muscles, keeping the affected joints as flexible as possible and preventing deformity (Clark, 1959).

A large number and variety of drugs have been tried in the treatment of this disease. Among them have been the salts of gold, corticosteroids, phenylbutazone (butazolidin), pregnelone methyl ester, and that old reliable aspirin along with numerous others. Almost all of them have been found to be of some value in the hands of their proponents, but in almost all instances the side effects and the dangers inherent in some of the drugs have discouraged many practitioners from their regular use. One of the few exceptions has been the salicylates, the most popular of which is acetyl-salicylic acid (aspirin). This continues to be the drug of choice for the alleviation of pain. Most practitioners agree that when this drug is given in proper dosage every day "it relieves pain without damaging the heart" (Clark, 1959).

The "steroids," gold compounds, and many of the other drugs are used from time to time to meet specific problems in therapeusis. It is highly important that the patient's reaction to these agents be closely watched by the physician so as to minimize any possible side reactions.

Osteoarthritis. Here, as was true of rheumatoid arthritis, the treatment is very largely symptomatic. No one has thus far found a means of halting the aging process, and, as a result, this pathological condition does not seem to lend itself to being halted. Good physiotherapy to maximize the retention of function, supplemented by use of the salicylates is thus far the most effective treatment. The use of X-ray therapy, vitamins, and the corticosteroids have been used with varying effects but none seem to have universal endorsement (Lowman, 1959; Hollander, 1954; Smyth and others, 1959; Robinson and others, 1956; American Rheumatism Association, 1952; Clark, 1959).

Gout. Unlike the above, considerable advance has been made in the drug treatment and control of this form of arthritis. Perhaps this is because gout is actually a metabolic disease with arthritis resulting from the effects of the urate deposits in the joints. The advances that have been made have been largely in the development of drugs that are capable of moving the excess uric acid and its salts out of the system, thus eliminating the source of the irritation to the joints. These are called uricosuric drugs. Most prominent among these have been phenylbutazone (butazolidin) and probenecid (benemid). These agents, when properly prescribed and controlled, not only are capable of relieving the acute attack of gout but also, when given on maintenance dosage, are capable in many instances of preventing or minimizing the recurrence of attacks. The use of these drugs requires medical supervision since they can and do produce side effects that can be generally avoided when the physician sees the patient with sufficient frequency to watch for evidence of such action. It should also be kept in mind that, whereas these drugs do succeed in overcoming the symptoms and the principal source of gouty arthritis, they do not appear to correct the faulty metabolic processes that produce the disease. Stoppage of the drug, therefore, is very likely to lead to return of the symptoms. Like insulin in diabetes, they control the disease but do not cure it.

Other important factors in the control of gout involve attention to weight reduction, avoidance of foods high in purines, avoidance of excess consumption of alcohol and red meat, and the avoidance of any agents that are found to precipitate acute attacks (Lowman, 1959).

PHYSICAL RESTORATION AND RECOVERY. The physical restoration of the sufferer from rheumatism or the arthritides often goes through three stages. These have been delineated by Kersley, Barker, and Cox who state:

> There are three main stages in the management of the arthritic patient: the acute stage, where hospitalization is necessary, the subacute stage, where the disease is still active, but the patient is able to lead a fairly normal life, and the stage where the disease may have burned itself out but the patient is left with residual deformity of the joints and loss of muscle power. [Kersley, Barker, and Cox, 1957, p. 94.]

Each phase involves its own unique aspects not only in the approach to the medical care of the patient from the standpoint of physiotherapy, the election of drugs of preference, nursing care, and the like but also in the approach to serious problems of social work and psychological services to the patient and his family. As these authors point out, basically the treatment of arthritis has not undergone much change in the past two decades. Although new pharmacologic preparations, advances in physical medicine, orthotics, and the like have made some gains, they are still dealing with symptomatic relief. However, a new approach has been added that is concerned with extension of greater insight to the personal needs of the patient, including his economic, social, and psychological preparation to live with what his disability leaves in its wake. The focus of returning the patient to a useful and meaningful position in his community give promise for more complete rehabilitation in the future (Kersley, Barker, and Cox, 1957).

Gafton (Gafton, 1957), in discussing rehabilitation in arthritic disease based upon a two-year survey made by the British Columbia division of the Canadian Arthritis and Rheumatism Society, came to the conclusion that the general attitude of pessimism in the treatment of this type of disease was not entirely warranted. Actually, except for patients over the age of sixty-four, a very high proportion of the patients did show some improvement. In the age group under forty years of age less than 10 percent remained unimproved. Whereas complete remission varied from 15 percent in those under forty to 7 percent in those over sixty, the results are indeed somewhat encouraging.

It is quite clear that the outcomes of rehabilitation in the arthritides and rheumatism will be greatly influenced by the extent to which actual permanent joint changes have or will take place. In those conditions where destruction of the components of the joint (cartilage, synovium, bone, etc.) are minimal or do not occur at all, the relief of pain, correction of known etiological factors, and the maintenance of the general functional efficiency of the tissues through a suitable physiotherapeutic program and pain-relieving drugs is likely to result in complete or nearly complete physical restoration. But, where the destructive process is very marked, "Functional improvement should be the primary goal, rather than the complete relief of discomfort" (Jackson, Sigler, Ensign, Fleming, and Long, 1955).

DURATION. The duration of rheumatism and the arthritides is subject to considerable variability. Each of the various types and forms of these diseases follows its own pattern. Many of them are rather insidious in their onset; many of them have no known cure; a few, such as the infectious forms of rheumatism, are preventable; others, such as gout, lend themselves to virtually complete medical control; but most of the so-called "collagens" respond in a rather unpredictable fashion to therapeusis and they are never "cured"—at times they may be subject to spontaneous arrest but even then may leave in their wake rather severe and limiting types of residuals. Fortunately, with proper care and the cooperation of the patient, in about 70 percent of the cases the sufferers from these diseases do show marked improvement following treatment, and deformity is prevented through physiotherapy.

FUTURE MEDICAL NEEDS AND SERVICES. Much more research is essential to understand the various forms of arthritis and rheumatism. Careful and well-controlled studies in the laboratories and clinics that will yield information on the etiology, pathology, control, and prevention of these crippling illnesses will ultimately lead to an answer for future sufferers. But these are not the only elements that need to be studied. Far more information is needed regarding the role that personality, motivation, and stress may play in triggering many forms of these diseases and determining how well the patient can be helped toward rehabilitation. As Clark points out:

> We still know almost nothing about the causes of arthritis. Virus infection is not ruled out, though we have as yet isolated no responsible virus. Heredity may be another source; but we have no proof beyond the observation that certain types of arthritis run in families. Psychological tensions have been known to trigger attacks, but we still don't know how this works. Allergy and hypersensitive reaction is yet another avenue for causative research. These tentative clues lead us into such varied sciences as virology, genetics, biochemistry, enzyme chemistry, psychotherapy, immunology and epidemiology. Promising leads exist in all these fields. Now they must be followed up. [Clark, 1959.]

We can do no better than to say "Amen" to this.

PSYCHOLOGICAL IMPLICATIONS. Thus far we have devoted a great many pages to the discussion of factors other than psychological as they apply to rheumatism and arthritis. This is necessary since we cannot hope to understand the problems of sufferers unless we have at least a modest appreciation of what happens to them physiologically and medically when they become the victims of such diseases. With this background we can now intelligently approach the even more intangible, oftentimes vague psychological aspects that, in spite of our limited knowledge, we have good reason to believe play a very fundamental part in making the patient's response to his illness what it is.

IMPLICATIONS ARISING FROM THE IMPAIRMENT. Relatively modest attention has thus far been expended upon the psychological factors that play a role in rheumatism and arthritis, and the major part of this attention has been directed toward rheumatoid arthritis and psychogenic rheumatism. We shall therefore limit our discussions primarily to these two conditions. The readers are cautioned not to assume from this that there are not psychological implications in the many forms of the collagen diseases and in other forms of arthritis and rheumatism. Rather they would do well to look upon this discussion as using these two forms of arthritis as prototypes of others in which psychological factors may play an obvious or a covert role.

There are those who believe that most cases of muscular rheumatism have a physiological or pathophysiological origin but that psychological aspects must also be kept in mind. Those like Edström (Edström, 1957) point out that the new tranquilizer drugs are of value in treating these disturbances. One cannot help but wonder whether the values of these agents lie in their physiological effects on muscle tension or in their psychologically "quieting effects," or both. Along similar lines, the glib opinion that rheumatic pain of the joints and muscles occurring in the absence of any objective symptoms are of psychogenic origin emphasizes the need for the utmost care in the exclusion of physiological pathology before assigning a psychic cause.

The painful back has long been an important problem in medicine. The causes of backache are numerous and varied, but in instances where no organic basis can be found they are often attributed to psychological sources, including both psychoneurosis and malingering. Unfortunately, in many instances organic, postural, occupational, mechanical, and psychological elements are all operative in one and the same individual, thus making diagnosis and treatment exceedingly complicated with the result that patients often remain in a state of partial or even complete invalidism (Smyth and others, 1959).

Patients with backache or other disturbances of the musculoskeletal system, after all other causes have been properly ruled out, may be considered as suffering from a form of psychogenic rheumatism. This may occur in a "pure" form, as a functional overlay of minor organic disorder, or as the perpetuation of symptoms of a previous organic illness (Tegner, 1955).

Those who present this kind of complaint have been found to be psychologically tense, anxious, vigilantly hostile, and resentful, with deep-seated feelings of being hurt by life (Smyth and others, 1959). It is considered that the symptoms they present are representations of their subconscious reactions to their deep-seated emotional conflicts. As we shall see, this pattern of behavior is reported over and over again in all psychological descriptions of patients with rheumatoid arthritis.

Whether or not rheumatoid arthritis, psychogenic rheumatism, and other diseases categorized under arthritis and rheumatism can be properly considered psychosomatic is far from clear although there are a number of clinicians who do so consider them. Halliday (Halliday, 1953, pp. 174–75) has suggested a seven-point formula which he considers effective in establishing a given illness as psychosomatic. The criteria he recommends are:

1. *Emotion as a precipitating factor.*— . . . In a high proportion of cases the bodily processes emerged, or recurred, on meeting an emotionally upsetting event.

2. *Personality type.*—A particular type of personality tends to be associated with each particular affection.

3. *Sex ratio.*—A marked disproportion in sex incidence is a finding in many, perhaps most, of these disorders.

4. *Association with other psychosomatic affections.* . . .

5. *Family history.*— . . . A history of the same or of an associated disorder in parents, relatives, or siblings.

6. *Phasic manifestations.*—The course of the illness tends to be phasic with periods of crudescence, intermission, and recurrence.

7. *The prevalence is related to changes in the communal environment considered psychologically and socially.*— . . . [There is a change in the incidence with changes in the social environment.]

Applying these criteria to rheumatoid arthritis, Halliday has found that the emotional factor, personality type, sex ratio disproportion, family history, and certain associated psychosomatic affections do occur in such a fashion as to warrant considering this disease as classifiable in the psychosomatic category (Halliday, 1953). To some degree psychogenic rheumatism and some forms of fibrositis in which organic pathology cannot be found follow a similar pattern.

The answer to the question of which comes first, the psychic "chicken" or the somatic "egg," must await considerably more research. In the meantime there is little room for doubt that both systems are involved in such diseases as rheumatoid arthritis. This would account for the failures of physical or symptomalogical treatment in the absence of psychic support.

There are those who like the Solomons (Solomon and Solomon, 1949) are quite definite in their opinion that "tension, repressed hostility and resentment have been recognized as factors in the etiology of arthritis." This they attribute to changes that are produced in the neuroendocrine system of the body as a result of emotional tensions. These physiological changes in turn are considered to be the basis for the pathology observed in the joints and tissues of the patient with arthritis. Others such as Hillman (Hillman, 1950) suggest that changes in the pituitary-adrenal system are the results of imbalance produced in the endocrine system by emotional tensions. He goes so far as to suggest that "a patient with rheumatoid arthritis would cure himself if his hypothalamus and pituitary would interlock to increase the secretion of ACTH." It is not surprising that such concepts should develop in view of the fact that some benefits are found through the administration of cortisone, ACTH, and other corticosteroids.

One must exercise caution, however, in accepting too readily any such explanations until the true etiological sources of these diseases have been established and verified. The preponderance of the evidence is that rheumatoid arthritis and other of the arthritides that display actual tissue pathology are not "cured" by the ingestion of corticoids in anything like the manner one might anticipate if these conditions were the result of a basic endocrine disturbance of psychic origin. The answer must await a great deal more in the way of crucial experimentation.

IMPLICATIONS ARISING FROM CHARACTERISTIC INDIVIDUAL REACTION. Perhaps as good a description of individual reaction to arthritis as is likely to be found exists in Ludwig's report (Ludwig, 1954) upon his psychoanalytic investigations of eight patients with rheumatoid arthritis. It is significant to note that "this group of patients presented gross abnormalities (of personality), both in the prearthritic stage, before the onset of the disease, as well as during the remission of joint symptoms." The characteristic reactions found in these patients were: (1) profound immature personalities; (2) marked feelings of inadequacy; (3) weak ego structure; (4) diffuse primitive aggressive traits; and (5) severe anxiety.

Because of the presence of such serious psychic disturbances Robinson (Robinson, 1953) has been rather emphatic in expressing the need of a broadly defined program of psychotherapy in the management of the over-all treatment of the patient with rheumatoid arthritis.

Others, such as Sherwood and Zimmerman (Sherwood and Zimmerman, 1951) have been inclined to favor a less intense attack upon the psychic factors in the disease and maintain that providing treatment staff who are willing merely to listen to the patient may make the difference between improvement or progression in the illness.

What is obviously needed is intensive study of the role of psychotherapy in relation to the treatment of the arthritides and rheumatism to the end that a better and more complete understanding may be attained.

FAMILY AND COMMUNITY REACTIONS. "The physician who specializes in rheumatology realizes that rheumatism is a problem not only of classification but of social and constitutional medicine" (Bach, 1951). This comment made by Bach pretty well places the emphasis regarding the social implications of arthritis and rheumatism. Whereas the problems are more or less psychologically unique to each patient, undoubtedly the family, especially the mother, has a profound influence upon the patient. The article by King (King, 1955), the monumental study by Short, Bauer, and Reynolds (Short, Bauer, and Reynolds, 1957), and many others already mentioned make clear that patients with rheumatoid arthritis, psychogenic rheumatism, and other disorders that are classified under the broad banner of the arthritides or rheumatic diseases are greatly influenced by what is happening in their external environment particularly in the family.

It is obvious that such patients not only suffer repeated traumatization from an unhealthy family constellation but that they in turn return the compliment by the manner in which they attain a psychological hold on the family. Since proper handling of the patient's psychic problems cannot be accomplished in a vacuum, it is essential that any treatment of the patient's problem calls for family treatment as well. Research along the lines of coping with the family and the patient in treatment has begun, but it needs far more intensive as well as extensive study.

Very little is available in the literature regarding any specific reaction of the community toward the patient with arthritis or rheumatism. Since in the mind of the public both disease categories are rather generally associated with old age, in all likelihood there is a general acceptance of these disabilities. This has grown to be the case in those afflicted with poor vision, auditory limitations, and other conditions so common with aging. No one can be sure he will not be the next victim; we are inclined to be much more empathic with those who may soon include ourselves. However, those who suffer severe deformity and the very young who are the victims of rheumatoid arthritis or spondylitis may find much less understanding because they do not fall within an age range with which the general public tends to identify such disability. Although this is largely hypothetical, it would seem to be born out by facts and warrants scientific investigation.

SPECIAL EDUCATIONAL AND/OR VOCATIONAL PROBLEMS. As of the present, probably about 1,750,000 rheumatic or arthritic individuals are in need of either educational and/or vocational assistance. "The balance are subject to chronic or recurrent pain but lose little or no time from work or other duties." Included in this number are about 200,000 children. Of these, 35 percent "are able to continue a fairly effective and reasonable active existence" (National Health Education Committee, 1959). The balance either die at an early age or are left to spend most of their time in bed or a wheel chair.

We know relatively little of any special educational efforts applied to the specific needs of the arthritic. Thus far the number who have been served are relatively few, and apparently they have been the recipient of about the same kind of treatment as pupils with other orthopedic limitations. When they attend schools where special classes are available or when a physical therapist is present in the school situation, they are given such physical therapy as may be prescribed by their physician. Special arrangements, such as excusing them from physical education or reducing their need for climbing stairs by either authorizing the use of an elevator or assigning classes on the ground or first floor level, are made as requested by the physician.

What is urgently needed are many more treatment facilities, including both free and low cost hospital beds for children and adults with the various forms of arthritis and rheumatism. It is estimated that only 1 percent of patients with these diseases can get hospital care in free or paying beds, and, when they are able to do so, they cannot remain long enough to get any but minimal benefits (National Health Education Committee, 1959). This means that they hardly ever receive the benefits of a rehabilitation program and, when they do, it is started much too late to give them opportunity to develop optimal capacities, to maintain themselves in family and community as independent and productive human beings. With increasing attention to the needs of this group of disabled individuals this situation may be greatly improved in the future.

SPECIAL CONSIDERATIONS IN PSYCHOLOGICAL APPRAISAL. The patient with rheumatism or arthritis requires a careful, comprehensive work-up by competent medical specialists drawn from the fields of internal medicine and rheumatology, psychiatry, orthopedics, physical medicine, and a host of other fields as their specific problems call for special knowledge. In addition, they require careful study by those working in many of the associated medical specialties, such as medical social work, clinical psychology, and vocational counseling.

There are those who seriously question the introduction of so many professionals into the life of the patient (Brown, 1954). Philosophically we agree that there are inherent dangers if the team approach "is employed in the management of chronic disease." However, we would be less than frank if we were not to point out that in our own experience almost all of the medical specialists complain that time does not permit them to do the thorough exploration they consider necessary. So they quickly turn to other medical and associated medical fields for other specialists who will do the necessary studies and provide them with their findings. Admittedly this is often spoken of as the efforts of a "team" when in reality it is merely a poorly correlated fact-finding committee. What appears to be really needed is a more realistic approach in which a well-coordinated program designed to study the patient from every aspect is worked out. The fact that it takes several persons who are professionally trained to do certain more or less specific exploration in several fields should not, if properly presented to the patient, either shake him or his physician. On the contrary, it should make the patient feel increased confidence in the thoroughness with which the physician is going about establishing his diagnosis, treatment, and prognosis.

For the time being, the preponderance of effort in those instances where the patient does seek medical assistance in meeting the problems of his arthritis or rheumatism should be directed toward giving him comprehensive treatment that will include adequate attention to his social, psychological, and vocational needs. A well-coordinated "team" of medical social worker, clinical psychologist, and vocational counselor would appear to be invaluable in establishing an appropriate assessment of the patient, his family, and the community, so that treatment and the reestablishment of the patient in a normal pattern of behavior can be attained. We have stressed elsewhere the great value that is to be attached to the medical social worker in establishing the patient as a unique individual in the family and the larger social milieu (Seidenfeld, 1949).

Closely paralleling but not duplicating the contribution of the medical social worker is the contribution that can be made by the clinical psychologist. As has already been indicated, King (King, 1955) has reviewed a good many of the psychological studies that have been made regarding rheumatoid arthritis. Unfortunately other forms of arthritis and rheumatism have received little attention, at least insofar as they are concerned with impairment of joint function.

Nearly all the psychological evidence that has been gathered so far has either derived from psychoanalytic interview or from the use of projective tests. Whereas we are willing to concede that this is one way to go about investigating the matter, grave questions about the validity of such approaches have been raised.

Eysenck (Eysenck, 1960, b) and Cattell (Cattell, 1957) are but two examples of highly competent psychological investigators who have raised serious questions about the validity and reliability of the projective tests as well as of the psychoanalytic approach, and we are inclined to feel that psychologists working in the medical fields who ignore these criticisms run a grave risk of retarding gains in the determination of psychological factors that are basic in such physical diseases as arthritis and rheumatism.

Above and beyond the problems involved in the use of projective techniques and the psychoanalytic approach is still another factor. In dealing with rheumatism and the arthritides we are concerned with diseases that in a good many instances appear to involve the autonomic nervous system. It has been suggested that imbalances in endocrine function, faulty autonomic control, and other physiological changes are closely related to what is observed in the way of change within the joints. It would seem wise for the psychologic approach to include within its scope comparable parallel data on the psychological level. Thus, muscle tension, which has been considered as playing an important part in the development of certain diseases categorized as arthritis or rheumatism, might well be considered from the standpoint of its psychic counterparts in the patient. Applications of the techniques developed by Eysenck (Eysenck, 1947, 1960, a, 1960, c, and 1960, d) and his colleagues offer the promise of validity and at the same time appear singularly appropriate to investigations concerned with the psychological equivalents and concomitants of physiological changes in physical illness such as found in the patient with arthritis.

SPECIAL CONSIDERATIONS IN PSYCHOSOCIAL AND VOCATIONAL REHABILITATION. We have already given some indication of the problems involved in the diagnosis and treatment of sufferers from arthritis and rheumatism. In situations where the disease process is well defined etiologically and the treatment is essentially specific or in cases where crippling residuals are minimal to absent, rehabilitation from the psychosocial standpoint may be seen as consisting mainly of understanding and encouragement during periods of severe pain and/or associated functional restriction. In the case of the sufferer who is fortunate enough to live in an environment that encourages him to get well and return to normal activity at a rate commensurate with medical advice, it is quite likely that this will be all that is required.

There are, however, some patients who in spite of the mildness of their involvement become anxious and insecure as a result of exposure to severe pain, absence from the family constellation, and deprivation of vocational opportunity. Obviously such patients require and can profit from adequate medical social work and psychological services, including vocational counseling.

It is well to keep in mind that the anxiety, passive dependence, and covert aggression frequently reported in the arthritic patient, especially those with rheumatoid or so-called psychogenic arthritides, require a great deal more than casual recognition on the part of the physician and treatment personnel. It has been repeatedly observed that such patients do not tend to do as well in treatment as those in whom active steps are taken to alleviate and control their psychological, social, and vocational problems. This clearly indicates that it is not enough to give merely vocal recognition to these problems in a staff conference. Nor should the active correction of psychosocial problems be postponed until after the medical treatment has been completed. In our opinion the arthritides and rheumatism do not differ from other chronic diseases in calling for collateral psychosocial treatment running parallel and integrated with the medical treatment program.

We have already given some indication of the great importance we attach to the services of the medical social worker in the treatment phase of chronic arthritis and rheumatism. It is of the utmost importance that a competently trained medical social worker or psychologist meet with the patient at frequent enough intervals to identify the problems that harass the patient. Proper attention to the patient's overt and covert fears regarding his health, his family, and his work allow these specialists to orient the medical and medically associated staff to a patient's psychological needs thus permitting proper allocation of personnel to meet them. If time, the lack of which is so often used as the excuse for inadequate attention to such needs, is truly of the essence, more intelligent utilization of psychiatric, psychological, social, and vocational counseling staff members can thus be made so that patients with minimal requirements may yield their time to those with maximal ones. The greatest gains, however, will accrue to the patient, for he will have the assurance that the many nonmedical problems that plague him and that interfere with his acceptance of treatment will be sufficiently reduced to allow him to profit from the total treatment program.

The clinical psychologist may well find that patients with lesser degrees of involvement require relatively little special consideration in the way of psychological examination of a routine sort. The more severely involved or those with clear-cut psychological disturbances call for well-planned psychological assessment. The writer is not aware of any special tests or psychological instruments that are particularly designed for the sufferer from rheumatism or arthritis.

Any modification in the administration of performance tests by the psychologist or the vocational counselor will follow the pattern for any other type of orthopedic restriction in regard to the use of upper or lower extremities. These are discussed in the chapters on hemiplegia and amputation. Lower extremity involvements will usually not pose serious problems to the psychologist but may be of considerable concern in vocational or prevocational assessment. Upper extremity involvements are likely to furnish problems as they do in the case of patients with paralysis, amputees, and so forth. The one great difference from most other upper extremity disabilities lies in the fact that the arthritic patient often suffers restrictions because of painful movement of joints which will disappear later when in remission or when the disease process burns out. Thus, greater need for clarification of the limitation by the physician is essential and must be heeded in the interpretation of findings. In other instances joint destruction may be involved, and then the limitations are permanent, calling for quite different appraisal.

Much more complicated than the appraisal of the patient's intellectual capacity, his educational achievement, his interests and aptitudes will be the frequent demands for personality assessment. Unfortunately because some of the most difficult arthritides to treat are heavily laden with psychic components, there is a greater or lesser tendency on the part of psychologists to establish the etiological role of personality factors in bringing either the primary disease or secondary exacerbations of the process into being. Because the factors that have been found within the personalities of such patients are those related to adjustment to the family, especially the mother figure, much of what has already been done has been related to using repeatedly psychoanalytic explorations or their test counterpart, projective tests, as the primary if not the only method of personality appraisal (King, 1955).

There is no particular objection to the clinician, psychiatric or psychological, using such devices as a resource for assessment. However, it is important to recognize the limitations of such approaches and to avoid the inevitable compulsion to use them for building glittering generalities regarding the role of personality. It is our hope that in the future the consideration of the part that the psyche plays either as a causative or as a secondary influence in the production of arthritis and rheumatism will include consideration of the close relationship between altered physiology and resultant behavioral changes.

In our opinion it is in this area that the most fruitful psychological research could well be directed. To contribute to this area, the psychologist will have to display a great deal more imagination than has been evinced by his preferences for the less reliable and minimally validated projective tools of assessment. He would do well both as a clinician and as a researcher to pay some heed not only to the criticisms of Eysenck (Eysenck, 1947 and 1960, a, b, c, d), Cattell (Cattell, 1957), and others but also to consider the suitability of some of the instruments they have developed for getting at the true etiological relationship between psychological maladaptation and organic disease of the component parts of joints. This point of view does not deny for a moment that emotional disturbances originating in poor family adaptation are elements in the lives of some arthritics, but there is no evidence that it is universally so, nor that similar disturbances are not present in a wide variety of situations involving both the physically well as well as the ill who suffer from many other kinds of pathology. Treatment of psychic disturbances among arthritics should be conducted with the recognition that acceptable, comprehensive research evidence as to the direct role of psychic disturbance in the causation of arthritis has not been established, nor has alteration of the psyche been established as the basis for pathological changes observed in the diseased joint.

A final word about the very important part that the vocational counselor should and must play in a comprehensive program for the care and treatment of clients with arthritis and rheumatism. Whereas the medical social worker and clinical psychologist play fundamental roles which, coupled with the medical assessment, help to provide a picture of what the individual arthritic may be potentially capable of doing, it is the vocational counselor who must pull these facts together and with a realistic perspective develop a workable plan that his client can accept and that family and future employer will permit to come to fruition. The medical, social, and psychological assessment of the client provides the basic underlying philosophy that influences the outcomes of treatment, while vocational counseling concerns itself with translating this philosophy into an operational program that the client accepts, bending his efforts toward making the philosophy a reality.

This is, then, a very serious part to play and calls for the vocational counselor to divest himself of any preconceived ideas and any rigid commitments to limited concepts as to what he can do. He must think broadly and realistically so that he can guide the client to utilize his potential capacities in spite of psychosocial factors that reduce his motivation to a suboptimal level. This the counselor can generally accomplish through adequate prevocational study, work tryout situations, and careful placement where not only physical needs of the client can be met but where he can also be psychically comfortable.

The ease with which these ideas can be expressed is a far cry from the difficulty that the counselor may encounter in bringing them into being. Yet this does not lessen the need for seeking to bring them as near complete attainment as circumstances permit. To whatever extent they are unattainable the counselor should be aware that success may be limited. The limitations in attaining the desired vocational placement in a given case and the necessary compromises that are made should be a part of the clinical record. In some situations, other members of the staff may be able to assist in improving the situation. If compromise is necessary, it should at least be recognized that what was done represented the "best" solution that could be reached under the circumstances.

Next in importance to proper preparation of the client for work is preparation of the employer regarding the potential employee's needs on the job. Vocational counselors are well aware of this fact, but it is of particular importance in the placement of clients who in addition to their physical restrictions have need for a favorable working milieu. It is also recognized by most counselors that arthritis and rheumatism are diseases in which active change may go on continually over a long period of time. In spite of this fact, most of these patients must work for a livelihood and, except for the rare instances when crippling is ultimately so bad that the individual simply cannot carry on vocational activities, it is likely that he will be able to maintain himself all of his working life if placed in a suitable type of job. The vocational counselor, being aware of this, may be able to plan with the patient the kind of employment that will best meet his personal requirements in spite of the dynamic and progressive nature of his disability.

If the counselor succeeds in reconciling his client's physical, psychological, and social status with his actual motivation to work and with the demands of the vocational milieu, then he is far along the road to readying the client for employment. Fortunately only a relatively small number of those afflicted with arthritis and rheumatism are likely to place excessive demands upon the counselor, but the few who do well merit the effort, even though they may tax the skill and ingenuity of the counselor to the hilt.

As has been indicated by Lowman (Lowman, 1959), "Job placement of disabled arthritics remains the most difficult objective to attain." This has been related specifically to the limitations that the patient experiences in using public transportation and to the limitations that restrict his physical performance on the job. However Lowman observes that effective evaluation by the medical social worker, the psychologist, and the vocational counselor usually results in a satisfactory training program where required, followed by job placement. Finally, it is well to keep in mind Lowman's injunction that "testing, counseling and placement in employment must be done with intelligent care and patient understanding if the arthritic is to be successfully restored to a productive place in society." As a matter of fact *all* efforts—medical, social, psychological and vocational—must be done with "intelligent care and understanding" if the many sufferers from these diseases are to find an attained goal of successful rehabilitation.

REFERENCES

American Rheumatism Association. 1952. Rheumatic diseases: based on the Proceedings of the Seventh International Congress on Rheumatic Diseases. Philadelphia, Saunders.

Bach, F. 1951. The rheumatic diseases, in International Society for the Welfare of Cripples, World Congress 5th, Stockholm. Proceedings. pp. 63–69.

Brown, T. M. 1954. The doctor-patient relationship in chronic illness, in M. Harrower, ed. Medical and psychological teamwork in the care of the chronically ill. Texas Rep. Biol. Med. 12:577–82.

Cattell, R. B. 1957. Personality and motivation structure and measurement. London, Harrap.

Clark, W. S. 1959. Arthritis. National Foundation Publication No. 24. New York, The National Foundation.

Edström, G. 1957. Psychogenic rheumatism. Nordisk Medicin 58:51.

Eysenck, H. J. 1947. Scientific study of personality. London, Routledge.

—— 1960, a. Behavior therapy and the neuroses. New York, Pergamon Press.

—— 1960, b. A rational system of diagnosis and therapy in mental illness, in Progress in clinical psychology. Vol. IV. New York, Grune and Statton, pp. 46–64.

Eysenck, H. J., ed. 1960, c. Handbook of abnormal psychology. London, Pitman.

—— 1960, d. Experiments in personality. London, Routledge.

Gafton, J. P. 1957. Rehabilitation in arthritic diseases—a two-year follow-up. Ann. Rheum. Dis. 16:456–59.

Garrison, F. H. 1929. An introduction to the history of medicine. 4th ed. Philadelphia, Saunders.

Halliday, J. L. 1953. Concepts of a psychosomatic affection, in A. Weider, ed. Contributions toward medical psychology. New York, Ronald Press, pp. 173–86.

Hillman, L. 1950. Relation of life stress to arthritis. Ass. Res. Nerv. Ment. Dis. Proc. 29:412–17.

Hollander, J. E., ed. 1954. Comroe's Arthritis and allied conditions. Philadelphia, Lea and Febinger.

Jackson, W. M., J. W. Sigler, D. C. Ensign, J. L. Fleming, and C. Long. 1955. Rehabilitation in arthritis. J. Mich. Med. Soc. 54:330–32.

Kersley, G. D., E. C. Barker, and C. Cox. 1957. Self-help and the arthritic patient. Ann. Phys. Med. 4(3):93–103.

King, S. H. 1955. Psychosocial factors associated with rheumatoid arthritis. J. Chron. Dis. 2:287–302.

Lowman, E. W., ed. 1959. Arthritis; general principles, physical medicine, rehabilitation. Boston, Little, Brown.

Ludwig, A. D. 1954. Rheumatoid arthritis, in E. D. Wittkower, and R. A. Cleghorn, eds. Recent developments in psychosomatic medicine. Philadelphia, Lippincott, pp. 232–44.

National Health Education Committee, Inc. 1959. Facts on the major killing and crippling diseases in the United States today. New York.

Robinson, W. D. 1953. The present day treatment of rheumatoid arthritis. Postgrad. Med. 14:206–13.

Robinson, W. D., and others, eds. 1956. Rheumatism and arthritis: review of American and English literature of recent years (eleventh rheumatism review). Ann. Intern. Med. 45:831–945.

Seidenfeld, M. A. 1949. Psychological aspects of medical care. Springfield, Ill., C. C. Thomas.

Sherwood, K. K., and B. Zimmerman. 1951. Newer concepts in rheumatoid arthritis. Northw. Med. 50:176–81.

Short, C. L., W. Bauer, and W. E. Reynolds. 1957. Rheumatoid arthritis. Cambridge, Mass., Harvard University Press.

Sigerist, H. E. 1951. A history of medicine: Vol. I. Primitive and archaic medicine. New York, Oxford University Press.

Smyth, C. J., and others, eds. 1959. Rheumatism and arthritis; review of American and English literature of recent years (twelfth rheumatism review). Ann. Intern. Med. 50:633–787.

Solomon, R. Z., and C. I. Solomon. 1949. Psychosomatic aspects of arthritis and allied disorders. Conn. Med. J. 13:1027–32.

Tegner, W. 1955. Psychogenic rheumatism. Proc. Roy. Soc. Med. 48:69–70.

U.S. National Health Survey. 1960. Arthritis and rheumatism reported in interviews. July, 1957–June, 1959. Washington, U.S. Dept. of Health, Education, and Welfare.

U.S. Office of Vocational Rehabilitation. 1959. Number of persons disabled from arthritis rehabilitated, fiscal years 1945–58. Washington, D.C.

CARDIOVASCULAR DISABILITY

by FREDERICK A. WHITEHOUSE

ALTHOUGH the term "cardiovascular" includes all diseases of the heart and blood vessels throughout the body, this chapter will deal chiefly with coronary heart disease (coronary artery disease or arteriosclerosis of the coronary arteries) and hypertensive heart disease (often referred to as high blood pressure), since these conditions constitute about 93.6 percent of all deaths due to the cardiovascular diseases (American Heart Association, 1958, a) and are the major causes of disability resulting from cardiovascular impairment (U.S. Dept. of Health, Education, and Welfare, 1960, p. 37). Rheumatic and congenital heart conditions will be given only passing reference because of their relatively lesser importance. Cerebrovascular disease (strokes, cerebral arteriosclerosis), although a significant impairment, is too complex a subject to be treated in this chapter other than very briefly.

INCIDENCE. Cardiovascular diseases in 1955 caused 53.3 percent of all deaths in the United States (American Heart Association, 1958, a), the major cause of death being "heart attacks" technically known as coronary thromboses, occlusions, or infarcts. The survival rate is about four in five cases (Marvin, 1957) depending upon age, previous attacks, severity of attack, and other factors. About 75–85 percent of the survivors are able to

Frederick A. Whitehouse, Ed.D., is Director of Rehabilitation of the American Heart Association.

return to work, most to their former jobs, with little or no alteration in the amount of physical activity. However, the 1959 National Health Survey (U.S. Dept. of Health, Education, and Welfare, 1960, p. 37) found that compared to other disabilities, heart conditions were the causes of the greatest number of restrictions in physical activity, particularly in the category of "unable to carry on major activity." In this latter category, heart conditions totaled over 30 percent of all causes and was almost twice that of the second leading cause, arthritis and rheumatism (16 percent), and over twice that of visual impairment (12.8 percent).

As a psychological problem, many experts in the medical and psychological sciences are of the firm opinion that psychic factors can and may exert a tremendous influence on the cardiovascular system, and that their effect is frequently of greater consequence than the somatic impairment in assessing limitation (Gelfand, 1957; Hellerstein and Goldston, 1954; Sparkman and Wilson, 1956). MacIver (MacIver, 1960) goes so far as to state that the major heart conditions—hypertension, hypertensive heart disease, angina pectoris, and coronary heart disease—"are classed in the category of psychosomatic disorders."

Another aspect of heart disease of particular importance to psychologists is a condition that some authorities claim is purely functional or "nonorganic heart disease," a neurotic focus on the heart. Various estimates (Cohen, 1950; Higgins and Schwartz, 1951; Bronstein, 1959; Cardiac Work Evaluation Clinic, 1959, Table III, p. 11) of the incidence of such cases range from 10 to 48 percent of cardiac patients. "Cardiacs without heart disease" may well represent a substantial proportion of the neurotic population of this country.

A few estimates of the personal and community costs of heart disease will serve to indicate the enormous drain this disability places upon our human and social economy. It is estimated that 900,000 people die of heart disease each year (U.S. National Office of Vital Statistics, 1960) and that 10,000,000 persons have some form of cardiovascular impairment (U.S. National Health Survey, 1960). The cost in personal grief and discouragement, family anxiety, invalidism, medical care, and vocational and social disorganization are beyond calculation. To cite just one economic statistic, industry lost 69,000,000 man days of productivity in 1959 as a result of cardiovascular illness (U.S. National Health Survey, 1959) at an estimated cost of $1 billion in wages and of $133 million in federal income tax. The consequence is a staggering cost to the individual, the family, and the community. But even worse is the fact that we have become so accustomed to this tragic situation that we tend to treat it as inevitable.

MEDICAL-PHYSICAL ASPECTS. The heart has been called the strongest muscle in the body and the one that gets the most exercise. "Each day, it pushes from five to ten tons of blood (depending chiefly upon your size) through your blood vessels" (Marvin, 1957, p. 16). From early embryonic life to the moment of death, it never stops. It accommodates itself to extremes of physical stress and quickens its pace under emotion. Its only rest is the fractional hesitation between beats. As a powerful muscular pump that forces the circulation of blood-nutrients and oxygen throughout the body, the heart is vital to life.

The ramifications and complications of circulatory pathology are enormous. They can range, for example, from the toes, where amputation becomes necessary when they are deprived of their adequate supply of blood nutrients, to brain tissue, which malfunctions and soon dies if deprived of oxygenated blood. Kidney, lungs, other organs—the whole body, in fact—may be affected by faulty circulation. Emotional and psychic disturbances may be activated. Of particular interest to psychologists is the fact that improper circulation of oxygen or chemical imbalance in the blood can affect the brain in such a way to cause what appear to be psychotic disturbances; these respond to amelioration or correction of the physiological condition (McKerracher, 1958; Eisenberg, Madison, and Sensenbach, 1960; Scheinberg and Jayne, 1952; Lancet, 1954).

The major types of cardiovascular disease are (American Heart Association [n.d., d, e, and f]):

Congenital heart disease, which is a malformation of the heart occurring in fetal life, the cause of which is unknown.

Rheumatic heart disease, which damages the heart, its valves, muscles, and blood vessels by scar tissue. It is caused by rheumatic fever, of which the precise etiological agent has not been identified.

Hypertensive heart disease, or *hypertension*, which is commonly known as high blood pressure. The condition places a prolonged stress upon the heart and major arteries. The cause is not as yet agreed upon.

Coronary heart disease or *coronary artery disease* or *arteriosclerosis of the coronary arteries* is a condition in which the coronary arteries become sclerotic or hardened and narrowed, so that the passage of blood through the channel becomes more difficult. The cause is not clear, although there are a substantial number of possibilities suggested in the literature. Under exertion or excitement, because of an insufficient supply of blood to the heart, pain of varying severity may develop and is usually called *angina pectoris*.

CAUSES OF CARDIOVASCULAR DISEASE. The etiology of hypertensive and coronary artery disease has escaped the determined investigation of many researchers. It is not yet known whether the causative agent is a single pervading factor, a group of factors, a sequential series of factors that trigger in turn, an initial force (such as a genetic factor) exerted in increasing or decreasing strength with age and environment, or, a unique causal constellation for each case. The relative strength of events that may be provoking, predisposing, facilitating, intermediary, precipitating, or long term, in combination with a more or less susceptible organ system, are not evident but there are a number of opinions on the subject.

A discussion of the various opinions would be too lengthy for this chapter. However, a summary of the literature gives a picture of an abundant number of possible causes and associations. These might be grouped roughly in three general categories:

1. The *endogenous*, mainly genetic, hereditary, and constitutional factors. Such items as body type, blood type, and chemical, systemic, physiologic, histologic, and hypothalmic irregularities or hypersensitivities have been investigated.

2. The *exogenous*. These features cover the ecological, such as the cultural, sociological, epidemiological, and environmental. Such factors as nationality, religion, geographic locality, occupation, economic level, and others are treated.

3. The *multicausal*, *psychogenic*, *psychosomatic*, *somatopsychic*, and *miscellaneous* factors. The aspects examined are age, sex, conditioned responses, health habits (among which are diet, smoking, amount of exercise); furthermore, work, strain, tension, and exertion, personality type, emotional stress, and phylogenic lag in environmental adaptation.

These are not discrete divisions. Some items cross all three categories, and there are many combinations (Whitehouse, 1959).

MEDICAL DIAGNOSTIC PROBLEMS. One of the first challenges of cardiovascular pathology is that of diagnosis, which in some cases is unusually difficult, for it has been found to be complicated by:

1. *The relative degree of the physician's experience in cardiac practice.* Many advances have been made since the large majority of physicians left medical school and, as already said, the involvements of heart disease can be highly perplexing (Becker, Vasey, and Kaufman, 1960).

2. *The physician's own personal attitude towards heart disease.*

Some physicians are fearful of the disease or are understandably cautious about the diagnosis and wish to protect their patient as well as themselves personally and professionally. As a result, some are inclined to "over-diagnose," i.e., to say the patient has heart disease when he does not. The physician also may over-restrict and limit his patients unnecessarily. Other physicians may under-diagnose, although the former (over-diagnosis) is more prevalent (Gardberg, 1957; Cook, 1960).

3. *The validity of diagnostic measures.* Unfortunately, the findings of many of the objective tools and measures that medicine may use—such as the sphygmomanometer (blood pressure measurement device), electrocardiograph (measurement of the electric current produced by the heart), ballistocardiograph (recorder of stroke volume of the heart), the stethoscope, drugs, and others—may be highly influenced by the psychological attitude both of the patient and of the physician. These measures are also subject to mechanical error, observer error, or bias, as well as the primary limitations of the tool or measure itself. Without further delineation, it is clear that these uncertainties also complicate the physician's accuracy of diagnosis (Turner, 1959; Sensenbach, 1946).

4. *Soft signs.* There are subtleties of heart murmur (atypical sounds) that are sometimes considered significant when they are innocent. Even previous heart attacks may not be noted, since perhaps as high as 20 percent are "silent," i.e., the individual was not aware of his heart attack, although he may have had some minor discomfort that he attributed to other causes (Dawber and others, 1957; Fisher, 1958).

MEDICAL TREATMENT. Some types of congenital heart abnormalities are corrective by surgery with excellent results in terms of providing a normal or practically normal life. Other types are either not surgically remedial or, at the present time, the operative risk is too great (Marvin, 1957; American Heart Association [n.d., d, e, and f]; Hellerstein and Ford, 1957).

Prevention of recurrences of rheumatic fever, particularly after rheumatic heart disease, is highly important, since recurrences worsen the previous damage and either destroy or shorten life. Since it is known that most attacks of rheumatic fever are preceded by a hemolytic streptococcal infection (often in the form of a sore throat, infection of the middle ear, etc.), prevention through the use of sulfonamides or penicillin has been found effective. Some types of damage due to rheumatic heart disease are amenable to surgery.

The relatively uncomplicated case of hypertensive heart disease may be treated by drugs to lower pressure, sedation, mild physical exercise, diet, reduction in weight, and advice to maintain an even tenor of existence, including plenty of sleep and relaxation. In some cases, an operative technique (sympathectomy) is used to reduce blood pressure.

Treatment for coronary heart disease, if detected before an actual heart attack, would be similar to the treatment for hypertensive heart disease, depending upon the symptoms and signs.

If a heart attack has occurred, the individual is put under complete bed rest at the acute stage, with sedation and possibly oxygen to make breathing easier. Every effort is made to keep the patient calm and as unworried as possible under the circumstances. The physician endeavors to present a positive, constructive attitude to the patient. It is also important that the hospital staff display an optimistic demeanor.

After the acute stage, which usually ends about the third day to the fifth day, there begins a period of hospital convalescence, which may continue for three to four weeks. During this period, the patient is gradually permitted visitors who are undisturbing and slowly increases his physical exertion.

Upon return home, the patient spends a period of two weeks to several months of home convalescence, depending upon the severity of his attack and his progress towards recovery. In this interval, there are planned stages of increasing physical activity. During the entire convalescence, a special diet is recommended.

Restrictions on the use of tobacco and upon sexual intercourse are usually removed as recovery progresses. However, the patient may need to continue upon a drug therapy routine.

One important message is stressed: emotional excitement can be as taxing as physical exertion; and this is something that the patient needs to remember the rest of his life (Hellerstein and Ford, 1957).

Although, as mentioned earlier, about three in four cardiacs may return to their previous jobs with little or no restriction, sometimes outside recreational pursuits of a strenuous nature are cut down, moderation in the use of alcohol and smoking is recommended, as well as a diet that tends to keep down weight and a routine of life that ensures adequate rest and relaxation. However, moderate physical exercise, especially if one's job is not too active, is not only recommended but needed (White, 1957). The patient should continue to visit his doctor regularly, as frequent check-ups are advisable.

The physician interprets the amount of physical exertion permitted to the patient and usually designates a functional and a therapeutic classification of the patient's status as a kind of distillation of his opinion and for the use of other medical and employment personnel. (See the chart at the end of the chapter.)

The medical prognosis of a patient's condition is thus a product of the severity of the impairment, its possible amelioration or restoration, the skill of therapeutic treatment, and the mental state and motivation of the individual. The two latter are highly important prognostic factors.

The newly diagnosed cardiac, accustomed to the security of a society in which there is provision for man's basic needs, suddenly finds himself vulnerable to an enemy who cannot be defeated but must be lived with in a temporary truce that will be relieved only by his demise. As this foe grows more powerful with the cardiac's own deterioration, ominous warnings occur that cannot be argued away and that remind him frequently of the enemy's existence. The cardiac may feel as if he were on a tightrope, where caution is always necessary and disaster ever possible; the degree of balance oscillates with every physical and emotional challenge.

Gardberg (Gardberg, 1957) says: "There can be but one way in which an individual with an unalterable lesion can live a satisfactory and useful life. He must learn to do that which he must do to take care of himself as a matter of habit, and aside from this, live every day as if he were going to live forever." Helping the individual learn to relegate to automatic practice precautions required by his condition is good advice, but attempting to suppress or deny his fears to the extent suggested is impossible, or at least undesirable, as such an effort could result in a worse situation physically and emotionally.

PSYCHOLOGICAL IMPLICATIONS. As previously noted, the physical vagaries of cardiovascular impairment can cause both emotional disturbance and psychic disorder. Often a major cause of emotional disturbance among cardiacs is anxiety due to lack of sufficient knowledge of the disease. Giving the patient a detailed list of precautions to observe may be useful, but, unless he understands the physiological reasons for the precautions, they may either not be followed or they may be adhered to overzealously and perhaps with considerable apprehension. Furthermore, since no physician can predict all the circumstances with which a patient is apt to be faced, it is clear that a thorough explanation of the basic condition, its significance and manifestations, is needed (Ernstene, 1957 and 1958). The psychologist will frequently find that explanation may not have been given adequately by the physician, or was not understood by the patient because the patient was not ready to listen, could not "hear" what was said, had not comprehended, or was not fully informed. Some patients do not want to know, because knowing is an aspect of reality they cannot face. Others may distort or utilize the information to form their own neurotic dramas. Nevertheless, information in the vast majority of cases is the only foundation for a constructive approach and should not be by-passed without serious consideration.

In psychological practice with inadequately informed patients, the psychologist should request the treating physician to provide more information directly to the patient. This is obviously the physician's responsibility; his opinion is authentic, and it is better for the patient to receive the information authoritatively, since it will mean more to him. Such information may be supplemented by the very helpful booklets on various heart conditions published and distributed by the American Heart Association (American Heart Association [n.d., a, b, c, d, f, and g]).

Individual reaction to the knowledge that one has heart disease is based upon what is loosely called "premorbid" personality. The person's accustomed pattern of response to threat is perhaps the most significant clue to the nature of his reactions to heart disease. A man may have met his problems in the past with resistance or with submission; he may have become practiced in constructive solution and grown stronger; or he may have been continually defeated and therefore tend to avoid or retreat from positive combat. However, this is but a rough generalization. Some individuals who seem to meet life's problems with confidence are sometimes surprisingly infantile when illness occurs. Others, who seem aimless in their everyday situations, have been known to respond to disaster with apparent fortitude and strength. Yet often such response patterns are but surface habits and not any real indication of what to expect in a case when the challenge is great and sustained effort is required.

Emotional reaction to heart disease is in a large measure similar to reaction to any serious impairment. The difference is mainly one of degree, rather than kind, since most impairments do not pose the immediacy of death. Heart disease, however, does, for culturally and traditionally the heart is the symbol of life.

Unfortunately, there are further implications to burden the victim. Heart disease is not static, like the residuals of polio, an amputation, or other traumatic impairments. It is dynamic, since it is a definite sign of a deteriorating physical condition. Whereas we gradually become aware that we are aging by the visible changes of skin and hair, by weakened musculature, or the need for stronger eyeglasses, such recognition usually comes about slowly; but a heart attack is sharp reality.

The first reaction to a heart attack is fear of death, a condition of psychic shock, and this feeling may continue to remain prominently in the picture. The succeeding reaction may be either an obvious depression, which may persist in conjunction with other modes of maladjustment, or a masked depression covered by various regressive or denial patterns. Fears are also present. They are often expressed in questions as to whether normal living will be regained. Most fundamental and often unexpressed is the threat to the self, one's basic self-image and ego structure: Am I the same person? Did this really happen to me? Will this change me? Am I now less worthy, a different kind of person? Shall I lose the regard of my wife, my family, my friends? Can I trust myself to withstand this? Am I being told the truth? Do I know the possible consequences?

Some cardiacs react to their fears with regression and present a picture of helpless resignation and infantile dependency. These are often persons who have, in a sense, waited for an occasion in their lives that would suffice to provide a socially and an internally acceptable excuse to withdraw from responsibility. Now they have found it.

Furthermore, there may be some very real external burdens that can tip the psychological balance of those who had formerly been reasonably self-dependent. For example, picture a man in the middle fifties with little education. His job was that of a laborer, a steeplejack, or a construction worker. Through the years, it has been increasingly difficult for him to maintain the physical pace. He has two grown children upon whom he might depend. His wife, a very aggressive individual, has already taken over. It may be difficult for such a man to find his way back to another job, perhaps in a different field. He may withdraw, overaccept and overlimit himself, and thereby place substantial obstacles in the way of his return to an independent status.

Another type of reaction is a form of denial. True feelings are suppressed and the seriousness of the condition discounted. This "underacceptance" is a fear to face the reality of the problem. Often, the physician's advice is not taken or is made light of. Such people seem to be seeking death to avoid living a life of cliff-hanging torture. The only recourse they see is to accept death bravely, with a smile and a wave of the hand.

Another aspect of denial is expressed as negativism and suspicion by the patient that he has not been told the truth by his doctor or family. Openly aggressive, he tends to hold a resentment against those around him who remind him of his helplessness. He rages against fate, which he believes selected him as an innocent victim for an unjustified and unwarrented punishment. The resentment, a striking back, may be expressed as follows: "My doctor is incompetent; my wife gives me no support; my employer doesn't really want me back. Perhaps another doctor or another job would be better." Indeed, to express his real feelings, he is saying: "Another wife, another life, for this situation is not mine, it doesn't belong to me, it can't really have happened to me."

Usual reactions to heart disease are often composed of one or more such responses to a greater or lesser degree. Whereas all cardiacs share a rather common and immediate numbing fear, a trial of various adjustment modes, depending upon the severity of the condition and the stage of recovery, is usually made. In time, most patients gradually discard nonconstructive responses; however, residuals of maladjustments may persist in minor forms in the typical case, and they occasionally flare up under stress, especially when return to normal routine and work is imminent (Whitehouse, 1960, c).

FAMILY ATTITUDES. There is no question about the striking effect heart disease or a heart attack has upon the family. There is not only an arousal of fear of the possible loss of a spouse and parent, but the family members' own fears of death are brought to the surface. The family unit is threatened with the possibility of modification or dissolution. Plans of many kinds, whether for college, a new home or car, straightening the young daughter's teeth, and many other schemes may need to be altered or abandoned, or become highly questionable. Expenses may mount for treatment; there may be complete loss of income during the period of attack and convalescence; and there may be a continuing financial burden for medical care and for accommodation of the client to his or her work. Special provisions for travel may be required, or it may be necessary to move nearer to work or to an apartment on the first or second floor. Many other problems often arise that are costly, troublesome, and frustrating.

The man convalescing at home may become irritable, feel he has lost his paternal authority, his prestige as a man and a supporter of his family. The family may tend to overprotect him and encourage invalidism. Resentment may arise because the situation burdens the whole family. Anxious children may grow defiant and rebellious.

The wife of the patient may collapse into despair, helplessness, or passive aggressiveness, which will further complicate recovery. Some wives who are overtly aggressive tend to take over and manage affairs, and this may not lend comfort to the victim of heart disease. A heart attack in a husband can arouse in the wife fears that had been suppressed. She may become more conscious of her own aging. In many cases, she will be in her forties or fifties herself and perhaps in her menopause. The late Edward Weiss has often said: "Usually the husband recovers from his heart attack but frequently his wife doesn't."

COMMUNITY ATTITUDES. As with many other impairments, we often see rather irrational attitudes towards heart disease in the general community. Friends may act differently, depending upon their conception of the disease. The fact that heart disease is not as visible as an injury sustained in some traumatic way, that it frequently is not discrete in its ramifications or limitations; that, to some, the presence of the individual is a walking reminder of sudden death—all of these factors tend to develop a folklore, mystery, and uncomfortable feelings about the heart and cardiac patients.

Employers often show more mixed feelings about their cardiac employees than they do with other impairments. Again, the impairment to them is less tangible, less definable insofar as limits are concerned, and they do not care to admit their real reasons for rejection, because it may reflect upon their humanity, foresight, courage, and good judgment. Legitimate-sounding and businesslike reasons are offered for rejection, but, when questioned further, employers react with annoyance, confusion, and lack of answers, indicating the speciousness of some of their original reasons (American Heart Association, 1958, b; Federation Employment and Guidance Service, 1959; Olshansky, Friedland, Clark, and Sprague, 1955).

PROBLEM OF VOCATIONAL ADJUSTMENT. One of the major personal problems of the individual with cardiovascular disease is to live up to his residual physical capacities. It is natural to play safe, and certainly precautions are necessary. Yet, a person can get rebellious at his wife's head shaking, a friend's raised eyebrow, a fellow worker's instant help with a light package, and the anxious look on the face of his superior.

Frequently, a man's job is changed, sometimes in spite of his physician's belief that his old job is physically feasible. The change is sometimes a downgrading in level or pay or is a much easier, "old man's" type of job. A man who shortly before was a respected and skilled worker finds it difficult to accept a watchman's job or one as a timekeeper, regardless of possible equality in pay. He has already faced too many reminders of the fact that he may not be the man he was. Moreover, a kindly word of advice on the part of the personnel manager is resented as pity or pampering. The physician, on the other hand, is one who can supply him with a realistic and socially acceptable reason for accepting a lesser job or a changed job. The cardiac needs such authentic explanation, and a psychologist or counselor should always consider the value of obtaining the physician's cooperation in presenting such issues.

When a homemaker is limited by heart disease, it may have serious consequences for her family, especially if there are children to be cared for in addition to the burden of maintaining the home. If she has been a homebody with little social life, her present limitations often make for a lonely and discouraging existence. Older daughters may resent taking over some of the household tasks, and most husbands do not realize the amount of energy required to work in the home. Hellerstein (Katz, Bruce, Plummer, and Hellerstein, 1958) has pointed out that the energy cost of many household tasks are higher than the average job in industry. Age and impairment in a homemaker make for a heavy burden, especially in a society that glorifies youth and beauty.

If the young child or adolescent has a damaged heart because of congenital abnormality or rheumatic fever, one finds much of what is typical of other early impairment. School work is missed, and experiences may be few, narrow, and distorted. The fear of death may be instilled, overprotection is frequent, and invalidism, accepted, unless medical, parental, school, and vocational personnel are properly oriented to the young person's developmental needs. When the onset of disability occurs in childhood, habilitation is the word that characterizes the necessary process of the establishment and progression of orderly concepts, self-images, and increasing standards of age performance (Whitehouse, 1953, a, and 1960, d.; Lawrence, 1960).

THE "CARDIAC PERSONALITY." Articles on the subject of personality frequently speak of the "coronary personality" or more often of the "hypertensive personality" (Whitehouse, 1959). Some writers either by implication or directly conclude that there is a distinct constellation of traits characterizing a "cardiac personality." Others do not go this far but feel that certain personality traits are encountered among cardiacs with unusual frequency. However, all tend to describe the cardiac individual in rather similar terms, with those who do not believe the psyche influential in the genesis of heart disease less inclined to see a "cardiac personality" type but rather to attribute characteristic reactions to the consequences of the disease.

Some of the terms most frequently used to describe these characteristic traits or reactions are: overstriving, perfectionistic, laboring under a time urgency; resentful, tightly restrained, and unable to express aggression; insecure, conflict-avoidance, passive with a great need for and respect for authority; marked tendency to neglect health, minimize symptoms, reject illness.

The question of a unique cardiac personality is an arbitrary one. In one sense there is no unique disability personality because there are actual and philosophic connections among all disabilities. However, there are sufficient differences and distinctions about heart disease to warrant speaking of the psychology of heart disease without accepting the concept of cardiac personality or denying the many psychological similarities between heart disease and other impairments.

SPECIAL CONSIDERATIONS IN PSYCHOLOGICAL APPRAISAL. PRELIMINARY OBSERVATIONS. While it is obvious that personality function is dependent upon the brain and its physical health, as a rule psychologists seldom stop to think of the relationship among heart, brain, and personality function. Mental symptoms may be present in cardiac patients that are induced by lack of a proper flow of blood, lack of proper blood content, an abnormality of blood vessels, and by certain drugs that are prescribed for the heart but may have an adverse influence upon the brain.

There are other areas in which medical and psychodiagnostic problems arise. There are cardiacs diagnosed as organic who are functional, and in all probability those in whom the functional overlay is the primary problem and the organic secondary. Psychotics with heart disease are difficult medical patients and also present difficulties in psychiatric treatment (Abraham, 1959; Cook, 1960). There are numbers of other complex problems facing the practicing psychologist in this area.

Let us consider first the question of reduced blood supply to the brain. Scheinberg and Jayne (Scheinberg and Jayne, 1952) say: "The great reduction in cerebral flow in heart failure is a physiologic explanation for the mental symptoms frequently seen in cardiac patients." Other investigators report similar findings (Eisenberg, Madison, and Sensenbach, 1960).

Besides adequacy of blood flow, there are conditions of atypical blood content and impairment of the vascular channels of the arteries. The effect of long-term hypertension on the brain was studied by Hughes and Dodgson who report: "Emotional lability was a striking feature in most cases . . . [and was] usually associated with intellectual deterioration" (Hughes, Dodgson, and MacLellan, 1954). An article in *Lancet* remarks that "The well-being of the cerebral neurones can be disturbed by gross and permanent factors, such as deprivation of blood, or by subtle and temporary factors, such as changes—even perhaps minute changes—in the blood chemistry" (Lancet, 1954). Symonds says: "Rauwolfia serpentina prescribed for arterial hypertension may sometimes cause an illness hardly distinguishable from a depressive psychosis" (Symonds, 1960). Sherlock (Sherlock and others, 1954) has pointed out that cerebral disturbances caused by treatments to cure liver disease can be removed by a reversal of the therapy. Rullo and Allan (Rullo and Allan, 1958) report psychosis as the result of thyroid deficiency, and McKerracher, a psychiatrist, says: "Just as it does to other organs, generalized toxemia disturbs the function of the brain; cardiac and renal disease are common causes of such mental change." He also states that "sclerosis of cerebral vessels often precipitates emotional disorder" (McKerracher, 1958). In the realm of psychosis or apparent psychosis, we find some very involved problems (Marchand, 1955; Abraham, 1959; Noyes, 1955; Ward and Ross, 1960) of which psychologists working with cardiac patients must be aware.

In short, it is extremely important that a proper and definitive medical appraisal be at the disposal of the psychologist, and that the psychologist be alert to the *physiological* aspects of psychological disturbances. So prepared, he is better able to assess and manage the many complex psychological problems he will encounter in work with cardiacs, problems that have led the National Conference on Work Evaluation Units held at Arden House, May, 1960, to resolve: "That in realistic planning with the patient, it is necessary to evaluate those emotional and psychological factors that are important in determining the patient's work potential, employability and total life adjustment. Therefore, we resolve that the psychiatrist and/or psychologist are by nature of their specialized training desirable members of the Work Evaluation Unit Team" (American Heart Association, 1960).

THE PSYCHOLOGICAL EXAMINATION. *Case History*. Since cardiovascular disease usually has a long development, is a chronic condition, and entails much emotional involvement, the case history is of particular importance in psychological evaluation. In fact, the competence of the examiner in handling cardiac patients may be judged by the thoroughness with which he studies and evaluates the case history, since this is one of the basic reference points in forming clinical judgments.

Of critical importance in this area of disability is the medical history. Sometimes the importance of heart disease as a primary impairment tends to put other impairments the patient may have in such a secondary role that they are not fully evaluated. As previously mentioned, the broad impact of heart and artery damage may influence other organs of the body and create other debilitating conditions presently or in the near future. The psychologist must be aware of these facts and of their implications, and not depend automatically for medical information upon a given physical examination as telling the whole story or as being adequately diagnostic or prognostic. He should himself seek out all necessary medical details which may be directly or indirectly associated with cardiac disease. He should make personal inquiry and be sufficiently informed about the impairment and its possible physiological and psychological ramifications to pose good questions, particularly regarding: (1) priority of cause; (2) major factor in inducing and/or precipitating the condition; (3) major treatment emphasis; (4) priority of treatment approach; (5) major physiological determinants in prognosis; and (6) major psychological factors in prognosis. In obtaining the medical information, it is obvious that the psychologist must have access to and close working relationships with medical specialists.

Other history information of special importance in work with cardiacs includes an answer to the question: What is the meaning of illness or disease to the patient? Does it represent a moral evil (a punishment)? a personal evil (the result of individual failure)? an hereditary curse? a medical failure? a fortuitous escape? a natural event? and so forth. The patient's interpretation of his illness provides a significant clue to his actions and reactions.

The "why" of heart disease may also prove significant. Why was the heart "selected" as the organ for attack? How much does the symbolic belief one has about the meaning of the heart affect the consequence? For example, Meerloo (U.S. Veterans Administration, 1960) says that heart difficulty means symbolically a loss of love. Note has also been made of the "anniversary reaction" in heart disease, which Weiss explains as follows: "Illness of emotional origin often seems to occur on the anniversary of a significant event in the life of the patient. This is usually the death of a key figure with whom the patient has established a complex identification in which hostility is usually noted" (Weiss, 1958).

In addition to the possible "anniversary" significance of a heart attack the psychologist may wish to review the situational aspects of the attack, i.e., time, day, and circumstances. Was the occasion or general situation of the episode parallel to earlier life episodes in which threat was met with irresolution or suppression? A number of investigators (Weiss and others, 1957; Russek and Zohman, 1958) report that a gradually mounting tension occurred in patients before the attack. Or perhaps one could say that the heart attack might be an expression by the individual of a mock suicide. It causes worry and threat to one's family and friends; it is a justification for unappreciated hard work; and the situation also has the comfort of much solicitude without the onus of public scorn or disapproval. Furthermore, one views and savors all while remaining alive.

Everyone must justify his illness in some way. The reasons designated by the patient are always of significance and provide clues to the deeper reasons as well as to psychological diagnosis and prognosis.

Finally, the psychologist should be aware of so-called "silent" heart attacks, which sometimes cannot really be specified but only approximated between thorough physical examinations and are described by such expressions as "felt extremely tired," "went to bed for a day," "disturbing pains attributed to indigestion at the time," "remained out of work because he wasn't feeling well." The psychologist will naturally need help from the physician in identifying such incidents; but the reporting by a client of a "heart attack" for which the physician has no confirmatory evidence, as well as the occasion and circumstances of the attack, may prove of significant psychological value.

The reasons behind the onset of congestive heart failure (inability of the heart to keep the blood circulating normally) should also be reviewed with the physician. The onset is often instigated by neglect of the patient to follow the regime prescribed by his physician, but the occasions and frequency of congestive difficulty may be related to psychological stresses or emotional upset.

The effect of frequent bouts of rheumatic fever upon personality function should be known to the psychologist. Schooling—or at least normal classroom experiences—are lost; hours are spent alone in a dependent state; and the dire consequences of overactivity are the frequent sermon of physician and parent. Consequently, the number of rheumatic fever attacks, their length and severity, and the restrictions imposed are clues to the effect these factors may have had on the client's life and should be contained in the case history.

Interview. The story behind the cardiac illness and its particular purport to the patient, including how he lived his life on the day of the "attack," obtained directly from the patient often fills in other history information with "live" and significant details.

To learn the various impact of events, the examiner may ask the patient to describe a typical day in his life, a typical Saturday night, or a typical week at a selected time in the past. Or he may ask the client to describe the period when he was ill with rheumatic fever; when he got his first job; how his routine changed after his marriage; how he spent the week before his heart attack; how he spent last week, now that he has recovered; and other queries in a similar vein.

An examiner often obtains a great deal more psychological insight by listening to a patient's direct reporting of events in his own words and by noting which events were selected for reporting than by direct questions about feeling and reaction (Whitehouse, 1958–59). Of course, reported feelings must be supplemented and checked on; for how one may feel is not necessarily how one may act; nor does action invariably indicate feelings. And we must also be aware that a patient's claimed activities may be fantasized in his present reporting. But because an individual with cardiovascular disease must change his life in terms of attitudes and habits, it is particularly important to hear what he has to say.

It is obviously difficult to estimate the significance to an interviewer of heart disease and the threat of death as personified by the interviewee. How well could an examiner work with a patient who was about the same age as his father who died of heart disease? Or the examiner himself may have heart disease. Sometimes reactions are aroused on a conscious or unconscious level that "take the form of strong positive identification with a subject, or hostility and rejection" (Levine, 1960, p. 89). However, as Galen said: "He cures most in whom most are confident." If this concern can pervade the interview, it may obviate much of the subjective feelings aroused and help psychologists be reasonably objective about their subjectivity.

While the cardiac client has undoubtedly reported various symptomatic complaints to the physician, it is important that the psychologist also review them with the client for the following three reasons:

1. The physician may not have responded to or noted the significance of some complaints, either through possible oversight, or because he may not be psychologically oriented.

2. The client will often report different symptoms or additional symptoms, or he will place altered value on some symptoms, because a psychologist is asking.

3. Hearing directly from the client how he speaks about his complaints, the facial and bodily movements he exhibits, the kinds of instances he gives—all provide a more vital picture of their meaning to the client when observed first hand.

A review with the physician of the session on this subject may be helpful to him as well as to the psychologist.

The cardiac client, like other people whose impairments are threatening, may make various attempts to mask his feelings. He may claim he is not afraid, but he emphasizes at great length how fearful his wife is about his condition. He may also exaggerate the "struggle" his physician had to "pull him through," going on to describe the exceptional technical excellence of his doctor. The psychologist must be alert to such diagnostic clues.

It is also important to find out how a client spends his leisure time. Assuming he is working within his physical limitations, it may be that the emotional stress of his job is more taxing than realized. It could be, that he retains an image of himself as an invalid, unable to socialize or be accepted socially. A significant criterion is to compare how much of a change his present activities are from his previous social and vocational involvements.

Whether he has resumed sexual relations, assuming his medical condition permits it, may be an obvious clue to his adjustment to his impairment. It may also be a resignation to a previously poor relationship with his spouse. His wife may, of course, use expressed concern about his impairment as an excuse for abstention desired by her.

If the client is convalescing from a heart attack, he should be questioned about whether his physical tolerance has been increasing as it should be, and what he has been doing. Whereas this is obviously a question that would be asked by his physician, his reaction to the statement and his account of the process may be indicative of the strength of his convictions about his perceived future role. Certain physical actions of greater exertion may be taken without strain while lesser ones of symbolic content provoke breathlessness and pain. The significance of these discrepancies should be of concern to the psychologist.

Another area would be reaction to a special diet. The compliance or lack thereof may be indicative not only of personal but of interpersonal problems with one's spouse. There are those who are resigned to a special diet because they are dependent; those who conform because it is a mark of invalidism that permits resentment and complaint. The resistors may be resigned to an inevitable short existence, punishing their spouse by apparently increasing the threat, punishing themselves, and so forth.

An individual whose heart condition does not produce angina under moderate physical effort does not ordinarily get anginal pain during an interview unless the occasion or topic is psychologically "painful." Such topics should, of course, be noted by the psychologist and eventually followed through. Similarly, breathlessness on the part of a client—unless he has just climbed a flight of stairs—or apparent or reported palpitations during the interview are also probably due to emotional stress.

Observation. The brief sample of behavior that psychologists are able to observe in their offices should be supplemented, if one has the opportunity, by whatever other available settings there may be: home, job, sheltered workshop, rehabilitation center, occupational therapy department of a hospital, and so forth. The cardiologist is interested in observing how a cardiac responds to various forms of physical exertion and stress, the psychologist in how a cardiac responds to various forms of psychological effort and stress. In making such observations, the area of what has been loosely termed "nonverbal" communication should not be overlooked, such as the setting and positioning of the individual involved, the tone of voice, the hesitations, choice of words, gestures of hands, body, and head, and many other aspects of "nonverbal" behavior. A particularly good setting for client observation is the comprehensive rehabilitation center, which permits economic, vocational, medical, psychological, and social estimations to be checked and compared (Whitehouse, 1953, b).

Psychological Testing and Interpretation. Apparently the cardiovascular patient needs no special test adaptation. It would be well however to note some of the factors involved in test *interpretation* so that the psychologist is prepared for possible areas in which some modification is required for valid appraisal.

If the subject is a child or an adolescent and has been somewhat divorced from a normal environment because of early cardiac impairment, the examiner should anticipate, because of this constricted experience and loss of schooling, a naivete about life, a below-grade academic level—particularly in reading—and a general immaturity and dependency (Whitehouse, 1953, a; Lawrence, 1960; Neuhaus, 1958).

The majority of cardiacs however are apt to be found in the aging and aged group, over forty-five years of age. Here the psychologist will often find, besides heart disease and its associated consequences for the mind and body, a number of additional impairments and physical conditions—as well as the mental habits of a lifetime—to take into consideration that may cause special interpretative difficulties (Whitehouse, 1960, b). These of course will have to be appraised on an individual basis.

SPECIAL CONSIDERATIONS IN MANAGEMENT AND REHABILITATION. THE REHABILITATION TEAM AND THE

PSYCHOLOGIST. Work Evaluation Units, sponsored by the American Heart Association in all sections of the country, have demonstrated the value of a more comprehensive approach to the rehabilitation of cardiovascular patients. Whereas, in their early beginnings in 1941, cardiac rehabilitation teams consisted of a cardiologist and an employment counselor, they now include social workers, rehabilitation counselors, psychiatrists, psychologists, and sometimes others (nurses, physiologists, nutritionists, occupational therapists, etc.), all of whom focus on the one disability—cardiovascular disease. The team functioning and problems are generally similar to those of other rehabilitation teams (Whitehouse, 1951, a, 1951, b, 1953, c, 1955, and 1957). The values, limitations, and procedures of Work Evaluation Units have been delineated elsewhere (Hellerstein and Goldston, 1954; American Heart Association, 1960; Bronstein, 1959; Clark, 1959; Gelfand, 1959). While a comprehensive rehabilitation center offers more facilities and a larger team than a Work Evaluation Unit, it does not handle most cardiac cases as capably as the Unit unless it, too, offers specialization.

As a team participant, the psychologist should be involved in the entire process of cardiac rehabilitation within the scope of the team, the agency, or the facility. He functions not only as a therapist, psychometrician, clinical evaluator, advisor, and teacher to other professions, as well as a contributor to all team decisions, but also as a competent observer and commentator on the rehabilitation setting, its organization, operations, and administrative procedures; for, if the milieu is of inadequate psychological structure, the psychologist as well as the cardiac client will inevitably be adversely affected.

Accordingly, the psychologist should endeavor to persuade the physician or physicians to provide the medical counseling a patient may require. He should also recognize the value of and should appraise the other kinds of counseling given the patient by other team members. The psychologist may feel the physician's counseling is too authoritative for a particular patient or that the vocational counselor's is too directive. He may have other ideas about what the social worker, the physical, occupational, speech therapists, or others may offer. Yet a client may have distinct needs for these various kinds of counseling at various stages of physical recovery and psychological adjustment. Some of this "counseling" may not be counseling at all in the psychologist's view, but, whatever he chooses to call it, it is a relationship in which ideas and feelings are exchanged. It is the responsibility of the psychologist to appreciate such relationships and guide when necessary all the psychological traffic involving client rehabilitation.

PSYCHOTHERAPY. The literature on the subject of therapeutic counseling for the cardiac emphasizes the importance of a reduction in anxiety for such patients. The educational approach to anxiety reduction stresses the importance of interpretation to the individual of his heart condition (Bellak and Haselkorn, 1956; Ernstene, 1957). Another approach speaks of "emotional re-orientation [which] for the timid . . . will mean the mastering of complex fears and the finding of ways to release pent up emotions. The ambitious cardiac will need to realize that he can still meet his obligations even though he may have to take a less strenuous and less remunerative job" (Gelfand, 1957).

In addition to alleviation of anxiety, reduction in blood pressure as a result of psychotherapy is also reported (Moses and others, 1956; Wolf, 1958; Reiser, Brust, and Ferris, 1951). In this connection there is far from universal agreement that psychotherapeutic procedures can reverse the physiological process (Binger and others, 1945). However, a number of investigators agree with Weiss that "because of the involved emotional problems frequently presented by patients with hypertension . . . psychoanalysis is sometimes advised" (Bellak and Haselkorn, 1956; Weiss and English, 1957, p. 243).

There are those however who would go for more limited goals and procedures in psychotherapy with cardiacs. They agree with Bellak and Haselkorn that "the use of uncovering therapy to produce permanent character change is impractical" and that the therapist should aim rather for personality restoration on the level of pre-illness adaptation rather than on total reorganization (Bellak and Haselkorn, 1956). Obviously there is need for much further exploration. It may be that any therapy is a holding operation with some ameliorative benefit.

It is in the area of angina pectoris, which presents so many emotional factors, that psychotherapy appears most helpful. Anginal symptoms should, incidentally, be of the highest interest to psychologists because the condition is a prime example of the psychosomatic-somatopsychic envolvement in heart disease as well as of the psychological significance of pain. The neurotic element in anginal pain has long been recognized (Kowal, 1960; Roberts, 1931; Cole, Kaye, and Griffith, 1958; Eskwith, 1960). The point at which a cardiac perceives and/or accepts a sensation and decides it is painful enough to report to his physician and others, as well as to limit his activities to some degree, is a significant decision. The point of pain perception is obviously influenced by the individual's readiness to feel pain (Hardy, Wolff, and Goodell, 1952), and this in turn may be influenced by a wide variety of psychological determinants. In some cases, pain is welcomed as a distorted "therapy of expiation"—a desired punishment and payment for guilt. Or it may represent hostile dependency, a displacement for a fear of greater psychic pain, a retreat, an excuse, an avoidance of reality, a socially acceptable reason for failure, a death testing—a practicing of fear when the greater fear of death is considered possible. On the other hand, some patients apparently deny organic pain when it should be noted. One might ask whether acknowledgment of pain in such cases represents a move down the road to disaster and is therefore suppressed and, thus, whether such cases represent an even more fearful group than those who readily admit and even augment the pain psychologically. There may well be far more uses for pain both from an organic and functional aspect than we now suspect.

The questions the psychologist must ask himself are: What seems to be the most potent motivation for the patient's pain? What does it symbolize? What therapeutic procedure will tend to relieve the symptoms? In answering these questions, the psychologist is in a position to help the physician estimate the possible influence of functional factors, suggest methods for establishing rapport, and alert the physician as to the quality of compliance he may anticipate, thereby enabling him to arrive at more appropriate recommendations for limiting the patient's activities than would be possible from the patient's subjective account of the occasion, amount, frequency, and duration of anginal pain.

"CARDIACS" WITHOUT HEART DISEASE. Whereas the most fascinating subject of " 'cardiacs' without heart disease" does not, strictly speaking, belong in this chapter, the psychologist must at least be alerted to the possibility that some "cardiacs" with whom he may deal are not truly organic cases. The perceptive, experienced psychologist is often in a position to offer the physician sufficient information about the individual to enable him to make a diagnosis of "no heart disease" with greater assurance. Unfortunately, even a brief account of this large and involved subject would be too lengthy for this chapter. Obviously there is need for further exploration of all psychological aspects of cardiac involvement, with MacIver voicing the exciting prospect "that early identification and 'adjustment' of [related] behavior or reaction patterns will enable us to abort [cardiac] diseases before any significant amount of organic pathology has been produced" (MacIver, 1960).

WORK AND THE CARDIAC. Work within cardiovascular limitations is good for the cardiac, and the physical employment and mental occupation are conducive to continued adequacy of function (Hellerstein and Ford, 1957). The cardiac work situation may be briefly summarized as follows:

1. Cardiacs can work if properly evaluated psychologically and physically, and appropriately placed in a satisfying job.

2. About three in four cardiacs return to work after a heart attack, most to their previous jobs with little or no job alteration, but sometimes with certain off-job restrictions. The seventy-five percent figure varies, of course, with age, severity of condition, type of skills, and the nature of the employing company. An older unskilled man would find work difficult in an undiversified heavy industry, but, with skilled men of a favorable age in a paternalistic light industry, the statistic may change to eighty-five percent or higher (Franco, 1951; Crain and Missal, 1956; Bruton and Jocz, 1957).

3. The emotional strain of a job, particularly in terms of its meaning, its deeper significance, and its mode of satisfaction for the individual can be as great or greater than the physical demands; and, since most jobs in industry require a low level energy cost, the emotional component may prove to be the determinant of job adequacy.

4. Some cardiacs can accept heavier work than others with comparable physical conditions if their circulatory system has been accustomed to heavier work, if they have a higher degree of skill in performance, if the work is familiar and psychologically satisfying, and if the individual suffers no fear or tension on the job.

It is obvious that an accurate determination of the question of physical capacity, psychological fitness, job demands, and the development of job opportunities requires the collaborative efforts of rehabilitation team and community. An "expectation of the ideal" often motivates psychologists in job selections and placements. In this connection, it is important to bear in mind that there are no ideal jobs any more than there are perfect therapeutic results, and a placement counselor must balance the therapeutic complex with the reality of the industrial complex.

RESEARCH. References to a sampling of research studies have been given in the preceding sections and can be found in the bibliography. The vast majority of cardiac studies is based on the assumption that some genetic, nutritional, constitutional propensity or biochemical failing is the cause of cardiovascular disease, and the major portion of research is conducted in these areas. Most of the work is done in laboratory settings, and much less in the epidemiological area. Recently, however, this latter approach is assuming increased importance. Only a modest amount of attention has been given to some of the practical aspects of work-physiology and to the value of the Work Evaluation Unit as an aid in selective placement. Little work has been done in rehabilitation facility settings.

There is also a scarcity of research in the psychosomatic area and in psychosomatic therapy. What has been done is rather narrow and has been conducted mostly by the somaticist and the physician, less often by the psychiatrist, and seldom by the psychologist. In regard to personality studies, the vast majority have been conducted through clinical observation usually by cardiologists and internists rather than by psychiatrists or psychologists. Psychologists and psychological instruments have played a very small role in this area.

In a study using the Rorschach test with hypertensives, Thaler (Thaler and others, 1957) reports that the subjects "had traits reminiscent of paranoid character disorders . . . they seemed to feel that other people were dangerous, derisive, untrustworthy and threatening." They desired to avoid close relationships and projected their hostility on others, being in turn provoked by the response. She also states: "When they are unable to defend themselves against direct emotional contact and conflicts, critical elevation of blood pressure occurs" (Thaler and others, 1957).

Using the Rorschach test and the Minnesota Multiphasic Personality Inventory, Ostfeld and Lebovits (Ostfeld and Lebovits, 1959) compared two types of hypertensive subjects, one "presumably renal" and the other essential (basic) in origin. They report that both groups "exhibited marked similarity in the Rorschach and Minnesota Multiphasic Personality Inventory," and little difference was found between the two groups and the controls. The investigators also found the percentage of hostile responses to be far smaller than that reported by Thaler.

In an attempt to predict whether individuals are hereditarily susceptible to heart disease, Thomas (Thomas, 1957) used the Rorschach test in a study of subjects whose parents had heart disease. When the Rorschach protocols of subjects with positive and negative parental history were compared, the investigator found that certain differences in temperament were suggested. "Those with a heritage of hypertension or coronary disease showed more aggression-hostility, more obsessive-compulsive trends, and more feeling of inadequacy, but less impulsiveness and less total affective reactivity than did their fellows with negative parental history."

As Lewin sees the research picture involving the effect of psychologic events upon physiologic processes, "the best hope for a breakthrough" is the team approach (Lewin, 1959). As Brown elaborates the idea (Brown, 1958), "in psychosomatic medicine . . . adherence to a coordinated and holistically oriented research strategy calls for close cooperation between the biologist who studies internal physiochemical processes, the clinical psychologist and psychiatrist, who study social interactions and their mental representations, and the social psychologist and anthropologist, who probe into the cultural framework within which motivational and characterological factors are given form and direction." There is unfortunately a lack of such studies of cardiacs.

The following are also among the needed studies in this area:

1. *Psychological investigation of medical instruments, measures, drugs, and procedures to identify the emotional reactions to their use, the natural sources of error, errors of observation and judgment, and general validity of such approaches.* There is a great deal of work reported in the literature pointing out the high emotional involvement in all such evaluative measures. However, the actual studies have generally been carried out by physicians, often cardiologists, but seldom by psychologists.

2. *The physician-patient and psychologist-client relationships and their implications for good treatment in heart disease.* The therapeutic significance of interpersonal relations, particularly of "nonverbal communication" have been amply demonstrated by the beneficial effects of pseudo-operations, placebos, and a patient's faith in a given procedure (Whitehouse, 1960, a; Boshes, 1960; Cobb and others, 1959). Interpersonal relationship is a far more intricate affair than verbal exchange particularly in heart disease (Dunbar, 1954; Meares, 1957; Whitehouse, 1960, a; Birdwhistell, 1952; Ruesch and Bateson, 1951) and warrants intensive investigation.

3. *Studies of the relationship between a person with cardiovascular disease and his physiological and psychological responses to work.* If the psychologist through research develops a clearer relationship between the individual psyche and its relation to an individual's applied psychophysical expression in work, then physiological and emotional responses that may be damaging to the heart may become predictable.

4. *Broader, longer-term studies of an epidemiological nature, but with a maximally feasible clinical content.* While not denying the value of clinical studies, their nature is such that they need broader confirmation. Studies of ten or fifteen years or even of lifetime dimension would be greatly rewarding.

In addition to studies such as these, there is a need to establish better standards for field terms and terminology. Twenty psychologists might classify a cardiac as "dependent" and yet mean

The Classification of Patients with Diseases of the Heart

FUNCTIONAL CAPACITY

Class I — Patients with cardiac disease but **without resulting limitation of physical activity.** Ordin physical activity does not cause undue fatigue, palpitation, dyspnea or anginal pain.

Class II — Patients with cardiac disease resulting in **slight limitation of physical activity.** They are co fortable at rest. Ordinary physical activity results in fatigue, palpitation, dyspnea or anginal pa

Class III — Patients with cardiac disease resulting in **marked limitation of physical activity.** They c comfortable at rest. Less than ordinary activity causes fatigue, palpitation, dyspnea or anginal pa

Class IV — Patients with cardiac disease resulting in **inability to carry on any physical activity witho discomfort.** Symptoms of cardiac insufficiency or of the anginal syndrome are present even at re If any physical activity is undertaken discomfort is increased.

THERAPEUTIC CLASSIFICATION

Class A. — Patients with a cardiac disease whose physical activity need not be restricted.

Class B. — Patients with cardiac disease whose ordinary physical activity need not be restricted, but w should be advised against severe or competitive physical efforts.

Class C. — Patients with cardiac disease whose ordinary physical activity should be moderately restricted, a whose more strenuous efforts should be discontinued.

Class D. — Patients with cardiac disease whose ordinary physical activity should be markedly restricted.

Class E. — Patients with cardiac disease who should be at complete rest, confined to bed or chair.

NO HEART DISEASE: PREDISPOSING ETIOLOGICAL FACTOR*

These are patients in whom no cardiac disease is discovered, but whose course should be followed by periodic examinations because of the presence or history of an etiological factor that might cause heart disease. These cases should be recorded as *No Heart Disease: Predisposing Etiological Factor* and it is essential that the etiological diagnosis also be stated.

UNDIAGNOSED MANIFESTATION*

Patients with symptoms or signs referable to the heart b in whom a diagnosis of cardiac disease is uncertain shou be classified tentatively as *Undiagnosed Manifestation.*

Reexamination after a suitable interval will usually help establish a definite diagnosis. When there is a reasonab probability that the signs or symptoms are not of cardi origin, the title *Undiagnosed Manifestation* should not used. The diagnosis then should be *No Heart Disea*

*There are patients in whom the symptoms or signs, though suggestive of cardiac disease, do not justify a definite diagnosis, and from whom is obtained a history of an etiological factor which might cause heart disease. The diagnosis in such cases should include both *No Heart Disease: Predisposing Etiological Factor* and *Undiagnosed Manifestation.*

From *Nomenclature and Criteria for Diagnosis of Diseases of the Heart and Blood Vessels,* Fifth Edition, 1953.

Prepared by the Criteria Committee of the New York Heart Association
Distributed by American Heart Association, 44 E. 23rd Street, N. Y. 10, N. Y. and its affiliates

many different things in the broad spectrum of levels of depth and accessibility. What is needed is some system of scaling or classification for our important concepts that will give us more precise degrees of estimation and tend to define our approximations more accurately.

And finally, a concluding word to psychologists: In working with cardiacs, indeed, in working in any area of physical disability, it is not enough that the psychologist know psychology, even the psychology of a particular impairment. He must also understand the philosophy of rehabilitation (Whitehouse, 1953, a) and of teamwork in order to apply psychological methods and procedures appropriately and effectively. Psychologists must explore with caution but with courage fields not previously or ordinarily engaged in by them because they have a legitimate discipline that can make an important contribution to areas that indeed cry out for their services.

REFERENCES

Abraham, A. 1959. Cardiovascular disease in psychotics. Amer. J. Card. 3:597–604.

American Heart Association. 1958, a. Cardiovascular diseases in the U.S.—facts and figures. New York.

—— 1958, b. Medico-legal and Insurance Committee statement No. 1, Workmen's Compensation. New York.

—— 1960. Proceedings of the National Conference on Work Evaluation Units. New York.

—— [n.d., a] Facts about congestive heart failure. New York.

—— [n.d., b] The facts about employment and heart disease. New York.

—— [n.d., c] Fears, fables, and facts about heart disease. New York.

—— [n.d., d] Heart disease caused by coronary arteriosclerosis. New York.

—— [n.d., e] Heart disease in children. New York.

—— [n.d., f] High blood pressure. New York.

—— [n.d., g] How the doctor examines your heart. New York.

Becker, M. C., W. Vasey, and J. G. Kaufman. 1960. Social aspects of cardiovascular rehabilitation. Circ. 21:546–57.

Bellak, L., and F. Haselkorn. 1956. Psychological aspects of cardiac illness and rehabilitation. Social Casework 37:483–89.

Binger, C. A. L., and others. 1945. Personality in arterial hypertension. Psychosomatic Monograph No. 8. New York, American Society for Research in Psychosomatic Problems.

Birdwhistell, R. G. 1952. Introduction to kinesics: an annotation system for analysis of body motion and gesture. Louisville, Ky., University of Louisville.

Boshes, B. 1960. The status of tranquilizing drugs—1959. Ann. Intern. Med. 52:182–90.

Bronstein, L. H. 1959. Experience of the work classification unit at Bellevue Hospital, in F. Rosenbaum and E. Belknap, eds. Work and the heart. New York, Hoeber, pp. 305–10.

Brown, F. 1958. A clinical psychologist's perspective on research in psychosomatic medicine. Psychosom. Med. 20:174–80.

Bruton, M. F., and M. W. Jocz. 1957. Myocardial infarction in industrial workers: a study in their progress, performance, and prognosis after return to work. Industrial Med. 26:551–55.

Cardiac Work Evaluation Clinic of University of Pittsburgh and Western Pennsylvania Heart Association. 1959. Determination of basic data concerning work ability and rehabilitation of one thousand persons with heart disease. Special Project No. 31–56. Pittsburgh.

Clark, R. J. 1959. Experience of the cardiac work classification unit in Boston, Mass., in F. Rosenbaum and E. Belknap, eds. Work and the heart. New York, Hoeber, pp. 311–21.

Cobb, L. A., and others. 1959. An evaluation of internal-mammary-artery ligation by a double blind technic. New Engl. J. Med. 260: 1115–18.

Cohen, M. E. 1950. Neurocirculatory asthenia and other psychoneuroses, in National Conference on Cardiovascular Diseases. Proceedings. New York, American Heart Association, pp. 139–54.

Cole, S. L., H. Kaye, and G. C. Griffith. 1958. Assay of antianginal agents; the rapport period. J. Amer. Med. Ass. 168:275–77.

Cook, W. L. 1960. Cardiacs should work, in Pennsylvania Heart Association, First Statewide Cardiac-in-Industry Conference. Proceedings. Harrisburg.

Crain, R. B., and M. E. Missal. 1956. The industrial employee with myocardial infarction and his ability to return to work: follow-up report. New York J. Med. 56:2238–44.

Dawber, T. R., and others. 1957. Coronary heart disease in the Framingham Study. Amer. J. Public Health 47(Pt. 2):4–24.

Dunbar, F. 1954. Emotions and bodily changes. 4th ed. New York, Columbia University Press.
Eisenberg, S., L. Madison, and W. Sensenbach. 1960. Cerebral and hemodynamic and metabolic studies in patients with congestive heart failure. II: Observations in confused subjects. Circ. 21:704–9.
Ernstene, A. C. 1957. Explaining to the patient. Arch. Intern. Med. 100:687.
—— 1958. Explanation in cardiologic practice. Circ. 18:1081–84.
Eskwith, I. S. 1960. Holistic approach in the management of angina pectoris. Postgrad. Med. 27:203–6.
Federation Employment and Guidance Service. 1959. Survey of employer's practices and policies in the hiring of physically impaired workers. New York.
Fisher, P. 1958. Painless myocardial infarction. Northw. Med. 57: 315–18.
Franco, S. C. 1951. Cardiovascular disease in industry: the role of degenerative disease. Industrial Med. 20:308–15.
Gardberg, M. 1957. Remarks on the rehabilitation of the cardiac patient. J. La. Med. Soc. 109:335–38.
Gelfand, D. 1957. The cardiac and his job. Med. Sci. 2(7):17–22.
—— 1959. Experience of the cardiac work classification of the Heart Association of Southeastern Pennsylvania [Philadelphia], in F. Rosenbaum and E. Belknap, eds. Work and the heart. New York, Hoeber, pp. 322–29.
Hardy, J. D., H. G. Wolff, and H. Goodell, 1952. Pain sensations and reactions. Baltimore, Williams and Wilkins.
Hellerstein, H. K., and A. B. Ford. 1957. Rehabilitation of the cardiac patient. J. Amer. Med. Ass. 164:225–31.
Hellerstein, H. K., and E. Goldston. 1954. Rehabilitation of patients with heart disease. Postgrad. Med. 15:265–78.
Higgins, J. W., and B. Schwartz. 1951. Cardiac symptoms in adolescents—psychiatric viewpoint. Ohio Med. J. 47:1129–32.
Hughes, W., M. C. Dodgson, and D. C. MacLellan. 1954. Chronic cerebral hypertension disease. Lancet 267:770–74.
Katz, L. N., R. A. Bruce, N. Plummer, and H. K. Hellerstein. 1958. Rehabilitation of the cardiac patient: panel discussion. Circ. 17:114–26.
Kowal, S. J. 1960. Emotions and angina pectoris: an historical review. Amer. J. Card. 5:421–47.
Lancet. 1954. Some origins of mental symptoms. Lancet 267:795.
Lawrence, E. M. 1960. Career plans for young cardiac patients. Heart Bull. 9:108–10.

Levine, E. S. 1960. The psychology of deafness. New York, Columbia University Press.

Lewin, K. K. 1959. Psychosomatic research: problems in methodology. Ann. Intern. Med. 50:122–28.

MacIver, J. 1960. Psychiatric aspects of cardiovascular diseases in industry, in L. J. Warshaw, ed. The heart in industry. New York, Hoeber, pp. 317–45.

McKerracher, D. G. 1958. Emotional disorders in later life and their treatment. Can. Med. Ass. J. 78:880–83.

Marchand, W. E. 1955. Occurrance of painless myocardial infarction in psychotic patients. New Engl. J. Med. 253:51–55.

Marvin, H. M. 1957. You and your heart. New York, New American Library.

Meares, A. 1957. The medical interview: a study of clinically significant interpersonal reactions. Springfield, Ill., C. C. Thomas.

Moses, L., and others. 1956. Psychogenic factors in essential hypertension: methodology and preliminary report. Psychosom. Med. 18:471–85.

Neuhaus, E. C. 1958. A personality study of asthmatic and cardiac children. Psychosom. Med. 20:181–86.

Noyes, A. P. 1955. Mental deterioration in the presenile period. Amer. Practit. 6:1488–92.

Olshansky, S., S. Friedland, R. J. Clark, and H. B. Sprague. 1955. Survey of employment practices as related to cardiacs in Greater Boston. New Engl. J. Med. 253:506–10.

Ostfeld, A. M., and B. Z. Lebovits. 1959. Personality factors and pressor mechanisms in renal and essential hypertension. Arch. Intern. Med. 104:43–52.

Reiser, M. F., A. A. Brust, and E. D. Ferris. 1951. Life situations, emotions, and the course of patients with arterial hypertension. Psychosom. Med. 13:133–39.

Roberts, S. R. 1931. Nervous and mental influences in angina pectoris. Amer. Heart J. 7:21–35.

Ruesch, J., and G. Bateson. 1951. Communication, the social matrix of psychiatry. New York, Norton.

Rullo, F. R., and F. N. Allan. 1958. Psychosis resulting from myxedema: report of a case. J. Amer. Med. Ass. 168:890–91.

Russek, H. I., and B. L. Zohman. 1958. Relative significance of heredity, diet, and occupational stress in coronary heart disease of young adults. Amer. J. Med. Sci. 235:266–77.

Scheinberg, P., and H. W. Jayne. 1952. Factors influencing cerebral blood flow and metabolism: a review. Circ. 5:225–36.

Sensenbach, W. 1946. Some common conditions, not due to primary heart disease, that may be associated with changes in electrocardiograms. Ann. Intern. Med. 25:632–47.

Sherlock, S., and others. 1954. Portal-systemic encephalopathy; neurological complications of liver disease. Lancet 267:454–57.

Sparkman, D. R., and J. L. Wilson. 1956. Evaluation of the cardiac worker. Northw. Med. 55:406–9.

Symonds, C. 1960. Disease of mind and disorder of brain. Brit. Med. J. 5191:1–5.

Thaler, M., and others. 1957. Exploration of the doctor-patient relationship through projective techniques: their use in psychosomatic illness. Psychosom. Med. 19:228–39.

Thomas, C. B. 1957. Characteristics of the individual as guideposts to the prevention of heart disease. Ann. Intern. Med. 47:390–401.

Turner, R. W. D. 1959. Diagnosis and treatment of essential hypertension. Lancet 1:897–903, 953–58.

U.S. Dept. of Health, Education, and Welfare. 1960. Health, education and welfare trends. Washington, D.C.

U.S. National Health Survey. 1959. Disability days, United States, July, 1957–June, 1958. Health Statistics, Series B, No. 10. Washington, D.C., U.S. Dept. of Health, Education, and Welfare, Table 31.

—— 1960. Heart conditions and high blood pressure. Health Statistics, Series B, No. 13. Washington, D.C., U.S. Dept. of Health, Education, and Welfare.

U.S. National Office of Vital Statistics. 1960. Monthly Vital Statistics Report 8, No. 13.

U.S. Veterans Administration. 1960. Third annual Neuropsychiatric Institute, Veterans Administration Hospital, Coatesville, Pa. Summary.

Ward, T. F., and H. F. Ross. 1960. Geriatric psychiatric patients in general hospital and mental hospital. Can. Med. J. 82:1151–54.

Weiss, E. 1958. The clinical significance of the anniversary reaction. G P 17(4):117–19.

Weiss, E., and O. S. English, eds. 1957. Psychosomatic medicine. 3d ed. Philadelphia, Saunders.

Weiss, E., and others. 1957. Emotional factors in coronary occlusion. Arch. Intern. Med. 99:628–41.

White, P. D. 1957. The role of exercise in aging. J. Amer. Med. Ass. 165:70–71.

Whitehouse, F. A. 1951, a. Teamwork: a democracy of professions. Exceptional Children 18:52–54.

—— 1951, b. Teamwork: an approach to a higher professional level. Exceptional Children 18:75–82.

Whitehouse, F. A. 1953, a. Habilitation—concept and process. J. Rehab. 19(2):3–7.

—— 1953, b. The rehabilitation center: some aspects of a philosophy. Amer. J. Occup. Ther. 7:241.

—— 1953, c. Teamwork: clinical practice in rehabilitation. Exceptional Children 15:143–53.

—— 1955. Teamwork: philosophy and principles, in American Association of Medical Social Workers. Social work practice in medical care and rehabilitation settings. Monograph II. Washington, D.C., pp. 1–19.

—— 1957. Teamwork: some questions and problems, in National Conference on Social Welfare. Social Welfare Forum. New York, Columbia University Press, pp. 148–57.

—— 1958–59. The rehabilitation counselor as a professional. Reach 6(4):9; 7(2):9.

—— 1959. Psychological aspects of heart disease. Presidential address to the National Council on Psychological Aspects of Disability. Cincinnati, Ohio.

—— 1960, a. Communication: an introduction to some basic constructs. Paper presented at National Rehabilitation Convention, Oklahoma City, Okla., October, 1960. New York, American Heart Association.

—— 1960, b. Rehabilitation and the life cycle. J. Rehab. 27:30–32.

—— 1960, c. Some psychological factors that influence rehabilitation of the cardiac. J. Rehab. 26:4–7.

—— 1960, d. Vocational counseling of the adolescent cardiac. Exceptional Children 26:275–79.

Wolf, S. 1958. Cardiovascular reactions to symbolic stimuli. Circ. 18:287–92.

HEMIPLEGIA

by LEONARD DILLER

HEMIPLEGIA is not a disease, but a disability, a paralysis of one side of the body. It usually follows an injury to the brain, caused by disease or accident popularly known as a "stroke" or "shock" or apoplexy. The damage to the brain is on the side opposite to the paralysis, so that a person with a lesion of the left cerebral hemisphere will incur a right hemiplegia or right-sided paralysis and a person with a lesion of the right cerebral hemisphere will incur a left-sided paralysis. If the paralysis is not total, it is then known as paresis; hence the term hemiparesis is used to refer to weakness or partial paralysis of one side of the body.

Hemiplegia affects voluntary movement of both the affected arm and leg. Contractures are a frequent problem (Rusk, 1956), for in the human body the muscles pulling the limbs toward the body are generally stronger than those pushing the limbs away from it. The hemiplegic will therefore show a characteristic stance, with the paralyzed arm flexed at the elbow, wrist, and fingers, the shoulder rotated inward to the middle of the body, the lower extremity and hips rotated inward, and the knee and ankle flexed. In walking, the hemiplegic will tend to swing the affected leg outward in a semicircle.

Although the hemiplegia is the primary disability, seldom is paralysis the only symptom. There is often residual weakness

Leonard Diller, Ph.D., is Director of Psychological Services at the Institute of Physical Medicine and Rehabilitation, New York.

of the lower two thirds of the face so that the nasolabial fold appears flattened; and, when the patient talks, the mouth turns down on the involved side and pulls to the uninvolved side. Vasomotor changes on the affected side occur so that the skin of the affected side eventually becomes dry and cold. Very often changes in response to sensation are present. The hemiplegic may show dulled response to touch, temperature, and pain on the affected side. Vision and hearing may be impaired in both gross and subtle ways. Food no longer tastes the same. Despite diminished sensation, complaint of intractible pain may be present. This may be accompanied by uncontrollable weeping. Minor personality changes (Harris and Towler, 1955), irritability, lethargic states, psychotic manifestations, lapses in memory and judgment may appear. In fifty percent of the hemiplegics—usually those associated with a right-sided paralysis—aphasia will occur. Whereas hemiplegia is basically a motor disability, more often than not it involves a whole psychomotor symptom complex.

INCIDENCE. Although the incidence of hemiplegia is difficult to assess, it is known to be the largest residual disability that follows cerebrovascular accident. Estimates of the number of hemiplegics in this country range from 1,000,000 (Harris and Towler, 1955; American Heart Association, 1956) to 4,000,000 (Howard, 1960).

Hemiplegia strikes at all ages; it occurs, however, most often at birth and in middle and old age, the incidence following a bimodal distribution. Hemiplegia in childhood is usually categorized as one of the cerebral palsies. By far the greatest incidence of hemiplegia occurs in people over fifty years of age. Increasing life expectancy in our society has unfortunately been shadowed by an increasing incidence of cerebrovascular disease (Harris and Towler, 1955).

MEDICAL-PHYSICAL ASPECTS. The greatest single cause of hemiplegia is a cerebrovascular accident or stroke. Technically a paralytic stroke may be defined as a neurologic disorder of abrupt development due to a pathologic process in blood vessels (American Heart Association, 1956 and 1958). In addition to its focal etiology, the notable feature of a stroke is its chronological profile, which is characterized by abrupt onset and rapid progress, the symptoms reaching a peak in seconds, minutes, or hours. If not at once fatal, a partial or complete recovery occurs in a period of hours, days, weeks, or months. In some cases, with slow progression, a careful history will reveal the advances of the disease by a series of small strokes. The stroke itself may vary in pattern and severity from a violent assault in which the person falls in his tracks deprived of sense and motion with one arm and leg paralyzed—apoplexy means "to be struck down"—to a very slight deficit or derangement in speech, thought, voluntary motion, sensation, or vision. While the chronological pattern can be discerned from the history, evidence for the focal character of the brain damage is manifested by the nature of the motor paralysis. Hemiplegia is thought to be a consequence of damage to a specific area of the brain, known as the motor cortex, and adjacent subcortical structures that play important roles in the regulation of voluntary movement.

From the medical standpoint, once the physician has decided that the symptoms are due to cerebrovascular accident, two questions arise of particular importance in diagnosis and prognosis, namely: (1) which part of the vascular system was damaged; and (2) why did the stroke occur. The answer to the former can be inferred from a careful evaluation of the neurologic symptoms, for these occur in relation to the specific parts of the brain that have died and ceased to function because their particular vascular supply system has been choked. In regard to the origin of the stroke, the physician tries to deduce whether the damage is due to the blocking of a blood vessel by a thrombus (clot) or an embolus (floating clot) or whether it is due to the rupture of a blood vessel (hemorrhage). Whereas it was formerly believed that most strokes were due to hemorrhage, it is now generally recognized that cerebral thrombosis ranks first as cause, cerebral hemorrhage second, and cerebral embolism third (Merritt, 1951).

The differential diagnosis of the causes of the hemiplegia is important, particularly in the early stages, for a number of reasons (Harris and Towler, 1955). First, rates of survival and recovery differ according to cause. Those due to hemorrhage have a grave prognosis, with 60 percent mortality in the first week. Strokes due to thrombus or embolus have a better prognosis, with a much lower mortality rate—thrombosis having a mortality rate of 30 percent during the first week and embolism even less. Second, the varieties of treatment and medication vary with etiology. Ingenious neurosurgical techniques are currently applied to remove clots or replace diseased segments of an artery by arterial grafts. In addition, powerful drugs are now at hand which alter the coagulability of the blood, dilate blood vessels, suppress infections, reduce cerebral blood pressures from dangerously high levels, or elevate them after circulatory collapse. Once administered, some of these drugs have to be continued over a lifetime. Hence, the hemiplegic may require medical care for the rest of his life. Finally, rehabilitation procedures are also influenced by etiology. Such procedures for hemiplegia due to thrombosis or embolism can be instituted within the first week of the disability whereas patients with hemiplegia due to hemorrhage may have to wait up to six weeks. It is difficult to forecast how much spontaneous recovery will occur. Some recovery may be due to the gradual clearing of cerebral edema and circulatory disturbance, altered intracranial pressure, and return of function to cellular elements that have suffered reversible damage.

In regard to physical treatment, the extent of disability resulting from the cerebral lesion is first measured by a series of tests, which include muscle examination to determine the power of both the affected and the unaffected muscles, the range of motion in the joints, and the patient's proficiency in activities of daily living (Rusk and Marx, 1953; Rusk, 1956). The importance of preventing and treating deformities cannot be overstressed (Peszczynski, 1954). The principal deformities are a frozen shoulder and a shortened heel cord. Heat, massage, and stretching are generally useful in treating the deformity.

In ambulation a careful analysis of the hemiplegic's gait, including the swinging and stance phase, is a necessary prerequisite for a training program. A knowledge of body mechanics as well as of corrective procedures for pathological movement is used by the physician to prescribe a series of exercises, mechanical appliances including braces, wheelchairs, or special lifts for the shoe. The retraining activities are carried on for the most part by a physiotherapist. The gait of a hemiplegic, its pathology and its treatment, has been the subject of a number of detailed studies (Peszczynski, 1954).

In treatment it is important to begin training the *unaffected* arm as rapidly as possibly, for very often the unaffected arm must be used to take over the functions of the affected arm in caring for daily needs. Furthermore, the unaffected arm is often used in ambulation training wherein the patient holds a cane in his unaffected hand to control his walking. Training of the affected arm is started while the patient is developing one-handed skills with the unaffected arm. If the affected arm is flaccid, a reeducation program similar to that used in poliomyelitis is started. If the arm is spastic, treatment starts at the shoulder and proceeds distally to the fingers. Occupational therapy is of particular value in arm retraining as it combines exercise and retraining with interesting activity (Ayres, 1960; Reynolds, 1959). The fingers of the spastic hemiplegic are most difficult to re-educate for any useful purpose. If useful function is ever attained, it represents a great cost in time and concentrated effort by the patient (Rusk, 1958). It is of interest to note that many of the tasks used by occupational therapists to elicit purposeful movement involve psychomotor skills (Carroll, 1958; Rusk, 1956). Proficiency in their execution resembles the proficiency on performance tests of intelligence. A number of occupational therapists have pointed out that perceptomotor rather than manual skills seem to be crucial for success in retraining hemiplegics. They have noted a very curious fact: left hemiplegics who still retain use of their dominant hand tend to do poorer than right hemiplegics who not only have lost use of the dominant hand but often demonstrate aphasia.

Speech therapy for those hemiplegics suffering from language disorders is integrated into the rehabilitation program.

PSYCHOLOGICAL IMPLICATIONS. The psychological implications of hemiplegia shall be considered in terms of the following aspects: (1) personal reactions; (2) the question of brain damage; (3) the influence of premorbid personality, intelligence, and educational level; (4) motivation; (5) intelligence; (6) body image; (7) the family; and (8) vocational problems.

PERSONAL REACTIONS. Beginning with what hemiplegics say about their disability and how they experience it, we can consider (*a*) the perceived cause; (*b*) the perceived deficits; and (*c*) the expected goals of rehabilitation.

Perceived Cause. Because a cerebrovascular accident strikes with a frightening suddeness so that a person may find his entire way of life changed in a moment, patients commonly ask themselves: Why did this happen to me? The answers they give are highly varied and serve as useful cues to the way patients define the disability. Whereas this same question is posed by many disabled people, the answers are more striking in hemiplegia by reason of a number of distinctive circumstances. A stroke happens mysteriously and suddenly, giving the person no time to adapt. The "stroke" itself is usually thought of as being due to "high blood pressure and repressed rage"—a view that is common in both folklore and medicine although the evidence for it is far from conclusive (Seidenberg and Ecker, 1954). Many hemiplegic patients with brain damage respond in regressed, primitive ways that are reflected in their beliefs, e.g., the female patient who thought her hemiplegia was due to childbirth many years before, or the male who believed it was due to his visits to a prostitute. In general, the perceived cause may reflect not only the direction of an individual's anger, whether toward himself or others, but also the level of rational control over his beliefs, whether on a level of perceptual maturity or perceptual primitiveness. Individuals who state that their stroke was an act of nature or who are able to cite medical reasons for its happening tend to have more mature beliefs and manifest more mature defenses on projective tests while those with primitive beliefs tend to have primitive perceptual styles on such tests.

Perceived Deficits. How does the hemiplegic experience his paralyzed limb? Many hemiplegics report different sensations and awareness on the involved side of the body. A common tendency is to push the affected side out of awareness (Nathanson, Bergman, and Gordon, 1952; Weinstein and Kahn, 1955), e.g., "I felt like I didn't have a right side at all," "At first it felt as if it wasn't my arm, as if it was out in the air," "I didn't feel like I had an arm," "It seemed like something attached that wasn't mine," "I didn't even know I had it; I would go to sleep at night and I couldn't find it." Another reaction, although less common, is to invest the disabled member with personal meanings, e.g., the woman whose husband had died in bed next to her commented: "My arm felt funny. Like somebody else's arm. I thought it was my husband's arm. I kept feeling it and started to get up to look at it." In general, this type of overt denial occurs more often during the acute stage of the illness. As rehabilitation progresses, the denial becomes less overt and is manifested in indirect ways, e.g., refusing to think about the future (Ullman, Ashenhurst, Hurwitz, and Gruen, 1960).

Expected Rehabilitation Goals. Both the perceived cause and the perceived disability are related to what the hemiplegic expects of the rehabilitation program. Many patients who cannot accept their disabilities invest them with private meanings and look for irrational solutions to their problems. They look for complete cure rather than for an opportunity to help themselves. Such people tend to alternate between denial and depression because they cannot accept the goals of the rehabilitation program since these goals often fall below their expected criterion of complete recovery.

THE QUESTION OF BRAIN DAMAGE. In hemiplegia, while it is clear that brain damage occurs, mental and behavioral functioning are not always adversely affected. Indeed, the varieties of response are very great. It may help us understand these responses by considering some of the distinguishing traits of hemiplegics with and without mental and/or behavioral dysfunction. The former are commonly referred to in the literature as "organic brain-damaged"; the latter as the "nonorganic." Although these terms shall be used here for convenience' sake, it must be stressed that they refer to mental and behavioral function rather than to actual brain damage. "Organic" refers to alterations in behavior and thought characteristically associated with brain damage. "Nonorganic" refers to the fact that mental and behavioral functioning appear to remain intact following brain damage. In trying to assess whether a particular sample of behavior is organic or not, it is best to consider patterns rather than single items of behavior, since isolated instances of organic behavior may occasionally be found in the absence of brain damage among persons under stress conditions.

We may then ask three pertinent questions: How often is organic behavior manifested in hemiplegia? Why is it present in some cases and not in others? What are the phenomena and problems associated with organic behavior? In answer to the first question, two independent studies (Birch and Diller, 1959; Weinblatt, 1959) report that about half the subjects exhibited organic behavior. To answer the question of why organicity occurs in some people and not in others involves the whole concept of brain function. As previously indicated, not all brain-damaged people behave in the same way. Let us, therefore, ask: Are there any basic attributes of brain function that, when impaired, result in uniform behavioral disturbances? Among the factors that warrant consideration are: size of lesion; site of lesion; nature of damage; age at which damage occurred; duration; and premorbid personality, intellect, and education.

Size of Lesion. For well over a century debate has raged over whether the amount of brain tissue that is destroyed, damaged, or diseased is or is not related to the amount of behavioral disturbance. The evidence thus far indicates that the size of the lesion per se is not the relevant factor in disturbances involving the "simpler behavioral functions," i.e., sensation, locomotion, etc. However, whether the size of the damage is related to disturbances of the "higher level functions," i.e., planning ability, motivation, etc., is still under dispute. While there are some who present evidence that a direct relationship exists (Chapman, Thetford, Beden, Guthrie, and Wolff, 1958), there is also evidence that an individual may be hemiplegic as a result of a hemispherectomy (removal of one side of the brain) yet show no basic impairment in higher level functions (Bruell, Albee, and others, 1958; Goldstein, Goodman, and King, 1956).

Location of Lesion. Location of lesion can present a highly important factor. As already noted in the case of hemiplegics, damage to the left side of the brain is associated with right-sided paralysis and aphasia, while damage to the right side of the brain is associated with left hemiplegia and spatial disturbances (L. Belmont, 1957; Hirschenfang, 1960, a, and 1960, b; MacDonald, 1960).

Nature of Damage. It has been suggested that if we view brain damage not in terms of the locus or size of the lesion but in terms of the nature of the lesion, meaningful insights into the behavioral consequences of brain damage can be educed (Birch and Diller, 1959). For example, brain damage that is due to a specific, focalized, clean-cut lesion, such as that generally induced by surgery or an embolus, may cause a subtractive loss wherein only specific functions (not "high level ones") are impaired. On the other hand, brain damage due to additive or disruptive lesions, which tend to occur when neurochemical or electrical forces of the brain are impaired, affects the brain in areas far removed from the site of the damage and tends to interfere with the functioning of the personality as a whole (Rosenzweig, Krech, and Bennett, 1960). This proposal has been advanced to explain the observation that an epileptic who suffers from increased seizures owing to scar tissue following surgery will perform better when the scar tissue is removed (Penfield and Jasper, 1953). The anomaly here is that more intact functioning occurs following seemingly increased brain-tissue destruction (of the subtractive type) than existed before when an additive lesion interfered with functioning. In other words, absent tissue is better than sick tissue. In general, hemiplegias occurring in arteriosclerotic populations would tend to show additive type losses because arteriosclerosis can produce widespread changes all over the brain (Birch and Diller, 1959).

Age of Onset. The author has found no studies comparing hemiplegics in terms of age of onset. However, a number of interesting observations have been made: (1) the incidence of spastic hemiplegia in infantile cerebral palsy is relatively large, representing nearly one half of the spastic cerebral palsied in one large study (Perlstein and Hood, 1957); (2) while only 10 percent of cerebral palsy is postnatally acquired, nearly one third of the spastic condition is postnatally acquired (Perlstein and Hood, 1957); (3) spastic hemiplegics show a delay of about nine months in walking and first words when compared with normal children, with the delay seemingly more closely related to intelligence and emotional factors than to the physical handicaps (Perlstein and Hood, 1957). One study comparing adult hemiplegics with brain-injured children on a series of perceptual tasks found many similarities (L. Belmont, 1957).

Duration. Since hemiplegia may occur because of a brain disease or through an external event that accidently damages an intact brain, it becomes important to know the nature and time of onset since recovery processes may differ in the two instances. In a diseased brain, recovery is more likely to be delayed than in a nondiseased brain. In the former case, the disease had already been active before the onset of hemiplegia and the process may still continue over a period of time. In general, there is no definitive evidence that would enable us to say that at a given time a patient has regained the optimum use of his abilities. The outlook is better for a healthy brain that has been injured than for a diseased one.

Whereas we have discussed organic and nonorganic reactions as if they were mutually exclusive, we should repeat that this is an oversimplification. In point of fact, there is probably a continuum with organic and nonorganic at opposite ends, rather than a pure dichotomy. What are the reactions of the typical organic and nonorganic hemiplegic? These may be summarized under the following major categories: (1) life rhythms; (2) psychological functions; and (3) contacts with environment.

1. *Life rhythms:* Many hemiplegics complain of difficulties in sleeping and in eating. These complaints occur with equal frequency among the organic and nonorganic and may be related to problems of aging. The organic, however, tends to report disruption of toilet habits, complaining particularly of con-

stipation. In addition, he complains of somatic pains, disturbances, and odd sensations and is irritable with people and events in his environment. As a matter of fact, these varied complaints are as characteristic of the organic as is their absence of the nonorganic (Weinblatt, 1959).

2. *Psychological functions:* The organic may be compared with the nonorganic on a number of important psychological dimensions, including perception, thinking, learning, and the emotions.

(*a*) *Perception:* In contrast with the nonorganic whose perceptions are basically unimpaired, the perception of the organic is marked by insecurity, fragmentation, and impotence. When presented with a task requiring the organization of a pattern of stimuli, the organic will complain about his inability to perform rather than proceed to try to solve the problem. These complaints are similar to the ones encountered when he faces complex tasks in his environment. Whereas perception refers to the pattern or meaning of sensation, it is quite clear that not only physical stimuli but also psychological stimuli can be "perceived." For example, one can perceive a feeling tone or a subtle communication between people. The relationship between perceptual problems in hemiplegia and deficits in visual sensation has not been well elucidated. It is probable that common disturbances in visual sensation found among hemiplegics, e.g., blind spots or field deficits, are found with great frequency among those presenting perceptual difficulties (Battersby, Bender, Pollak, and Kahn, 1956). However, it is possible to have perceptual disturbances when visual sensations are intact. In any event, perceptual difficulties are one of the signal characteristics of organic hemiplegics (Birch and Diller, 1959).

(*b*) *Thinking:* Thinking disturbances also distinguish organic from nonorganic hemiplegics. Organics have difficulty in assuming the "abstract attitude." This is reflected in difficulties in assuming a definite mental set; accounting to themselves for their actions and thoughts; shifting from one aspect of a situation to another; keeping in mind various aspects of a task; grasping the essentials of a problem or a *Gestalt;* voluntarily evoking previous images; assuming an attitude towards the possible future rather than the immediate concrete present; detaching themselves from the outer world; grasping conceptual symbols; and identifying common properties in diverse settings (Goldstein, 1959). Thus, the organic hemiplegic is preoccupied with his pain because it is immediately present in his environment. He finds it hard to talk about his future plans because he cannot consider anything beyond his immediate sensations and environment. Other examples of such concrete thinking are readily apparent in rehabilitation. The physiotherapist who asks the hemiplegic to walk to the end of the parallel bars while she tends to another patient may find that he has continued to walk back and forth in the parallel bars until told to stop. Various sensory paresthesias are accepted as real because of their immediacy. The patient performs well in one setting but not in another so that, when a program is changed, he becomes irritable and upset.

(*c*) *Learning:* Some psychologists have pointed out the consequences of concrete thinking for learning (Mednick and Freedman, 1960). People who think concretely cannot generalize or transfer the meaning of stimuli and experiences from one learning situation to another. The hemiplegic who can solve a space problem with one occupational therapist may be unable to solve the same problem with another. The context and the conditions of learning are much more influential with organic than with nonorganic hemiplegics.

(*d*) *Emotional reactions:* The most common reaction to hemiplegia is depression. Depression occurs equally often in organic and nonorganic patients. The difference between the two lies in the fact that depression may appear to be all-pervasive in organic cases because of the inability of such patients to shift their thinking and take their mind off their disability. Common sources of depression are the disability itself and the loss of mastery associated with the disability. This sense of loss often revives all other losses experienced in life so that the patient feels overwhelmed by loss, e.g., a female hemiplegic was able to say that she felt depressed because her paralysis reminded her of the time she spent in a concentration camp and of her husband's death following her arrival in America. In some hemiplegics, crying frequently occurs. The crying may be related to mood or emotional state but may also be on an organic basis. In the latter instance, it is thought to be part of a syndrome resulting from damage or irritation to the thalamus, or due to a release of control of higher (cortical) centers. The syndrome is accompanied by spontaneous pain, and overreaction to stimuli where there is normally a diminution of stimulus sensitivity. Some believe that this crying syndrome represents a type of social adaptation in dependent, worrisome people, serving to call attention to the disability, and is not a direct consequence of organic damage (Weinstein, 1955).

Anxiety is also a common reaction in hemiplegia. It is significantly more marked in organic than in nonorganic patients and appears to be one of the organic's distinguishing characteristics. The anxiety may be free-floating, fixed on somatic preoccupation, or experienced as a general uneasiness about the environment, and it is often total and profound as if the person were experiencing a series of catastrophes. At times it is founded on fear of a second stroke.

PREMORBID PERSONALITY, INTELLIGENCE, AND EDUCATIONAL LEVEL. The question arises whether premorbid personality, intelligence, and education affect reaction to brain damage. In the field of physical disabilities, it is often suggested that individuals with premorbid life patterns of high achievement and drive possess the greatest rehabilitation potential. Empirical evidence as well as common sense testify to this. Churchill, Pasteur, and

Mach led productive lives following hemiplegias. Working with animals, Harlow found that those who received more training before experimentally induced brain damage were able to learn more effectively. "The educated man can face arteriosclerosis with confidence—if results from animals can be extended to man" (Weinstein and Teuber, 1957, a, and 1957, b). However, this glibly applied generalization should be seriously questioned in dealing with hemiplegics. Observers have noted that people with consistent histories of successful vocational attainment may fail to adapt to hemiplegia and do poorly in rehabilitation. This is thought to occur in people who attain success at the price of denying their needs in other areas, e.g., those who have limited cultural interests, lack close interpersonal relationships, or are unable to admit illness or personal weakness (Weinstein and Kahn, 1955). In such cases, adaptation occurs not by accepting the disability but through denial. Denial, in fact, may be a characteristic defense in this type of personality structure. While premorbid personality, therefore, is an important consideration in evaluating response to a disability, its relationship to current functioning in hemiplegia must be very carefully evaluated. In general, it can be said that premorbid personality and intelligence are important—but they may be vitiated by a diffusion of large lesions in the brain, by lesions strategically placed, or by the nature of the lesion. All of these may interfere with the person's ability to act or to think. In cases where the damage is small, of a subtractive nature, and of a stable character, the effects of brain damage appear to be less potent. Under the latter circumstances, the total individual becomes a more important determinant than the specific characteristics of the damage.

MOTIVATION. Whereas depression and anxiety often interfere with motivation, they sometimes serve to increase it. The rehabilitation process itself affects motivation. In about one third of hemiplegic patients it serves to increase motivation. However, sometimes it has the opposite effect when the patient realizes he will not make the recovery he hoped for. Increased motivation in the course of rehabilitation tends to occur in nonorganic patients. In organic patients, it may decrease as often as it increases (Weinblatt, 1959). Since organic patients tend to be highly anxious, they also tend to be highly aware of failure. Consequently, attempts to motivate such patients by arousing anxiety only leads to more failure. On the other hand, some studies show that "urging" instructions on simple tasks rather than relaxing or supportive ones are more effective (Benton, 1960; Blackburn, 1958; Blackburn and Benton, 1955). At the present time, therefore, it is difficult to generalize about what kinds of incentives best influence performance for what kind of patient. One of the major problems of motivation with hemiplegics is the narrowing of interests and goals following paralysis. Both depression and organicity serve to narrow the individual's values, goals, and preoccupations; while concrete thinking serves to influence a patient to fixate on a goal long after it is clear that it is not feasible.

INTELLIGENCE. Is hemiplegia associated with changes in intelligence? The answer depends on which groups of hemiplegics are being considered (e.g., right vs. left, young people vs. old people) and which type of test is being used to measure intelligence.

Since most young hemiplegics who have been studied generally have been bracketed with the cerebral palsied, it is difficult to isolate a specific group. Some generalizations appear warranted concerning hemiplegics up to the age of 16 years: (1) They appear to be slightly higher in intelligence than the other types of cerebral palsied. (2) Approximately 35–40 percent of congenital hemiplegics test in a defective range (Rusk, 1958), whereas 20 percent test in the normal or higher range (Perlstein and Hood, 1957). (3) There appear to be no differences in intelligence between right and left hemiplegics (Wood, 1959).

In adults the matter is a little more complicated. Most observors agree that right hemiplegia is associated with deficits in verbal skills. This deficit may be associated with aphasia. However, it sometimes occurs even when aphasia is not manifested clinically. In regard to left hemiplegia verbal skills appear to be intact, while performance skills tend to be impaired. This differential patterning has given rise to a considerable body of speculation that suggests that different sides of the brain are involved in verbal skills as opposed to performance or spatial skills (Heilbrun, 1956; Hirschenfang, 1960, a, and 1960, b; Masland, 1958; Reitan, 1955). One must be careful about generalizing from these studies, however, as many right hemiplegics with aphasia who might show impairment in performance tasks were excluded from the studies because they were unsuitable. From a practical standpoint the differential in skills is important because (1) some areas of rehabilitation require verbal as opposed to performance skills (e.g., speech therapy vs. occupational therapy) and (2) the manner of teaching motor skills should be examined for its dependence on verbal instructions as opposed to motor instructions.

BODY IMAGE. The term "body image" has become very popular in current psychology in referring to the concepts a person may have about himself and his body. It is less commonly known that the term had its origins in studies of brain-damaged people who literally acted as if they had lost familiarity with their bodily parts. To account for this phenomenon a British neurologist, Henry Head, postulated that in growing up we form a body schema that may be impaired when the brain is injured (Weinstein and Kahn, 1955).

Hemiplegics commonly suffer from disturbances in body image or body schema. These disturbances are more common in organics than they are in nonorganics and may involve the physical body, the spatial surroundings, and the ego. In regard to the physical body, we find in hemiplegics (1) inability to follow instructions pertaining to parts of the body (Rusk, 1958), (2) inability to localize body parts or distances on the body correctly (MacDonald, 1960; Shontz, 1956), (3) denying or misrepresenting the presence of a paralyzed limb (Bender, 1952), and so forth. In regard to location in space, we find that hemiplegics may easily become lost in new surroundings or ignore or distort objects that confront them on their paralyzed side. Some hemiplegics report difficulty in driving a car, following their disability, because they do not trust their spatial judgment. Finally, disturbances in ego functioning generally accompany body-image problems. These are manifested by feelings of low self-esteem and inadequacy. Frequently, they are related to sexual problems.

Disturbances in body image may pose major problems in rehabilitation. The hemiplegic who is not aware when his foot hits the ground may be afraid of falling. The patient may forget to lock his brace because he is unaware of his left side. It is our impression that body image disturbances are manifested differently in right and left hemiplegics. Right hemiplegics have difficulty in carrying out verbal directions involving their body, whereas left hemiplegics have difficulty in localizing themselves in space (Masland, 1958).

THE FAMILY. Hemiplegia poses profound problems for the family. To begin with, hemiplegia usually strikes middle-aged and old people. The hemiplegic may not recover sufficiently to be completely independent in activities of daily living, so that he requires help. Families become frightened because there may be some mental changes or because the patient's depression may transmit a sense of hopelessness. Since the deficits may be multiple—ranging from gross to subtle—they are hard to assess so that some are overestimated while others are overlooked. The family may also be afraid of a second stroke. Finally, the family may have to adjust to the effects of visual field problems, e.g., in a left-sided field defect (left hemiplegia) the patient may ignore objects, including even a plate of food, on his left side.

The responses of families are quite varied. In general where family relations have been strained, hemiplegia causes a further strain. Sexual impotency, associated with feelings of low self-esteem and depression, is not uncommon. Where marital problems had existed before, they now become magnified. In one case, marital infidelity on the part of the male who was hemiplegic had occurred some thirty years before the cerebrovascular accident; it now became the source of bitter conflict. Where marital relations had been good, they can be resumed after a period of adjustment. In general, the resolution of the multiple marital problems posed by hemiplegia will depend on the dynamics of the marital relationship. When the family cannot take the person back, he becomes a custodial problem. This looms as an ever-increasing choice because of the advanced age of many hemiplegics.

VOCATIONAL PROBLEMS. Vocational evaluation must take into account the limitations of the disability that have been reviewed. In addition, work history, vocational goals, motivation, and environmental alternatives that enter into vocational planning must also be considered. Whereas planning should begin as early as possible, one of the major tasks is to induce patients who are still preoccupied with physical cure to think about the future. Careful individual evaluation, using standard vocational tests, are often not as fruitful as prevocational work sample tasks. While stress is placed on training the individual for one-handed activities, the most important use of these tasks is to assess and encourage motivation. Vocational placement is also influenced by the fact that in certain sections of industry, with well-ingrained and systematized personnel practices, the employment of hemiplegics can be achieved only with the greatest of difficulty. A set of specific objections, not only from management but also from line supervision, exists, centering primarily around increasing the liability ratio and the manufacturing costs for the industry. In general, the barriers affecting the use of hemiplegics in industry are (1) the medical policy of the company; (2) the size of the company; (3) the additional demands of job-related tasks; and (4) the attitudes of personnel. An active placement program is often necessary to break down these barriers (Howard, 1960).

SPECIAL CONSIDERATIONS IN PSYCHOLOGICAL APPRAISAL. An evaluation of a hemiplegic is a complex affair involving any or all of the following medical specialists: physiatrist, neurologist, psychiatrist, and ophthalmologist as well as those from the nonmedical disciplines, including social worker, vocational counselor, speech therapist, physiotherapist, occupational therapist, nurse, and psychologist. For the psychologist, the principal aims of the evaluation are (1) to assess and analyze behavior from the standpoint of the rehabilitation program and its goals, (2) to assess the effects of brain damage on behavior, and (3) to help plan therapeutic strategies.

The examining psychologist should be familiar with the patient's social and vocational history. In addition, the medical examination should be utilized. Some useful cues which may be culled from the medical examination are (1) age (older people do less well than younger) (Bruell and Simon, 1960); (2) etiology (e.g., arteriosclerotic hemiplegics tend to give more impaired performances) (Birch and Diller, 1959); (3) time since disability (e.g., it has been noted that hemiplegics who do well were referred to a rehabilitation program much earlier than those who do not) (Bruell and Simon, 1960); (4) the presence of sensory defects (in addition to helping the examiner account for possible defects in test performance, sensory losses are thought to be one of the causes of failure in retraining procedures) (Van Buskirk and Webster, 1955); (5) the type of medication (e.g., tranquilizers are generally prescribed for organic patients to alleviate their anxiety, whereas prune juice may be prescribed for depressed patients to relieve constipation) (Birch and Diller, 1959); (6) presence of recent seizures (e.g., this occurs more often among organics who may show signs of disruptive cortical activity) (Birch and Diller, 1959); (7) complaints of pain which are unrelieved by medication (e.g., thalamic pain may often become the basis of somatic preoccupation), (8) nursing notes pertaining to life rythyms (e.g., anxious patients have difficulty in falling asleep because of uncontrolled thoughts) (Weinblatt, 1959).

Formal psychological testing should be preceded by an interview to establish rapport as well as for diagnostic purposes. The interviewer should generally be seated on the hemiplegic's nonparalyzed side in order to minimize the effects of sensory difficulties, including visual field and auditory defects that may be present on the paralyzed side. The interview should be conducted along the same lines that guide interviews with other types of patients. However, a number of points specific to hemiplegia should be noted. Some hemiplegics cry easily. Discussion of personal problems often does not bring relief and catharsis but provokes depressed thoughts that are difficult to dispel. The depressed affect of the hemiplegic is often not helped by ventilation. On the contrary, because an organic perseverates, he may perseverate the affect. A change of topic is a simple useful device to break up depressive perseveration. Sometimes, the hemiplegic may burst into tears that do not seem to be provoked by the interview. The patient complains that the tears are not caused by sadness, rather he feels depressed because he cannot stop the crying. Suggesting a substitute motor act, such as gripping the side of his chair, may be useful. This phenomenon brings to mind the classical James Lange theory of emotion that states that the muscular response precedes the emotional experience: "You see a bear in the forest, you run, and then you are frightened."

In the course of the interview, several key areas provide useful insights into mental functioning: (1) *The patient's perception of the cause of his disability*. (*a*) Organics tend to embellish the cause of the disability more than nonorganics (according to L. Stern in an unpublished doctoral dissertation in progress at Teachers College, Columbia University). (*b*) Organics tend to blame themselves more than twice as often as nonorganics. (2) *Current adjustment to the rehabilitation setting or home*. (*a*) Many hemiplegics in chronic disease settings appear to accept their disabilities with too little complaint at the expense of being passive and resigned (Weinblatt, 1959). (*b*) Hemiplegics in more active rehabilitation institutes react in an opposite way. Those who appear to accept the setting without complaint actually profit more from a program, while those who do not, fail to learn. (3) *Statements about the disability itself, including changes in sensation*. (4) *The patient's goals in rehabilitation*. (5) *Life history*. In selecting events to describe his background, the hemiplegic may select positive ones designed to impress the interviewer and win his sympathy, or else he may recount traumas and failures—a mark of his depression.

In conducting the testing itself, the examiner should be aware that hemiplegics often have a difficult time adapting to a new setting. The examiner can safeguard against this by scheduling several test sessions. In general, a variety of different instruments may be utilized. These include the following: (1) standard global omnibus psychological tests, which tap a variety of skills and capacities; (2) tests for specific functions, which tap a narrower range of skills; (3) specific tests designed to replicate the tasks utilized in rehabilitation; (4) tests adapted from experimental and neuropsychology.

1. *Standard omnibus global measures.* These include such well known instruments as the Wechsler Adult Intelligence Scale (Hirschenfang, 1960, a), Rorschach test (Birch and Diller, 1959; Weinblatt, 1959), Draw A Person test (Bruell, Albee, and others, 1958), Bender Gestalt test (Hirschenfang, 1960, b; Weinblatt, 1959), and Thematic Apperception test. Most of these instruments have a body of literature in the field of hemiplegia, including (*a*) identification of organicity (Birch and Diller, 1959), (*b*) prognostic value (Weinblatt, 1959), and (*c*) comparison of right and left hemiplegics (Heilbrun, 1956; Hirschenfang, 1960, a, and 1960, b; Masland, 1958). It is sometimes helpful to obtain a more detailed picture of patients with deficits by utilizing children's tests, e.g., Stanford Binet. One study, analyzing the sources of failure in block design performance, for example, points out that, while perceptive motor functioning may be impaired, perception may be intact. Binet may sometimes be more sensitive to the regression imposed by brain damage because it taps lower level functioning in more detail (Bortner and Birch, 1960).

2. *Specific tests adapted for the disabled.* These are less well known. However, the following have been used for hemiplegia: (*a*) Columbia Mental Maturity Scale (Shontz, 1957), (*b*) Knox cube (Shontz, 1957), (*c*) Full range vocabulary test, (*d*) Raven's progressive matrices, (*e*) Hooper Visual Organization Test (Weinblatt, 1959), and (*f*) Macdonald Howard Electric Maze Test (Howard, 1960).

3. *Techniques designed to replicate task demands of rehabilitation.* When one attempts to do a job analysis of some of the tasks the hemiplegic is required to master, it is possible to isolate a number of aspects of learning and select or create tasks to measure these aspects, e.g., (*a*) a hemiplegic is required to follow a series of directions in learning how to get into a wheelchair, so that he must be able to keep the goal in mind while carrying out a sequence of activities, (*b*) he must remember

an act even after others have intervened—a task well known to psychologists as delayed recall, (*c*) he must be able to follow directions involving his body parts, (*d*) he must be oriented, (*e*) he must be able to profit from verbal cues (for instance, can the patient solve a performance task that he has failed when he is given additional cues). This type of analysis can help a psychologist select tasks that are more in line with the demands of rehabilitation than most standard tests. They can readily be adapted from standard tests by altering the instructions or selecting specific tasks from well-known tests (Belmont, Birch, and Diller, 1960).

4. *Tests adapted from experimental psychology.* (*a*) Rod and Frame test (Werner and Wapner, 1952). This task, requiring a subject to judge when a luminous line appears vertical in a dark room, was used in American psychology over a decade ago in the study of personality. It was generally concluded that people who used their bodies as cues tended to be more independent while those who relied on their visual senses tended to be more dependent. The task was adapted by a group of psychological theorists (Werner and Wapner, 1952) interested in the sensory tonic influences on perception. It was discovered that the perception of verticality was related to asymmetrical bodily influences. Hemiplegics, in a sense, are a natural example of asymmetric body influences so that they may be expected to show distortions in perceiving the upright. Studies show that hemiplegics do indeed show distorted judgments of the vertical. These distortions are thought to be related to disturbances in spatial perception and even to the ability to learn how to walk. Hence the perception of the vertical may be a useful diagnostic test. (*b*) Double simultaneous stimulation (Bender, 1952). When two sides of the body are stimulated equally at the same time the stimulus on the nonparalyzed side is acknowledged while that on the paralyzed side is not. This may be an additional reason for communicating with a hemiplegic from his less involved

side. A variant of this technique, the face-hand test, is often used by neurologists (Bender, 1952). (*c*) Two point touch. Since hemiplegics demonstrate body-image disturbances, a number of studies indicate that hemiplegics: (1) underestimate distances on their body surface (Shontz, 1956); and (2) misplace the point touched toward the body midline in left hemiplegics (but not in right hemiplegics). (*d*) A variety of techniques adapted from comparative and experimental psychology to study concept formation, the effects of visual field defects, and learning.

REHABILITATION. Whereas the first stage in treatment is devoted to maintaining life and restoring physiologic balance by skillful nursing and conservative management, it is advisable to begin rehabilitation procedures as early as possible. The immediate goals of a rehabilitation program for hemiplegics are as follows: (1) to prevent and to correct any deformities that have developed; (2) to retrain the patient in walking; (3) to retrain the affected upper extremity to its maximum degree of usefulness; and (4) to teach the patient to perform the eventual activities of daily living. In about half the patients retraining of speech skills is necessary. The long-term vocational rehabilitation results may be divided into the following categories: (1) patients able to return to full-time work either in the previous job or in another job; (2) those able to return to part-time work in ordinary employment, sheltered work or home work; (3) those capable of independent self-care; and (4) those who will require care (American Heart Association, 1956 and 1958).

Most hemiplegics prove to be suitable for a rehabilitation training program. However, certain conditions militate against an optimal outcome, namely: (1) severe brain damage when mentation is severely affected and relearning ability is impaired; (2) malignant nephrosclerosis and hypertension both of which may lead to hemorrhages; and (3) intractable, chronic, congestive heart failure or coronary insufficiency that does not respond to medical treatment. Where mental impairment is present, the full cooperation of the patient is not a prerequisite. Frequently he can be gently but firmly urged to participate in rehabilitation training activities.

Although it is difficult to generalize about principles of management or cite specific techniques that may be unique to hemiplegia, a number of considerations might prove helpful in framing a course of treatment. Those hemiplegics who respond in a nonorganic way can be treated the same as any other group of disabled. Those who respond in an organic way may require special management, with their rehabilitation program and goals generally more limited and with fewer activities prescribed. Special attempts are made to keep the environment constant for the organics so that therapists and classes remain stable. A great effort is made at drill and repetition in teaching. Many trials are necessary for the organic hemiplegics to attain mastery in a skill, and these trials should be spaced rather than massed together. Training materials should be lifelike and meaningful, and it is important that the patient be made aware of his progress as well as of the immediate goals. Staff members are encouraged to build warm, personal relationships with the patients. They are told about the patients' psychological problems so that they will not personalize aggressive or abusive behavior that may be directed against them. They are also informed that firmness is as important as gentleness in patient management. A firm physiotherapist presents a fixed predictable stimulus figure in a world that has become otherwise distorted.

In regard to counseling and psychotherapy, hemiplegics generally require (1) environmental information and (2) supportive help. Although depression is common, support rather than insight therapy is warranted, for the depression is often on a realistic basis. Because many hemiplegics struggle with problems of dependency at the same time that they require supportive therapy, special care must be taken so that the patient does not become unnecessarily dependent on the therapist or counselor.

In conclusion, the impact of hemiplegia on rehabilitation can be deduced from the vast increase in the number of hemiplegics in active rehabilitation programs. For example, the Kessler Institute for Rehabilitation reports ten times as many hemiplegics in 1959 as in 1949 and that hemiplegics constitute one fourth of the total number of new admissions (Kim, 1960). Other centers report a parallel increase (Knapp, 1959). When we realize that many hemiplegics require the assistance of one to four persons unless they can become independent, the impact of hemiplegia on the community becomes apparent.

RESEARCH. How successful is rehabilitation in achieving its goals? This question is hard to answer scientifically, for, in addition to the problems of obtaining adequate measurements for each of the subgoals and the problem of relating a specific gain to a complex, uncontrolled therapeutic process, it is difficult to obtain control groups of patients who have not been subjected to rehabilitation procedures. Most clinicians working in the field are reluctant to withhold rehabilitation procedures from needy patients for the sake of research. And without controls it is difficult to assess the efficacy of specific therapeutic modalities. However, the following observations have been made.

1. *Ambulation and Self Care.* Numerous studies over the last forty years have demonstrated that 75–90 percent of hemiplegics improve sufficiently to ambulate successfully (Lee and others, 1958). The results must be considered in terms of other factors, such as age; time of beginning treatment; sensory factors; motivation; etc. Among an aged group of over 80 years, for example, only 56 percent were able to ambulate. The importance of beginning treatment as early as possible is demonstrated by the finding that among unrehabilitated hemiplegics of long duration only 35 percent were able to learn to walk (Lee and others, 1958). Some evidence exists that sensory factors influence the

ability to function independently (Van Buskirk and Webster, 1955). However, these findings have not been confirmed in all cases (Lee and others, 1958). Other factors, such as motivation, and family support, have been found to be related to success (Lee and others, 1958). Is it the specific training through rehabilitation procedures that is responsible for the high rate of success in ambulation? An answer may be deduced from a follow-up of 230 patients at the Bellevue Rehabilitation Service. Although 85 percent showed improvement in skills in activities of daily living, only 50 percent showed improvement in motor function while only 23 percent improved in sensory function. This would suggest that the amount of acquired skills exceeds the gains in motor and sensory functions, both of which may be more related to spontaneous recovery. The reader should accept these results with caution because the evidence here is inferential rather than direct. The only controlled study in this area (Lee and others, 1958) reports that the gains of patients undergoing rehabilitation exceeds those not undergoing rehabilitation; however, the number of patients involved was too few for broad generalization and the problems of measurement require refinement.

Do patients maintain the gains made in rehabilitation programs? For the most part they do, although there appears to be a gradual decline in motor skills over a long-term period, manifested by increased use of mechanical devices, such as leg braces, crutches, canes, wheelchairs, and other ambulation aids. It should be noted that the data for this particular observation were based on patients with a mean age of 55 at the time of their rehabilitation so that advancing age may have operated against the benefits of the rehabilitation program. However, in none of the instances showing decline were people worse off than they were before rehabilitation (Lee and others, 1958).

2. *Vocational Status.* The findings are unclear, but a number of studies indicate that 30–40 percent of hemiplegics who have

completed rehabilitation programs are working on a full-time or part-time basis (Lee and others, 1958). Nearly 50 percent of one large sample of patients were considered to be employable following rehabilitation (Lee and others, 1958). On the other hand, another large study reports that only 23 out of 122 patients were judged to be employable (Knapp, 1959). Yet of those judged employable, 6 of 11 right hemiplegics were actually working, while 2 out of 12 left hemiplegics were working. Recent attempts to use a workshop setting for hemiplegics has met with some success in that 10–14 percent of hitherto unemployed hemiplegics between the ages of 16 and 55 years were able to be placed successfully (Howard, 1960). The true employability status of hemiplegics is, of course, governed by many considerations, of which age is an important one. In older hemiplegics, the employability figures are lower than in the younger. Other considerations in the employment of hemiplegics have been previously reviewed.

To conclude, although hemiplegics present a single disability group, for the psychologist they pose problems that tax his skills and literally require him to stretch the frontiers of his knowledge. Research needs span all of the fields of psychology. The investigations themselves tend to move in cycles. For the last half dozen years there has been considerable interest in comparing the behavior of right and left hemiplegics. At the present tim there is a growing interest in the problems posed by the management of hemiplegics. Toward this end, the next half dozen years will see more studies in sociology, vocational psychology, neuropsychology, and learning theory. The pattern seems to be similar to the flow of interests that psychologists have followed in the mental hygiene movment, from the task of gathering reliable measurement in order to compare different populations, to the attempt to understand processes that initiate behavior and therapeutic change.

At present, there are no specific foundations nor voluntary

agencies to offer sponsorship to this field. However, the incidence of the problem is so great that all major rehabilitation settings and an increasing number of general hospitals are offering services to hemiplegics.

REFERENCES

American Heart Association. 1956. Cerebral vascular disease, 1st conference transactions. New York, Grune and Stratton.

—— 1958. Cerebral vascular disease, 2d conference transactions. New York, Grune and Stratton.

Ayres, A. J. 1960. Occupational therapy for motor disorders resulting from impairment of the central nervous system. Rehab. Lit. 21:302–11.

Battersby, W. S., M. B. Bender, M. Pollak, and R. L. Kahn. 1956. Unilateral spatial agnosia. Brain 79:68–93.

Belmont, I. 1957. Psychoneurologic problems of the hemiplegic patient in rehabilitation. N.Y.J. Med. 57:1383–86.

Belmont, I., H. Birch, and L. Diller. 1960. Rehabilitation potential of nursing home patients, a report of psychological consultants. Unpublished report, Department of Physical Medicine and Rehabilitation, New York Medical College, New York.

Belmont, L. 1957. A comparison of the psychological effects of early and late brain damage. Unpublished PH.D. dissertation, New York University.

Bender, M. B. 1952. Disorders in perception. Springfield, Ill., C. C. Thomas.

Benton, A. L. 1960. Motivational influences on performance in brain damaged patients. Amer. J. Orthopsychiat. 30:315–22.

Birch, H., F. Proctor, M. Bortner, and M. Lowenthal. 1960. Perception in hemiplegia. (I) Judgment of vertical and horizontal by hemiplegic patients. (II) Judgment of the median plane. Arch. Phys. Med. 41:19–27, 71–78.

Birch, H. G., and L. Diller. 1959. Rorschach signs of organicity: a physiological basis for perceptual disturbance. J. Project. Techn. 23:184–97.

Blackburn, H. L. 1958. Effects of motivating instructions on reaction time in cerebral disease. J. Abnorm. Soc. Psychol. 56:359–66.

Blackburn, H. L., and A. L. Benton. 1955. Simple and choice reaction time in cerebral disease. Confinia Neurologica 15:327–38.

Boone, D. R. 1959. Communication skills and intelligence in right and left hemiplegics. J. Speech Hearing Dis. 24:241–48.

Bortner, M., and H. Birch. 1960. Perceptual and perceptual motor dissociation in brain damaged patients. J. Nerv. Ment. Dis. 130:49–54.

Bruell, J. H., and M. Peszczynski. 1956. Space perception in hemiplegic patients as related to rehabilitation, in International Congress of Physical Medicine, 2d. Proceedings, pp. 254–60.

Bruell, J. H., M. Peszczynski, and N. Volli. 1956. Disturbance of perception of verticality in patients with hemiplegia: preliminary report. Arch. Phys. Med. 37:677–80.

—— 1957. Disturbance of perception of verticality in patients with hemiplegia, second report. Arch. Phys. Med. 38:776–81.

Bruell, J. H., G. W. Albee, and others. 1958. Intellectual functions in a patient with hemispherectomy. Paper read at American Psychological Association meeting.

Bruell, J. H., and J. I. Simon. 1960. Development of objective prediction of recovery in hemiplegic patient. Arch. Phys. Med. 41:564–70.

Carroll, V. B. 1958. Implications of measured visuospatial impairment in a group of left hemiplegic patients. Arch. Phys. Med. 39:11–14.

Chapman, L. F., W. N. Thetford, L. Beden, T. C. Guthrie, and H. G. Wolff. 1958. Highest integrative functions in man during stress, in Association for Research in Nervous and Mental Disease. Brain and human behavior: proceedings of the Association, December 7–8, 1956. Research Publications 36. Baltimore, Williams and Wilkins, pp. 491–534.

Critchley, M. 1953. The parietal lobes. Baltimore, Williams and Wilkins.

Goldstein, K. 1959. Brain damage, in S. Arieti, ed. American Handbook of psychiatry. New York, Basic Books.

Goldstein, R. L., A. C. Goodman, and R. B. King. 1956. Hearing and speech in infantile hemiplegia before and after left hemispherectomy. Neurology 6:869–75.

Gordon, V., J. S. Young, C. Cobb, and J. DeTurk. 1960. Functional significance of disturbances in cortical integration in the nondominant hemiplegic patient. Unpublished paper read at Conference of American Occupational Therapy Association, Los Angeles.

Harris, T. H., and M. D. Towler. 1955. Intracerebral vascular disease, in A. B. Baker, ed. Clinical neurology. New York, Harper.

Heilbrun, A. B. 1956. Psychological test performance as a function of lateral localization of cerebral lesion. J. Comp. Physiol. Psychol. 49: 10–15.

Hirschenfang, S. 1960, a. A comparison of WAIS scores of hemiplegic patients with and without aphasia. J. Clin. Psychol. 16: 351–52.

—— 1960, b. A comparison of Bender Gestalt reproductions of right and left hemiplegic patients. J. Clin. Psychol. 16:439.

Howard, J. A. 1960. A demonstration and research study of the rehabilitation of the physically rehabilitated hemiplegic in a workshop setting. Unpublished report to U.S. Office of Vocational Rehabilitation, Washington, D.C.

Kahn, R. L. 1955. Delusional reduplication of parts of the body after insulin coma therapy. J. Hillside Hosp. 4: 134–47.

Kim, K. H., and others. 1960. Rehabilitation manual for hemiplegia. Orange, N.J., Kessler Institute for Rehabilitation.

Kløve, H. 1959. Relationship of differential electroencephalographia patterns to distribution of Wechsler Bellevue scores. Neurology 9:871–76.

Knapp, M. E. 1959. Problems in rehabilitation of the hemiplegic patient. J. Amer. Med. Ass. 169: 224–29.

Lee, P. R., and others. 1958. An evaluation of rehabilitation of patients with hemipareses or hemiplegia due to cerebral vascular disease. Rehabilitation Monograph No. 15. New York, Institute of Physical Medicine and Rehabilitation.

Linn, L. 1953. The role of perception in the mechanism of denial. J. Amer. Psychoanal. Ass. 1:690–705.

Lowenthal, M. J. Tobis, and I. R. Howard. 1959. Analysis of the rehabilitation needs and prognoses of 232 cases of cerebral vascular accidents. Arch. Phys. Med. 40: 183–86.

MacDonald, J. C. 1960. An investigation of body scheme in adults with cerebral vascular accidents. Amer. J. Occup. Ther. 14:75–79.

Masland, R. 1958. Central nervous system, higher functions. Ann. Rev. Physiol. 20: 533–57.

Mednick, S. A., and J. L. Freedman. 1960. Stimulus generalization. Psychol. Bull. 57: 169–201.

Merritt, H. H. 1951. Cerebral vascular accidents, in R. L. Cecil and R. F. Loeb, eds. Textbook of medicine. Philadelphia, Saunders, pp. 1458–69.

Nathanson, M., P. S. Bergman, and G. G. Gordon. 1952. Denial of illness: its occurrence in 100 consecutive cases of hemiplegia. Arch. Neurol. Psychiat. 68: 380–87.

Penfield, W., and H. H. Jasper. 1953. Epilepsy and the functional anatomy of the human brain. Boston, Little Brown.

Perlstein, M. A., and P. Hood. 1957. Infantile spastic hemiplegia. Amer. J. Ment. Defic. 61:534–68.

Peszczynski, M. 1954. Ambulation of the severely handicapped hemiplegic adult: (1) Early management, (2) Gait training. Paper read at American Congress of Physical Medicine and Rehabilitation, 32d, Washington, D.C.

Reitan, R. M. 1955. Certain differential effects of left and right cerebral lesions in human adults. J. Comp. Physiol. Psychol. 48:474–77.

Reynolds, G. M. 1959. Problems of sensorimotor learning in the evaluation and treatment of the hemiplegic patient. Rehab. Lit. 20:163–72.

Rosenzweig, M., D. Krech, and E. L. Bennett. 1960. A search for relations between brain chemistry and behavior. Psychol. Bull. 57:476–93.

Rusk, H. A. 1956. Rehabilitation of the elderly neurologic patient in Association for Research in Nervous and Mental Diseases. Neurologic and psychiatric disorders of aging, proceedings of the Association, December 9–10. Research Publication 35. Baltimore, Williams and Wilkins, pp. 224–33.

—— 1958. Rehabilitation medicine. St. Louis, C. V. Mosby Co.

Rusk, H. A., and M. Marx. 1953. Rehabilitation following cerebrovascular accident. Southern Med. J. 46:1943–57.

Seidenberg, R., and A. Ecker. 1954. Psychodynamic and arteriographic studies of acute cerebral vascular disorders. Psychosom. Med. 16:374–92.

Shontz, F. C. 1956. Body concept disturbances of patients with hemiplegia. J. Clin. Psychol. 12:293–95.

—— 1957. Evaluation of intellectual potential in hemiplegic individuals. J. Clin. Psychol. 13:267–69.

Teuber, H. L. 1960. Premorbid personality and reaction to brain damage. Amer. J. Orthopsychiat. 30:322–30.

Travis, A. M., and C. N. Woolsey. 1956. Motor performance of monkeys after bilateral and total cerebral decortication. Amer. J. Phys. Med. 30:273–310.

Ullman, M., E. M. Ashenhurst, L. J. Hurwitz, and A. Gruen. 1960. Motivational and structural factors in denial in hemiplegia. Arch. Neurol. 3:306–18.

Van Buskirk, C., and D. Webster. 1955. Prognostic value of memory defect in rehabilitation of hemiplegics. Neurology 5:407–11.

Weinblatt, B. A. 1959. The role of the organization of intellectual and emotional processes as it relates to performance on a physical rehabilitation program. Unpublished PH.D. dissertation, New York University.

Weinstein, E. A. 1955. Symbolic aspects of thalamic pain. Yale J. Biol. Med. 28:465–70.

Weinstein, E. A., and R. L. Kahn. 1955. Denial of illness: symbolic and physiological aspects. Springfield, Ill., C. C. Thomas.

Weinstein, S., and H. L. Teuber. 1957, a. Effects of penetrating brain injury on intelligence test scores. Science 125:1036–37.

—— 1957, b. The role of preinjury education and intelligence level in intellectual loss after brain injury. J. Comp. Physiol. Psychol. 50:535–39.

Werner, H., and S. Wapner. 1952. Toward a general theory of perception. Psychol. Rev. 59:324–38.

Witkin, H., and others. 1954. Personality through perception. New York, Harper.

Wood, N. E. 1959. Comparison of right hemiplegics with left hemiplegics on motor skills and intelligence. Perceptual and Motor Skills 9:103–6.

CEREBRAL PALSY

by ROBERT M. ALLEN

CEREBRAL PALSY is a condition, not a disease. Its manifestations are as varied as are the possible results of the accompanying lesions within the brain upon motor control of the body. This means that the physical involvements of cerebral palsy run the gamut from the scarcely observable to the most seriously involved, disabling, and handicapping conditions.

INCIDENCE. Statistical estimates of cerebral palsy include such numbers as: 1 cerebral palsied infant born every fifty-three minutes in this country; 1 cerebral palsied infant out of approximately 175–200 live births; estimated cerebral palsied population in this country between 500,000 and 600,000 persons, or 3 per 1,000 individuals (Abbott, 1956). With the increase in birth rate, the percentage will remain the same but the raw numbers of cerebral palsied will increase markedly. Cardwell (Cardwell, 1956) commenting on Wallace's study of the incidence of cerebral palsy in New York City states: "Using an annual incidence rate of 6 cases for 1000 live births, cerebral palsy would be increased by a total of 900 new cases a year" (Wallace, 1954, p. 477).

ETIOLOGICAL FACTORS. Etiology of this condition may be ascribed to factors operating during the pre-, para- (or actual

Robert M. Allen, Ph.D., is Professor of Psychology at the University of Miami, Coral Gables, Florida.

birth), and postnatal periods. In approximately 60 percent of the recorded cases, damage to the brain occurs with equal frequency during the first two of these periods, with hereditary and acquired etiologic agents accounting for the prenatal brain lesions, and anoxia and toxic conditions representing the major etiologic factors for paranatal injury. Trauma, infections, anoxia, and toxic conditions comprise the 10 percent of cerebral palsy cases occurring in the postnatal period. This leaves approximately 30 percent with unknown etiology (Parke, Davis & Co., 1959).

DEFINITIONS AND CLASSIFICATIONS. Abbott points out that there is no agreement among leaders in the field "as to the precise limits and extent of the term cerebral palsy" (Abbott, 1956). In 1954 the Nomenclature Committee of the American Academy for Cerebral Palsy adopted a classification that was derived from observable symptoms.

1. *Spastic Type*, in which stiffness is the characteristic sign and is attributable to increased muscle tone. Other diagnostic features include the ready eliciting of the stretch reflex (vigorous muscle contraction when suddenly stretched), clonus reaction (involuntary rapid contractions and relaxations of a muscle), and persistent muscular contractions giving a characteristic appearance to the various affected limbs.

2. *Athetotic* (*Athetoid*) *Type* is recognizable by the variety of involuntary and incoordinate movements of body parts. These range from mild and wormlike motions to those which involve the trunk, arms, and legs in a seeming endless profusion of contorted movements. Subtypes are classified as tension, nontension, dystonic, and tremor athetosis. In the tension state, the muscles are so "tight and tense" (Phelps, Hopkins, and Cousins, 1958) that athetoid movements have a spastic quality; the opposite state, muscular flaccidity, is seen in the nontension athetoid; the dystonic reaction is seen in the patient who maintains a distorted

position for a length of time; and finally, the tremor type is recognized by the gross, slow movements of the body or limbs. Phelps, Hopkins, and Cousins (Phelps, Hopkins, and Cousins, 1958) list these additional athetoid types: shudderlike, flail, cerebellar release, emotional release, hemiathetoid, neck-and-arm, and deaf reactions. Engle (Engle, 1959) adds the following as subtypes of the dyskinesias: rotary, head and trunk, kernicteric, and balance release.

3. *Rigidity Type*, in which the agonist-antagonist muscles are not functionally coordinated, that is, the antagonist of the pair is more strongly affected so that movement of the limb is slow, either consistently or intermittently. In the former case, with consistent resistance to motion, the term "lead-pipe" rigidity is used diagnostically. Intermittent or irregular assymetry between the agonist-antagonist muscles results in "cogwheel" rigidity.

4. *Ataxic Type* cerebral palsy is manifested in disturbances of equilibrium that become overtly evident in walking.

5. *Tremor Type* is evidenced by a rhythmic movement. The alternation of contractions between the flexor and extensor muscles is usually constant. However, there are individual variations in the tremor pattern with regard to the degree of motion depending on whether the person is at rest or active and whether the movement is voluntary or involuntary.

6. *Atonic Type* is also known as flaccidity. However, this condition is not due to a lack of muscular innervation but to a lack of, or very weak, muscle tone. Hypotonia is another descriptive term.

In addition to the above somewhat discrete systematic categories, there are mixed types and unclassified types of cerebral palsy. Of the 500,000 cerebral-palsied population, 50 percent are spastic; 25 percent, athetoids; 13 percent, rigidities; and the remaining 12 percent are divided among ataxia, atonia, tremor, mixed, and undiagnosed cerebral palsy states.

Unfortunately, different medical authors use classificatory

systems that do not focus on the symptomatic approach as does the one presented above. Courville (Courville, 1954) classifies in terms of the cortical syndromes, thus emphasizing the locus of cerebral pathology as the differential diagnostic basis. Diagnostic categories of mild, moderate, and severe involvement are also used, but these have little meaning in themselves since at best they are subjective evaluations that would differ markedly from one rater or diagnostician to another. A more valuable approach is a description of the patient in terms of locus of impaired function. It is more meaningful to describe a patient as having athetoid movements, gross or fine, in a particular limb than to resort to such general descriptions as "mildly involved athetoid." Categorical terms merely conjure up stereotypes rather than individuals. Nevertheless, diagnostic classification is essential for administrative and other purposes and some acceptable system is therefore followed by the medical member of a diagnostic or evaluation team.

Russ and Soboloff define cerebral palsy as follows:

> A. A non-progressive central nervous system lesion (or lesions) is present.
> B. Motor dysfunction has occurred as a result of this lesion.
> C. Sensory, emotional, or psychological disturbances can coexist. [Russ and Soboloff, 1958, p. 4.]

This view of the condition recognizes the physical and psychological correlates that are present in varying degrees. The definition is flexible in its inclusiveness depending upon the nature and interpretation of the terms "lesion," "motor dysfunction," and psychological concomitants. The presence of a lesion may or may not be established, motor (and sensory) disturbances may or may not exist, and the psychological facets of the condition may or may not be overtly observable or incapacitating intellectually, personally, socially, and/or vocationally. In many instances interpretations are made which would not find acceptance from one clinic to the other. The author is acquainted with one center that accepts mentally retarded youngsters for physical, occupational, speech, and counseling therapy on the assumption that psychological ineptitude must arise from some kind of undetected brain pathology.

In addition to the diagnostic categories used, the physician further describes the condition in terms of topographic involvement, such as hemiplegia, diplegia, and so forth. Differential diagnosis among the types and subtypes of the classifications systems is difficult at times. This may account for the variations in medical diagnoses seen in the case records of patients. A patient seen over a period of years by one physician or at different times by several physicians may very easily give the appearance of being a diagnostic paradox when in reality both time and/or classification systems are the major factors in this seeming diagnostic anomaly.

MEDICAL ASPECTS. The medical management of cerebral palsy is a very complex procedure. Treatment includes such medical specialties as pediatrics, orthopedics, orthopedic surgery, neurosurgery, and physiatry. An important aspect of treatment is drug therapy for coping with the various neuromuscular difficulties involved and with the control of seizures. The paramedical professions, physical and occupational therapy, are also in the picture. Other medical consultants who play an important role in treatment are the ophthalmologist, otolaryngologist, and the dental specialists. Nonmedical specialists include the psychologist, audiologist, speech and hearing therapist, special teacher, and the vocational counselor.

The degrees of effectiveness of medical treatment cover a wide range. Generalization is practically impossible since treatment encompasses numerous aspects of management and therapy designed to handle very specific pathologies as well as larger dysfunctions of the persons affected. Russ and Soboloff comment on the treatment of the handicapped cerebral palsied person as follows: "In summary, it therefore should be pointed out that in *all* prognosis, whether we are concerned with the hopelessly, moderately, or mildly handicapped, the direction must be realistic, and not mere wishful thinking indulged in by the medical or treating teams or the parents" (Russ and Soboloff, 1958, p. 64).

Medical treatment has accomplished a great deal with and for the cerebral palsied. The research in prevention and amelioration is tremendous, but it must be recognized that there are aspects of the total situation that require the treatment skills and attention of the nonmedical professions. This appears to be the essence of Russ and Soboloff's summary of the picture concerning the treatment of the cerebral palsied person.

It is evident that, with such neural pathology as is present in cerebral palsy, there will be definitive physical and psychological implications. In regard to the former, physical dysfunctions on the one hand, and, on the other, the associated problems of disability, handicap, rehabilitation (physical and vocational), continued medical, social, and personal care, and institutionalization are complicated problems not easy to solve. In the younger years, medical care is the major concern, and medical attention in all its specialties and ancillary therapies is central. With increasing age, the medical problem is joined by the intellectual, emotional, educational, and vocational aspects of daily living. These are the aspects that require the ministrations of the nonmedical specialists: psychologist, speech therapist, special educator, audiologist, social worker, and vocational rehabilitation personnel (counselor and training staff).

Since cerebral palsy most frequently yields a multiple-handicapping condition, either one or any combination of handicaps in the following abridged listing is apt to be present: intellectual retardation, speech and hearing difficulties, visual defects, seizures, sensorimotor dysfunctions, perceptual anomalies, dental dysplasias, sensory disorders, drooling, and incontinence. In addition, there are the usual psychological concomitants, such as mental retardation, disturbed behavior (sometimes called the "organic syndrome behavior"), personal immaturity, social isolation, lowered educability, and/or sensory deprivation and/or motor inefficiency.

The preceding lists do not tell the whole story. Nevertheless, despite his complex problems, the cerebral palsied individual can be helped medically, psychologically, educationally, and vocationally, but in varying degrees ranging from institutionalization for complete personal care to rehabilitation wherein the client is rendered vocationally feasible and capable of meeting most of his needs quite independently. Rehabilitation approaches are more fully discussed in a subsequent section of this chapter.

PSYCHOLOGICAL ASPECTS AND IMPLICATIONS. Whereas the medical aspects of the condition are quite obvious to anyone who has had contact with a cerebral palsied person, the psychological aspects are equally important for a complete understanding of the problems associated with cerebral palsy. A roll call of associated psychological difficulties includes mental retardation and its implications for learning, emotionally disturbed behavior, impaired communicative ability, and perceptual disorders.

Hohman and Freedheim indicate the extent of actual and *as if* mental retardation in these words: "The number of CP's who are truly educable for any economic independence is probably much less than 40%; because from the 40% which have IQs above 70, there must be subtracted a number of cases whose physical handicaps are sufficiently severe to prevent useful or usable education" (Hohman and Freedheim, 1958, p. 97). Cardwell (Cardwell, 1956) tabulated findings of thirteen studies directed to ascertaining the intellectual levels among cerebral palsied children. For the mentally retarded portion of the intelligence continuum (i.e., IQ below 70), she reports a range from

30.5 percent to 58.6 percent of the cerebral palsied children. The borderline-dull category (IQ 70–80) shows a spread of 11 percent to 38 percent. A review of the reports is characterized by inconsistency since many factors, such as test used, skill of the tester, and the physical status of the testee, contribute to differences among the findings (Allen and Collins, 1955; Allen, 1958, a). This is highlighted in the reports of studies with children classified according to type of cerebral palsy. Table 1 summarizes this aspect of the problem. Previously, Burgemeister and Blum (Burgemeister and Blum, 1949) had reported somewhat similar findings, that the ataxic group had the highest percentage of mental retardation, and the athetoid types the lowest.

TABLE 1. *Psychological Findings; Analysis by Groups Above and Below 70 Intelligence Quotient*

N = 933

	Below 70 Intelligence Quotient		*70 Intelligence Quotient and Above*		
Type of Cerebral Palsy	*Number*	*Percent*	*Number*	*Percent*	*Median*
Spastic	215	44.1	272	55.9	91.9
Athetoid	95	40.9	137	59.1	93.5
Ataxic	86	70.5	36	29.5	84.5
Rigidity	61	66.3	31	33.7	91.3
Total	457	49.0	476	51.0	91.8

SOURCE: Reproduced with permission from T. W. Hopkins, H. V. Bice, and K. C. Colton. 1954. *Evaluation and Education of the Cerebral Palsied: New Jersey Study*. Washington, D.C., International Council for Exceptional Children. Table 28, p. 39.

The mental retardation or intellectual deficit is complicated by a host of personal, social, educational, and vocational problems. Certainly sensorimotor involvements increase the limitations imposed by limited mental ability. There also seem to be serious social barriers in terms of community attitudes toward these children and adults. Not only are they set aside as being markedly deviant physically, but they may also be intellectually different and so a double burden on the community. The intellectual deficiency whether actual or due to impaired sensorimotor functioning adds to the total problems in their care and rehabilitation. Even if the goal were to help the patient achieve some measure of independence in the activities of daily living, the limitation of intellectual grasp would restrict the range of physical achievement on the one hand, or, on the other, the mental potential for better than average training and education could be seriously limited by the physical handicap. This is the basis on which Hohman and Freedheim point out that many cerebral palsied individuals with average or better intelligence behave *as if* they were mentally retarded. "It should be emphasized that although children with mentality between 70 and 90 IQ could acquire grade school education, many cerebral palsied are severely hindered by physical motor handicaps. It would seem clear, therefore, that only a small portion of CP's is educable for any useful economic purpose" (Hohman and Freedheim, 1958, p. 96).

The psychosocial behavior of the cerebral palsied child has received much attention and study. Disregarding the child with severe physical handicaps who, at best, offers major personal care problems, attention has been given to those who are capable of some mobility and who are more apt to react to their social milieu. In general, the cerebral palsied child seems to react with aggressive defensiveness as if to prove his right to be in the world. Complicated by damage to the brain, which is associated with intellectual deficits (in most cases), and some degree of impaired sensorimotor efficiency, the outlook is not promising because the opportunities are narrowed down. The parent, teacher, pediatrician, and psychologist well know the stereotype of the organic syndrome behavior described by Michal-Smith as a "hyperkinetic, impulse-driven youngster . . . the child who is always on the go, with short attention span and poor power of concentration. He is quite variable and unpredictable, unable to delay gratification, and he overreacts emotionally" (Michal-

Smith, 1960, p. 31). This behavior impedes education and training and may lead to the exclusion of the youngster from the regular classroom. Strauss and Lehtinen describe this situation:

> Behavior disorders are the most conspicuous manifestation of abnormality in brain-injured children. For the physician, psychologist, and teacher they are often the most difficult ones to treat. In some instances the medication of sedatives is indicated to help an unusually disturbed child begin his adjustment to a group situation. It is possible by these means to spare a child and those who are entrusted with his care the unpleasant impressions and experiences which would inevitably result from his uncontrollable drive and disinhibitions. [Strauss and Lehtinen, 1953, p. 97.]

Michal-Smith aptly points out that some difference is to be expected between prenatally and postnatally acquired cerebral palsy. In the former, the child's brain has not developed, so that intellectual potential is limited. In postnatally acquired cerebral palsy (through encephalitic infection or traumatic incident), the child or even the adult has previously had the opportunity to learn some skills, so that there are compensatory or coping mechanisms available that are denied to the prenatal cerebral palsied person. Goldstein's "catastrophic reaction" to brain injury (Goldstein, 1939) seems a logical explanation, for this kind of event brings with it a shift in the person's motivational pattern as well as other effects on his psychological outlook including perception of self and actual visual perception of the social milieu.

Related to the preceding discussion are the difficulties encountered by the cerebral palsied individual as he attempts to maintain communication with his immediate world. The difficulties may be receptive and/or expressive, that is, sense modalities involved in the reception of stimuli may be so impaired that the cerebral palsied individual is either unable to receive the written and spoken word, or there is receptive distortion. On the other hand, the child may have little or no difficulty in receiving and comprehending signals but may not be able to respond through the usual channels, viz., speech, writing, and gesture, because of motor impairment. (The reader is referred to the chapter on the language disorders for a fuller treatment of this subject.) The end result in either case is the same—social isolation due to an inability to interact with others in the social milieu. The youngster is reduced to the status of an inactive spectator of the social scene. This generates a continuing sense of personal frustration, which in turn results in deviant behavior.

With reference to actual speech, cerebral palsy may so involve the speech apparatus as to make comprehensible verbalization difficult to achieve. Although a system of vocal and gestural communication may be established between the cerebral palsied child and his family, it seldom extends beyond this small group. To all intents and purposes, isolation results, and this gives rise to a host of personal, educational, and vocational problems.

In the younger years, the problems center about appropriate diagnosis, treatment, and preparation for educational experiences. With time and physical growth, the horizon of difficulties widens to include the degree and nature of formal schooling, prevocational and vocational training, and preparation for independent living. Much of the personal, social, educational, and vocational difficulties of the cerebral palsied are related to perceptual difficulties; for with impaired perception there are bound to be distortions in the reception, organization, and interpretation of stimuli and, therefore, in reaction to physical, biological, and social forces. In attempting to introduce order into his life, the cerebral palsied individual usually acquires a number of coping mechanisms that generally take the form of a concretistic and perseverative mode of dealing with the events of daily living.

From a phenomenological point of view, the ideas and notions an individual has about himself comprise his self-concept. For the cerebral palsied person, self-concept is strongly influenced by the effects of sensory and motor dysfunction, which penetrate deep into his personal, social, and vocational adjustments. Call summarizing Block (Block, 1955, a) describes the major psychological problems of cerebral palsied children and the behavioral manifestations in these words:

1. Unresolved dependency feelings and excessive need of affection.
2. Excessive submissiveness and compliance underlying hostility.
3. Egocentricity with emphasis on expansive self-concepts.
4. Compensation for feelings of inferiority and inadequacy by fantasy.
5. Resignation rather than recognition of limitations imposed by the disability.
6. Superficial conscious recognition of the handicap, unconscious rejection of the self. [Call, 1958, p. 14.]

A careful study of this list discloses the possible range of coping behavior that would emerge from the basic needs for recognition, esteem, independence, and for participation in the experiences of childhood. Thwarting the underlying drives toward approval, acceptance, and self-actualization finds outlets in a multiplicity of behavioral manifestations—all designed to help bolster and perhaps enhance the self-concept. Call elaborates on this:

For example, a child who grows up in an atmosphere of over-solicitude, indulgence or over-protection, and who in essence is kept in an infantile, dependent state is quite likely to have many unresolved dependency needs, has no choice other than helplessness, and would retain the infantile expectation that others would revolve around him and that he possesses capacities which indeed he does not possess. Handicapped and injured children adopt those attitudes toward their handicaps and injuries that their parents have toward them. If the parent continually minimizes or denies the existence of the handicap, either through action or word, the child will also. He superficially will be forced to look at the handicap but the real meaning of it will not be accepted, and instead of being able to accept the limitations the handicap imposes, the individual compensates for them in grandiose daydreams or fantasies or will "give up completely" rather than accept compromise which would, of course, require a realistic appraisal of one's own limitations. [Call, 1958, p. 14.]

The resultant behavior would be immature, unrelated to social expectancy (but idiosyncratic to the individual's self-concept), and would manifest other signs of personal and social maladjustment. The empathic observer should see in this behavior the efforts of the cerebral palsied person to meet his personal needs, to organize his social milieu in terms that he can understand and can manipulate meaningfully, and to participate as a group member.

With the passing of years, other problems enter the picture, which, unfortunately, parents either do not foresee or refuse to see, or are unable to recognize. Allen spells out these significant problems in these terms:

Whether [the] self-concept can be expanded to include, in some instances, relevant notions regarding social and sexual roles, e.g., ideas regarding social dating, courtship, and marriage, is an important personal problem for many cerebral palsied who attain adolescence and young adulthood. Maturation of the glandular system and the social model of self-actualization as expressed in a marital situation bring with them biological and psychological stress. Adolescence and beyond are accompanied by the usual attitudes toward, and interests in, emerging needs for independence and in heterosexual concern. For the severely involved patient, neither of these needs usually comes to the attention of the family because of the emphasis on the problems of feeding, washing, toileting, and dressing. It would seldom occur to the parent that the handicapped adolescent boy or girl would have internal promptings. Recognition of these feelings is embarrassing and anxiety-laden for most parents. Suppressing these facts, however, cannot help the person cope wholesomely and constructively with his sexual drives and the matters of courtship and marriage. [Allen, 1960, a, pp. 42–43.]

These problems enter largely into the reactions of the mildly and moderately handicapped person since nonacceptance by the opposite sex is but another expression of rebuff by society and reenforces the cerebral palsied person's self-perception as a member of a minority group. Allen continues: "While some [of the cerebral palsied] may intellectually recognize the attitudes and reactions of the nonhandicapped member of the opposite sex, most cannot emotionally accept their position as rejected suitor" (Allen, 1960, a, p. 43). In personal counseling with several young male cerebral palsied adults the author was impressed with the counselees' "intellectual awareness of the limitations inherent in their physical condition. Yet each insisted that as *he saw himself* this should be no bar to being accepted. . . . The 'Yes, but . . .' attitude seemed to be uppermost in the thinking of each client" (Allen, 1960, a, p. 43).

In the past, the attitude of society and parents toward the cerebral palsied was marked by general indifference to treatment, to the alleviation of physical involvements, and to training; and the matter of socialization was dealt with by isolation, by hiding one's shame, and by limiting the opportunities for contact with the world. Today the general attitude is much more positive, so that parental concern for the care of the cerebral palsied is shared by large segments of society. This has resulted in a need to reconsider the person as a member of the larger societal group and not as the responsibility solely of the family, and to reevaluate modes of dealing with his personal, social, and vocational activities. This includes a reconsideration of the techniques of psychological appraisal so that the feasibility as well as the direction of the treatment and training program may be realistically conceived and executed.

SPECIAL CONSIDERATIONS IN PSYCHOLOGICAL APPRAISAL. The complete appraisal of the cerebral palsied person is a multifaceted task calling for the efforts of a team of professional personnel. The usual clinical or interprofessional team will be drawn from such areas as medicine, special education, psychology, speech and hearing, social service, and vocational rehabilitation, including vocational counseling and training.

The psychological, educational, and vocational assessment of the cerebral palsied must be undertaken within the conceptual framework applicable to the nonhandicapped, the guiding hypothesis being that psychological principles posited for the cerebral palsied do not differ from those which obtain for the nonorganically involved person.

In the appraisal of the cerebral palsied this matter becomes a real issue in the light of the contention that intellectual evaluation should be based on tests designed for, and standardized on, this unique population. The argument usually deplores the fact that the cerebral palsied subject is being unduly penalized when competing directly with the physically and mentally normal child. McCarthy meets this issue head on with these comments:

> Another tendency which I think is unfortunate for the whole field of [psychological] measurement is that with the development of highly specialized clinics for various types of cases in rehabilitation centers, speech and hearing clinics and cerebral palsy centers, workers not highly trained in psychometrics are being forced to develop their own batteries of tests and are using groups of items which are not standardized and on which they develop their own subjective norms on the basis of their clinical experiences. . . . The problem is: what do normal children do with the same tasks? Any one who works for a period of time with one type of handicapped child is bound to develop a distorted norm biased in favor of such cases and while discrimination of degree of defect may be made carefully, the perspective in relation to the normal child will be lost without the use of standardized tests based on representative sampling. [McCarthy, 1958, pp. 19–20.]

It is important that all those working with the cerebral palsied in a diagnostic relationship bear in mind that, if the appraisal and eventuating treatment are to be meaningful to the cerebral palsied patient, they must be within the framework of the real world of the client and not addressed solely to his disability. All assessment has to be within the context of the social, familial, personal-psychological, vocational, and economic factors of the client's world.

Further, the professional specialists of the clinical and rehabilitation teams must be cognizant of the fact that appraisal of the cerebral palsied is a continuous process that must be modified as short-term medical, educational, and training goals are achieved and as the client is ready to go on to the next step in treatment and training. For example, prescription and treatment in the medical specialties go along with ministrations of the physical and occupational therapists. With subsequent improvement, modifications in medical evaluation are indicated and open the possibility to further and more encompassing training goals commensurate with the progress made. Each of the disciplines represented on the clinical team contributes to this fluid evaluation-treatment-training activity, and each needs to change its own diagnosis, prognosis, and goal as progress is made.

With reference to psychological diagnosis, the usual concern is to examine in the areas of intellectual development, personality, educational and vocational feasibility. Each of these will be considered at some length.

INTELLIGENCE. In regard to intelligence testing, the goal of this procedure is to elicit behavior by any means that will yield insights into the individual's intellectual level, potential, and efficiency. In those instances where speech and motor dexterity are present, the selection of appropriate tests is usually a matter of the examiner's preference, influenced perhaps by the subject's verbal comprehension. It is with the more than moderately physically involved cerebral palsied client that modifications in the administration of standard tests becomes necessary. Such departures from the usual test directions are needed in order to obtain a representative picture of abilities, but the norms on which these test results are to be interpreted must derive from a normal or nonhandicapped population. Since the major concern here is with the assessment of individuals with motor, speech, and sensory impairments, the more widely usable tests of intelligence will be reviewed. In the author's experience, those apparently adequate for the purpose are as follows: Ammons Full-Range Picture Vocabulary Test (Ammons and Ammons, 1948), Columbia Mental Maturity Scale (Burgemeister, Blum, and Lorge, 1959), Raven's Progressive Matrices (Raven, 1951), the Leiter International Performance Scale (Leiter, 1952), Vineland Social Maturity Scale (Doll, 1953), Gesell Preliminary Behavior Inventory (Gesell and Amatruda, 1952), Cattell Infant Intelligence Scale (Cattell, 1950), and the Revised Stanford-Binet Scale (Terman and Merrill, 1937, and 1960).

Prior to testing it is helpful to survey the extent and nature of the cerebral palsied clint's impaired functioning. Katz has devised a form (see p. 177) that facilitates this kind of survey. Additional observations may include

> deviations or limitations in convergence and supraversion of the eyes; data on particular arm-hand restrictions to include the types of movements useful in test performance, e.g., ability to point, hold a pencil, draw, etc.; additional information regarding patient's reading and writing skills; and finally the extent to which a subject can indicate "yes" or "no" either verbally or gesturally. . . . This would assist the tester in the selection of tests, modes of administration and the manner of indicating responses. [Allen and Collins, 1955, p. 11.]

To assist the psychologist, Allen and Collins have devised a two-fold category of the intelligence tests listed above: *Type 1:* "techniques which assume an understanding of verbal directions . . . but do not absolutely require motor manipulation for responding" (Allen and Collins, 1955, p. 11). The tests in this class are the Ammons Full-Range Picture Vocabulary Test, the Columbia Mental Maturity Scale, Raven's Progressive Matrices, and the Leiter International Performance Scale. *Type 2:* these tests "emphasize the accumulation of information regarding the testee's development in various life areas from a source (or sources) other than the testee. In these procedures the major concern is to obtain reports of the testee's behavior from an observer presumed to have sufficient knowledge to relate valid information. This reduces somewhat dependence on motor performance and problem-solving activity by the testee in the presence of the tester" (Allen, 1958, a, p. 6). Included in this category are the Vineland Social Maturity Scale, Gesell Preliminary Behavior Inventory, and the Cattell Infant Intelligence Scale. The Revised Stanford-Binet Intelligence Scale will be discussed in the light of Katz's research (Katz, 1956 and 1958).

1. *The Ammons Full-Range Picture Vocabulary Test* consists of 16 plates with four pictures on each. A list of eighty-five words (for each form, A and B) is defined by the subject who indicates which one picture on the exposed plate illustrates the meaning of the word. The norms range from 2.5 years to adult. The format of the test items requires sufficient vision to see the pictures on each plate and verbal comprehension. The selection of the appropriate reply—one of the four pictures—may be indicated in one of several ways. Visual perceptual distortion will interfere seriously with taking this test.

Basically the individual's intellectual level is derived from the number of correct pictures selected as well as the level of the words pictorially defined. The choices range from the extremely concrete to the abstract. On the assumption that the level of verbal concept formation is a function of intellectual growth, the modal and the highest levels achieved will yield useful data regarding the subject's intellectual efficiency.

For the speech-comprehending and motor-impared client, the examiner explains the nature of the test and further indicates that his reply may be made in a particular way (in accordance with the subject's previously determined ability to do so). The "pointing" technique is most feasible. In this procedure, the psychologist asks for the desired word-definition and points with his finger to each of the four pictures on each plate. The pointing is done in a standard fashion by starting with the picture at the upper left-hand corner of the card, shifting to the upper right picture, then to the lower left corner picture, and finally to the

Name____________________ Sex________ No.________ Date________

Diagnosis______________________________ B.D.________

____________________ Rated by:____________ Age________

	NON-HANDICAPPING		HANDICAPPING		Comments
	Minimal	*Mild*	*Moderate*	*Severe*	
VISION	☐ No trouble with vision; no glasses needed	☐ Some correction needed; may wear glasses; not handicapped in seeing	☐ Quite handicapped in seeing; vision not correctible by glasses	☐ Almost blind totally blind	Left eye Rt. eye
HEARING	☐ No trouble with hearing	☐ Some difficulty in hearing; may wear hearing aid satisfactorily	☐ Quite handicapped in hearing; has difficulty when wearing hearing aid	☐ Almost deaf totally deaf	Left ear Rt. ear
SPEECH (verbal)	☐ Speech can be understood without difficulty by a stranger	☐ Some difficulty in being understood by a stranger; able to get ideas across in speech	☐ Speech hard for a stranger or immediate family to understand; hard to get ideas across in speech	☐ Almost totally unable to communicate by speech; totally without speech	
SITTING BALANCE	☐ No difficulty in sitting in a chair or at a table	☐ Some difficulty in sitting in a chair or at a table, but not handicapped in doing so	☐ Quite handicapped in sitting in a chair or at a table; needs a relaxation chair and tray	☐ Unable to maintain sitting balance unless fully supported	
ARM-HAND USE	☐ No difficulty in using arms and hands for self-help activity	☐ Some difficulty in using arms and hands for self-help, but not handicapped in doing so	☐ Quite handicapped in using arms and hands for many self-help activities	☐ Unable to use arms and hands for any self-help activity	Left arm Rt. arm
WALKING	☐ No difficulty in walking	☐ Braces needed; unsteady gait; but able to get around	☐ Quite handicapped in walking; cannot walk independently	☐ Unable to walk	Left leg Rt. leg

Survey of Degree of Physical Handicap

Prepared for Cerebral Palsy Program, Department of Pediatrics, University of California School of Medicine, San Francisco, by Elias Katz, Ph.D., Psychologist, Cerebral Palsy Program, with the cooperation of Dr. Peter Cohen, Associate Professor of Pediatrics, and Supervisor, Cerebral Palsy Program, and staff members.

Reproduced with permission from E. Katz. 1956. "A Method of Selecting Stanford-Binet Intelligence Scale Test Items for Evaluating the Mental Abilities of Children Severely Handicapped by Cerebral Palsy." *Cerebral Palsy Review* 17: 17.

picture on the lower right corner. At each picture the examiner asks, "Is this the one?" for the first few plates. After the third plate the subject usually understands the purpose of the pointing and stopping. It may be necessary occasionally to repeat the question in later cards as a reminder. The examiner should stop at each picture for an equal time interval, so that the pause may not be used as a clue to correct selection. Further, even though the correct item may be the first, second, or third picture on each card the examiner should point to all four pictures. Nor should the examiner start or stop with or at the correct item unless it is the first or last item respectively. This could also prove to be a clue to the subject. Starting and stopping the pointing in this way introduces a standard administrative procedure into this adaptive testing. The client may indicate his selection either by saying "yes" or "no" or by some other distinguishable sign to indicate yes or no: nodding of the head, blinking of an eye, a grunt—anything, so long as the individual's response is communicated satisfactorily. The value of the findings obtained by this procedure more than justifies the increased testing time.

If the cerebral palsied client is deaf but can read, an adaptive procedure would follow along these lines:

> The tester may use a 3 by 5 card to expose one word at a time from the printed list of words. The examiner should control the card to prevent more than one word appearing. The pointing procedure detailed above may be used to enable the motor impaired subject to signal his choice of response. If there is no motor incapacity, the usual point response may be given by the testee. [Allen and Collins, 1955, p. 13.]

2. *The Columbia Mental Maturity Scale* (revised edition) consists of 100 cards, 19 by 6 inches, with various pictures, designs, forms, words, and letters printed thereon. The subject has to utilize concept formation ability ranging from the completely concrete to the highly abstract. The purpose of the test is to

evaluate the ability to reason logically with space, form, color, number, and verbal concepts. Perceptual distortions play a role in the space and form items but may be detected or assessed in the light of the subject's achievement with the other types of items. The essential solution of the problem on each of the 100 cards is in the principle of *belongingness*. The subject must select the single item that does not belong or fit with the other three, four, or five items on the card. The norms range from a mental age of 3 years, 5 months, to 13 years, 11 months. For this test, vision and comprehension of verbal instructions are necessary. Pantomime of the principle of belongingness with some of the first cards is feasible, especially with the more intelligent subject. The motor or speech impaired individual may respond to the card by the pointing method described above with the active cooperation of the examiner.

3. *Raven's Progressive Matrices*, as used in this country, consists of: Sets A, B, C, D, and E for subjects 6 years of age and over (1938 booklet form); Sets A, Ab, and B (1947 color series) for children 5 to 11 years; and Sets I and II for persons 11 years of age and over with average intelligence or better. The norms are expressed in percentiles and grade classification.

The book forms consist of a large design or matrix on each page with six alternative inserts printed underneath each matrix. The subject selects the one insert that completes the large design. The appropriate choice is a function of a basic relationship to be grasped by the subject as he views the matrix and the six choices. The basic concept ranges from simple pattern coherence and completion to highly conceptualized number and form relationships. The format of the test invites the pointing method of response by gesture or vocalization. The examiner should start at the first insert and pause as he comes to each of the alternatives until the sixth or last one is reached. Instructions may be pantomimed, thus enhancing the test's usefulness. This test is not to be used if vision is impaired since incorrect responses may be due to visual distortion rather than to an inability to grasp the completion principle.

4. *The Leiter International Performance Scale* is the lengthiest of the devices in this category. The three trays contain fifty-four items ranging from 2 to 18 years. The task is to match items depicted on a model card placed in a wooden frame with individual items on block faces that fit into slots in the wooden frame. The problems to be solved vary from simple color matching to deriving a general principle that determines the matching procedure. Verbal comprehension is not necessary since the directions may be pantomimed. Vision is essential. This test offers no barrier to the person with cerebral palsy who may also be deaf or speech-impaired. The mode of response is to insert each block into its appropriate slot. This can be done for the subject by the examiner. Which block is to be inserted is selected by the subject. Since only four of the test items are timed, this aspect of the test situation is, for practical purposes, negligible so that the subject may manipulate the blocks himself without being penalized for time. Where this is not possible, the examiner and subject should agree on a method of indicating the latter's choices and have the former do the purely manipulative task of insertion. The examiner can present the response blocks in two ways: by showing the subject one block at a time and looking for the prearranged signal to notify the examiner to place the block in front of each slot in the frame until the subject communicates the selection. The examiner should start at the slot on his right at all times and proceed to the left until the subject disposes of it into one of the slots. According to a second method, wherein all blocks must be exposed simultaneously to the subject's view, the examiner places one finger on the first slot and with a finger of the other hand moves from one block to the next until the subject signals his choice.

In those instances in which direct testing with these Type 1 tests is not possible, or in which supplementary developmental and personal data are desirable, Type 2 tests referred to above may be utilized. In this category, the focus is on the accumulation of pertinent data from sources usually other than the subject. The prototype of this technique is the interview in which relevant information is obtained from one or many sources by direct questioning or by open-ended queries in which the informant is presumed to have valid information. Most closely approaching this interview method are the Vineland Social Maturity Scale (Doll, 1953) and the Gesell Preliminary Behavior Inventory (Gesell and Amatruda, 1952). Although it is true that neither of these two procedures are intelligence tests in the usual understanding of the term, "if a more liberal definition of the term is adopted, viz., to consider intelligence as a function of the degree of adequacy of behavior to the demands of a situation" (Allen, 1960, b), then an overview of the youngster's attainments in various areas of living will give a fairly representative profile of intellectual ability and potential" (Allen, 1958, a, p. 6).

5. *The Vineland Social Maturity Scale* is an age scale of 117 items from Year O-I to Adulthood (Year XXV+). The information obtained from a knowledgeable individual and the observations in the testing room can yield data in the major activities of daily living: self-help, general; self-help, eating; self-help, dressing; self-direction; occupation; locomotion; socialization; and communication. The personal and social maturity reflected in the activities of the person provide the basis for assessing his intellectual and emotional development. Thus, the kind of intelligence tapped with this device is more functional than that evaluated by the formal tests previously discussed. Both approaches are essential since it is desirable to know not only the potential and the efficiency of intellectual growth but also the extent to which this has been, and will continue to be, manifested in the problems of every day living. The Vineland Scale

furnishes the latter type of information. It is the kind of data on which realistic educational, training, and vocational goals must be predicated.

The method of administration is practically alike for all subjects. The informant is led into a discussion of the kinds of information sought by open-ended questions and rising-inflection statements (Allen, [n.d.]) or reflected comments by the psychologist. Direct question is avoided where possible since it limits the spontaneity of the informant's responses and could lead to a rather sterile, repetetive and boring question-answer session. Efforts should be made to learn not only whether the youngster can take care of his toilet needs but also the nature of the attitudes in the family with regard to this intimate activity of daily living. The "yes" or "no" of toileting can lead to insights into interpersonal relationships of major significance for goal planning.

Many of the items in the early age levels may be answered by direct observation since they are mainly neurological and motor in content. Hadley cautions the user to be sensitive to "not only the danger of uncritical acceptance of parents' reports of information rated on the Vineland Scale, but also the importance of observing behavior in various test situations and integrating and comparing these observations against a background of historical information" (Hadley, 1958, p. 10). The author's experience has led to the conclusion that this test is best used in conjunction with a formal test of intelligence.

6. *The Gesell Preliminary Behavior Inventory* is limited in its applicability to the years from birth to 3 years. It seeks to derive information regarding the infant's and child's motor, adaptive, language, and personal-social development. The data is obtained by observing the child, asking a reliable informant, and administering some test items (Allen, 1958, a, pp. 6–7). The first of these calls for rating the youngster's behavior in the testing room or the play room. Detailed previous knowledge of the test items helps the examiner focus on those activities which can

be checked on the convenient form. The second method (asking an informant) differs little in procedure from that suggested in connection with the Vineland Scale. The administration of test items—the third approach—is resorted to if spontaneous activity during the testing session does not elicit relevant behavior. Some of these items, like block tower building, may be beyond the child's motor ability owing to physical involvement, so that the examiner will have to be judicious in the inclusion and omission of specific tasks. This would be especially so for those test items that do not lend themselves to modification in terms of the subject's physical abilities.

7. *The Cattell Infant Intelligence Scale* is also restricted to the very early years, from 2 months to 4 years of age. The items for the infant years are similar to the Gesell inventory and are completed by observation and by information supplied by a reliable source. The guides given above are applicable. The items between 30 and 48 months are Year III, III-6, and IV of the Revised Stanford-Binet Scale (Terman and Merrill, 1937), which will be discussed next.

8. *The Revised Stanford-Binet* is one of the more widely used tests, along with the Wechsler series of tests. Katz published the results of his pioneer adaptation of the items of this test to the cerebral palsied. He calls this method the "pointing modification"—a term that adequately describes it. The reader is urged to consult Katz's two papers, "A Method of Selecting Stanford-Binet Intelligence Scale Test Items for Evaluating the Mental Abilities of Children Handicapped by Cerebral Palsy" (Katz, 1956) and "The 'Pointing Modification' of the Revised Stanford-Binet Intelligence Scales, Forms L and M, Years II through VI: a Report of Research in Progress" (Katz, 1958). The first of these two reports contains a detailed table that indicates the specific physical abilities necessary for the performance of the test items in Form L of the Revised-Binet and is very helpful to the examiner in selecting the items and adapting them for the particular sub-

ject. These abilities are classified according to vision, hearing, speech (verbal), sitting balance, arm-hand use, and walking involved in each test task. This analysis was made for all of the Form L items from Year II, 1, to Superior Adult–III, 6. (For those psychological examiners who are using the 1960 or Third Revision, Form L-M, of the Stanford-Binet Intelligence Scale, the suggestions contained in Katz's analysis still apply since the same or very similar items are utilized.) Table 2 illustrates a random selection of test items and physical abilities required (x) and not required (o) for tasks at various age levels.

Thus, in test Year II, 2, Identifying Objects by Name, the abilities required are vision, hearing, and arm-hand use. With the cerebral palsied the adaptation would center about the inability of the child to use his arm-hand satisfactorily. In this instance the examiner would point to each subject on the card while asking for the identification by name. The child signifies his response by some gesture or vocal signal. Adaptations come with experience, but the examiner must be sensitive to McCarthy's caution against formulating local norms based on sentimentality and almost total immersion in only one kind of testing population so that sight is lost of the larger referent, the nonhandicapped world in which the cerebral palsied person must live.

For the present, the upper age level items of this test and others, viz., the Wechsler series, will have to be adapted experimentally before a smooth procedure can be developed (see Sievers and Norman, 1953). The larger issues to be dealt with, however, are standardization and norms. These matters should be the concern of psychologists in the field of assessment of the physically disabled, but it must not impede experimentation. Katz comments:

> It is becoming evident that the cost of educating and rehabilitating a severely handicapped cerebral palsied child is considerably greater than the cost of educating and rehabilitating a cerebral palsied child with minor physical handicap. . . . Furthermore, it is now more

TABLE 2. *Classification of Physical Disabilities Required to Perform Test Items of the Stanford-Binet Intelligence Scale, Form L*

	Test Item	*Physical Ability Required*					
		Vision	*Hearing*	*Speech (Verbal)*	*Sitting Balance*	*Arm-Hand Use*	*Walking*
II, 1	Three-Hole Form Board	x	x	o	o	x	o
II, 2	Identifying Objects by Name	x	x	o	o	x	o
II, 3	Identifying Parts of the Body	x	x	o	o	x	o
II, 4	Block Building: Tower	x	x	o	o	x	o
II, 5	Picture Vocabulary	x	x	x	o	o	o
II, 6	Word Combinations	o	o	x	o	o	o
VI, 1	Vocabulary	o	x	x	o	o	o
VI, 2	Copying a Bead from Memory I	x	x	o	o	x	o
VI, 3	Mutilated Pictures	x	x	x	o	x	o
VI, 4	Number Concepts	x	x	o	o	x	o
VI, 5	Pictorial Likenesses and Differences	x	x	o	o	x	o
VI, 6	Maze Tracing	x	x	o	o	x	o
XIV, 1	Vocabulary	o	x	x	o	o	o
XIV, 2	Induction	x	x	x	o	o	o
XIV, 3	Picture Absurdities III	x	x	x	o	o	o
XIV, 4	Ingenuity	o	x	x	o	o	o
XIV, 5	Orientation: Direction I	o	x	x	o	o	o
XIV, 6	Abstract Words II	o	x	x	o	o	o
SA-III, 1	Vocabulary	o	x	x	o	o	o
SA-III, 2	Orientation: Direction II	o	x	x	o	o	o
SA-III, 3	Opposite Analogies II	o	x	x	o	o	o
SA-III, 4	Paper Cutting II	x	x	o	o	x	o
SA-III, 5	Reasoning	x	x	x	o	o	o
SA-III, 6	Repeating 9 Digits	o	x	x	o	o	o

SOURCE: Reproduced with permission from E. Katz. 1956. "A Method of Selecting Stanford-Binet Intelligence Scale Test Items for Evaluating the Mental Abilities of Children Severely Handicapped by Cerebral Palsy." *Cerebral Palsy Review* 17:13, 14, and 15.

widely accepted that the ability of cerebral palsied children to profit from intensive treatment and training is correlated with their mental ability. . . . A more precise knowledge of whether a severely physically handicapped cerebral palsied child is also mentally retarded is thus an important consideration as to whether or not to embark upon the complex and expensive training program necessary for his condition. [Katz, 1958, p. 700.]

Certainly this is a cogent and persuasive argument for extensive and adaptive intelligence testing in a reality framework.

Since perceptual processes are involved in intellectual functioning, as well as in learning and training, this area must not be overlooked. Some assessment may be obtained from the subject's performance on the intelligence tests mentioned, especially the Columbia Scale, the Progressive Matrices, the Leiter Scale, and the Gesell Scale (Allen, [n.d.]). Gross perceptual distortions become quite obvious in the nature of the responses. However, the examiner must make certain that it is not intellectual deficit that is yielding incorrect replies to the test items.

A major review of the research in this particular field may be found in Cruickshank, Bice, and Wallen's book, *Perception and Cerebral Palsy* (Cruickshank, Bice, and Wallen, 1957). Space does not permit a detailed discussion of the methodology and the results of this study. However, the over-all conclusion shows markedly inferior perceptual performance by cerebral palsied individuals when compared with nonhandicapped children on the various perceptual tasks. A note of caution that concludes the book warns against a generalized finding: "Thus, although this study indicates impaired perception in the cerebral palsy children, there appear to be more variables involved than forced responsiveness resulting in the observed figure-ground disturbances. Further research is needed to clarify this latter issue" (Cruickshank, Bice, and Wallen, 1957, p. 114). The role of perception in the functioning of the cerebral palsied person is almost the entire story of cerbral palsy as a condition. Perceptual distortions find experssion in the intellectual inefficiency of the individual, in the mode of reacting to the forces impinging upon him in his life space, and in the effectiveness of educational, training, and rehabilitation programs.

PERSONALITY. A thorough understanding of the personality of the cerebral palsied individual is predicated on a knowledge of personality dynamics. Mayman and Gardner write of this person:

> The world of a brain damaged person is radically different from the world of common experience. He thinks, feels, and functions at a more primitive level of organization. Objects of perception press in upon him in such compelling fashion that he becomes a bystander in respect to these external events. He is bound to be tangible, concrete in the impact of his experiences and loses the capacity to abstract several levels of meaning from sensorimotor events. He is easily confused if stimulation comes too rapidly or is more than minimally complex. [Mayman and Gardner, 1960, p. 26].

The effects upon organization of behavior—the observable aspects of personality—vary. But a thread of discomfort, unhappiness, and sense of social isolation cannot be dismissed. Lack of experience leads to a restrictive view of people, objects, and events, with concomitant narrowing of personal qualities and coping mechanisms available for use in problem-solving. Psychological disturbances are the rule rather than the exception in personality makeup for this individual.

It should be borne in mind that different parts of the body are involved for different cerebral palsied patients. Add to the physical variables the family variables, and the varied relationships engendered by empathy, sympathy, guilt and shame, rejection, oversolicitousness, and so forth; the social situation with its isolation, exclusion, toleration, and thoughtlessness (especially in peer group relations); and the inability to compete; and the conclusion is obvious that there can be no personality type for the cerebral palsied. The condition and its effects are too complex and too varied to permit "typing," and each patient must be considered individually in arriving at a personality description.

Personality evaluation is not too readily accomplished with the severely disabled, especially those whose speech is so impaired as to make oral response an almost impossible task. Where intelligible speech is feasible, the usual personality tests may be employed. A study by Linde and Patterson reports significant scale differences on the MMPI between normal and cerebral palsied groups, but they comment that "the conclusion that there are specific personality types or patterns associated with particular disabilities does not appear to be warranted" (Linde and Patterson, 1958, p. 212).

The author has been able to use the Rorschach Inkblot Test (Allen, 1953 and 1954), the Thematic Apperception Test (Murray, 1943), the various sentence completion forms (Forer, 1950; Stein, 1947), and a host of other projective and psychometric paper and pencil personality tests with the cerebral palsied (Allen, 1960, b). Each testing situation took into consideration the individual's ability to see, speak, hear, write, and otherwise indicate that he could receive and respond to the test requirements. Figure drawing tests, such as the Draw-A-Person Test (Machover, 1948), and the Visual Motor Gestalt Test (Bender, 1938; Hutt and Briskin, 1960) were sometimes possible to administer. An outstanding feature of the Rorschach test protocol was the presence of "organic signs," both gross and soft, in addition to those coping mechanisms reflecting the individual's manner of organizing the perceptual field. Beyond this, the distribution of Rorschach elements was individually determined and resisted categorization of the "typical picture" variety. Many of the figure drawings reflected the body-perceptions of the cerebral palsied subject with overcompensation for, or partial-to-complete denial of, the body part(s) involved in the condition. In those instances in which motor function permitted the administration of the visual-motor gestalt figures (and in which organic signs did not significantly overshadow the reproductions of the model designs) the protocols did lend themselves to personality interpretation (see Hutt and Briskin, 1960).

In short, personality tests and procedures may be utilized successfully with the cerebral palsied client provided the examiner is cognizant of the performance of the nonhandicapped on these tests and is further sensitive to the influences of impaired visual perception and/or dysfunction.

REHABILITATION. Basically, there are no cures for cerebral palsy. Under medical supervision steps may be taken to achieve a state of motor function that will render the individual more effective in caring for his personal needs. For many of the cerebral palsied, however, there is the persistent problem of care when adulthood is attained and when parents or other relatives are either deceased or unable to continue ministering to the individual. In general, the cerebral palsied person will continue to require help throughout his lifetime. A realistic attack on the problem looks to prevention as the major approach. Engle (Engle, 1959) suggests the following steps in prevention: good prenatal care, qualified obstetric care, adequate pediatric care for the full-term neonate, prevention of prematurity, and adequate care of the premature neonate, prevention of erythroblastosis fetalis and kernicterus, protection against communicable diseases and infection, protection against and adequate treatment for brain injuries, and promotion of protective legislation.

So far as the cerebral palsied individual is concerned, after medical, physical, orthopedic, neurological, educational, and psychological evaluation and therapy have been accomplished, what then? Then education in its broadest sense must be applied; exposure to experiences both in and out of the formal classroom situation; "an opportunity to develop . . . capacities and social relationships, and stimulate . . . interest so that [the cerebral palsied] will make an effort to overcome or adjust to their handicaps and so achieve the greatest possible competence and happiness" (Cardwell, 1956, p. 411).

At the school-age level, of particular interest to psychologists are the perceptual difficulties that mirror the encephalopathic condition and are manifested in classroom learning crises. Because of the cerebral palsied pupil's inability to deal with more than "minimally complex" stimuli, easy distractibility, tactile and visual anomalies, and lower order conceptualizing, the teacher has to create a special environment for such a student. Class size, emotional atmosphere, special equipment to increase pupil mobility or even to afford comfort in standing and sitting, special eating and toilet arrangements, unique teaching methods and materials, and patience are among the major special education issues.

In regard to efforts to rehabilitate the adult cerebral palsied for maximal (for the individual) independent living or vocational placement, the consensus seems to be that this singular population will require specialized vocational appraisal techniques (Arns, 1959). One such approach is the "work sample" procedure or the "miniature job task method" in use at the Institute for the Crippled and Disabled in New York City and at the Demonstration Project at the United Cerebral Palsy Rehabilitation Center of Miami. As with any vocational situation, the beginning point is the individual—his abilities, limitations, attitudes, likes, and dislikes. The very severely physically and/or intellectually involved patients are usually excluded from economically advantageous vocational rehabilitation. For the severely physically involved but intellectually capable, an avocational goal at best would be practicable. The focus of vocational rehabilitation efforts is ordinarily the moderately and mildly involved with slightly retarded or better intellectual ability.

Ideally, rehabilitation planning for the cerebral palsied has to begin literally at the beginning. It is not a matter of picking up from the time of the disability, for in most instances there has been no disability-free period. Nor is it a continuation of the vocational-counseling or career-planning program initiated in the junior and senior high school, since few go through the grades in regular classes. The rehabilitation program should therefore begin in prevocational activities that include ample opportunities to learn what is ordinarily assimilated during the formative years: accomplishing good interpersonal relationships, inculcating a sense of growing independence, formal scholastic learning, such as reading and writing (where possible), and acquiring attitudes of personal and social responsibility. Later these should develop into positive attitudes toward work habits and activities and lead to an awareness of the world of reality the individual will have to accept and live in. These goals can be accomplished by the rehabilitation center personnel with whom the growing child and adolescent come in contact—the occupational therapist, the special education teachers, the psychologist, and the vocational counselor.

Little in fact can be achieved at any level without the cooperative efforts and skills of the rehabilitation team, the principle of operation being to adapt team effort to individual need. By means of the medical, social, special educational, psychological, speech and hearing, and paramedical service information that is provided by the team, assessment, prescription and treatment of the individual can be planned to establish vocational feasibility. In consultation with the medical specialists, psychologist, and training personnel, the vocational counselor sets both immediate and ultimate vocational goals. In this endeavor, the psychologist plays a key role in three important ways: (1) psychological assessment of the patient; (2) modification of the patient's behavior through individual and/or group therapy; and (3) coordination of the services available to the patient. This final step is, of course, supervised by the vocational subteam—the vocational counselor, vocational trainer, and the community placement resource person. The ultimate goal is the effective vocational placement and adjustment of the client.

RESEARCH. As yet, research has provided too few answers to the many questions, issues, and problems of rehabilitation of the cerebral palsied. Much needs to be done to really understand the rehabilitation process, the rehabilitee, and the rehabilitators. A fine beginning in finding the answers is being made by the Office of Vocational Rehabilitation through its many grants to agencies in state and local government and to private voluntary groups. At the local levels, county and city governmental units operate through schools systems and through cooperation with such private voluntary agencies as the Jewish Vocational Service, the Sheltered Workshop, and so forth. In some communities rehabilitation programs are discrete entities so that a large city may have several agencies operating in an uncoordinated manner. In Dade County, Florida, for example, the United Cerebral Palsy Rehabilitation Center of Miami, the Rehabilitation Center for Crippled Children, Goodwill Industries, Dade County Sheltered Workshop, the Jewish Vocational Service Workshop, and several private organizations and employers are all active in training and vocational placement but have little interchange of experience, evaluation, or programming. The more enlightened communities plan for a comprehensive rehabilitation center that could serve larger number and varieties of rehabilitees more effectively because of the coordination such centers make possible.

Psychologists have many research possibilities open to them in the area of cerebral palsy, ranging from improved testing procedures and techniques to the conceptualization and testing of rehabilitation principles. However, Rusk, in an address before the Princeton Rehabilitation Conference, stated the case succinctly in these three questions about the rehabilitee (Wright, 1959, p. 105): "Did he have something to do? Did he have some place to go, a home? Did he have somebody to love him?" To answer all three in the affirmative is to achieve rehabilitation in its truest sense.

REFERENCES

Abbott, M. 1956. Cerebral palsy; its scope and management. Pamphlet No. 158A. New York, Public Affairs Committee.

Allen, R. M. 1953. Elements of Rorschach interpretation. New York, International Universities Press.

—— 1954. Introduction to the Rorschach technique. New York, International Universities Press.

—— 1958, a. Suggestions for the adaptive administration of intelligence tests for those with cerebral palsy, Part II. Cereb. Palsy Rev. 19(2):6–7.

—— 1958, b. Personality assessment procedures. New York, Harper.

—— 1959. Psychological assessment procedures for the cerebral palsied, in R. M. Allen and others, eds. Proceedings of the Postdoctoral Workshop in Psychological Services for the Cerebral Palsied. Coral Gables, Fla., University of Miami Press, pp. 21–24.

—— 1960, a. The cerebral palsied, the rehabilitation team, and adjustment: an overview. J. Rehab. 26:22–25, 42–44.

—— 1960, b. Guide to psychological tests and measurements. Coral Gables, Fla., University of Miami Press.

—— 1960, c. Intellectual evaluation in cerebral palsy: one point of view. Exceptional Children 27:202–4.

—— [n.d.] The appraisal of social and perceptual competence of school children, in J. Magary, ed. School psychology. New York, Prentice-Hall, Chap. 12. (To be published.)

Allen, R. M., and M. G. Collins. 1955. Suggestions for the adaptive administration of intelligence tests for those with cerebral palsy, Part I. Cereb. Palsy Rev. 16(3):11–14, 25.

Allen, R. M., C. C. Corrie, and T. W. Jefferson. 1960. Proceedings of the Second Annual Workshop on the Integration and Interpretation of Pre-vocational Information concerning the Neurologically Handicapped Client. Coral Gables, Fla., University of Miami Press.

Allen, R. M., and others, eds. 1959. Proceedings of the Postdoctoral Workshop in Psychological Services for the Cerebral Palsied. Coral Gables, Fla., University of Miami Press.

Ammons, R. B., and H. S. Ammons. 1948. The full-range picture vocabulary test. New Orleans, R. B. Ammons.

Arns, J. 1959. Evaluation of the vocational potential of the cerebral palsied by the work sample technique, in R. M. Allen, and others, eds. Proceedings of the Postdoctoral Workshop in Psychological

Services for the Cerebral Palsied. Coral Gables, Fla., University of Miami Press, pp. 19–20.

Baker, H. J. 1959. Introduction to exceptional children. New York, Macmillan.

Barker, R. G. 1948. The social psychology of physical disability. J. Social Issues 4:28–34.

Bender, L. 1938. A visual motor gestalt test and its clinical use. Research Monograph 3. New York, American Orthopsychiatric Association.

Block, W. E. 1955, a. Personality of the brain injured child. Exceptional Children 21:91–100, 108.

—— 1955, b. A study of somatopsychological relationships in cerebral palsied children. Exceptional Children 22:77–83.

Burgemeister, B. B., and L. H. Blum. 1949. Intellectual evaluation of a group of cerebral palsied children. Nervous Child 8:177–80.

Burgemeister, B. B., L. H. Blum, and I. Lorge. 1959. Columbia Mental Maturity Scale. Revised ed. New York, World Book Company.

Burks, H. F. 1960. The hyperkinetic child. Exceptional Children 27:18–26.

Call, J. D. 1958. Psychological problems of the cerebral palsied child, his parents and siblings as revealed by dynamically oriented small group discussions with parents. Cereb. Palsy Rev. 19:3–5, 11–15.

Cardwell, V. E. 1956. Cerebral palsy: advances in understanding and care. New York, Association for the Aid of Crippled Children.

Cattell, P. 1950. The measurement of intelligence of infants and young children. New York, Psychological Corporation.

Courville, C. B. 1954. Cerebral palsy. Los Angeles, Calif., San Lucas Press.

Cruickshank, W. M., H. V. Bice, and N. E. Wallen. 1957. Perception and cerebral palsy. Syracuse, N.Y., Syracuse University Press.

DiMichael, S. 1960. Current developments in diagnosing and counseling of the neurologically disabled, in R. M. Allen, and others, eds. Proceedings of the Second Annual Workshop on the Integration and Interpretation of Pre-vocational Information concerning the Neurologically Handicapped Client. Coral Gables, Fla., University of Miami Press, pp. 13–21.

Doll, E. A. 1953. The measurement of social competence. Minneapolis, Educational Test Bureau.

Engle, H. A. 1959. Outline notes—cerebral palsy. Miami, Fla., United Cerebral Palsy Association of Miami. Mimeographed.

English, H. B., ed. 1959. Psychological Abstracts (index number)

33, No. 6. Washington, D.C., American Psychological Association.

Forer, B. R. 1950. A structured sentence completion test. J. Project. Techn. 14:15–29.

Gesell, A., and C. S. Amatruda. 1952. Developmental diagnosis. New York, Hoeber.

Goldstein, K. 1939. The organism. New York, American Book Company.

Hadley, J. M. 1958. Clincial and counseling psychology. New York, Knopf.

Hohman, L. B., and D. K. Freedheim. 1958. Further studies on intelligence levels in cerebral palsied children. Amer. J. Phys. Med. 37:90–97.

Hopkins, T. W., H. V. Bice, and K. C. Colton. 1954. Evaluation and education of the cerebral palsied child: New Jersey study. Washington, D.C., International Council for Exceptional Children.

Hutt, M. L., and G. J. Briskin. 1960. The clincial use of the Revised Bender-Gestalt Test. New York, Grune and Stratton.

Katz, E. 1954. A "Survey of Degree of Physical Handicap." Cereb. Palsy Rev. 15:10–11.

—— 1956. A method of selecting Stanford-Binet Intelligence Scale test items for evaluating the mental abilities of children severely handicapped by cerebral palsy. Cereb. Palsy Rev. 17:13–17.

—— 1958. The "pointing modification" of the Revised Stanford-Binet Intelligence Scales, Forms L and M, years II through VI; a report of research in progress. Amer. J. Ment. Def. 52:698–707.

Leiter, R. G. 1952. Part II, Manual for the 1948 revision of the Leiter International Performance Scale. Washington, D.C., Psychological Services Center Press.

Linde, T., and C. H. Patterson. 1958. The MMPI in cerebral palsy. J. Consult. Psychol. 22:210–12.

Machover, K. 1948. Personality projection in the drawing of the human figure. Springfield, Ill., C. C. Thomas.

Mayman, M., and R. W. Gardner. 1960. The characteristic psychological disturbance in some cases of brain damage with mild deficit. Bull. Menninger Clin. 24:26–36.

McCarthy, D. 1958. Measurement of cognitive abilities at the preschool and early childhood levels, in Invitational Conference on Testing Problems. Proceedings. Princeton, N.J., Educational Testing Service, pp. 19–20.

Michal-Smith, H. 1960. Adjustment of the neurologically impaired, in R. M. Allen, and others, eds., Proceedings of the Second Annual

Workshop on the Integration and Interpretation of Pre-vocational Information concerning the Neurologically Handicapped Client. Coral Gables, Fla., University of Miami Press, pp. 30–36.

Murray, H. A. 1943. Thematic Apperception Test. Cambridge, Mass., Harvard University Press.

Parke, Davis & Co. 1959. Cerebral Palsy. Patterns of Disease. Detroit.

Phelps, W. M., T. W. Hopkins, and R. Cousins. 1958. The cerebral palsied child. New York, Simon and Schuster.

Raven, J. C. 1951. Progressive matrices. Beverly Hills, Calif., Western Psychological Services.

Rusk, H. A. 1959. Next steps in rehabilitation, in B. Wright, ed. Psychology and rehabilitation. Washington, D.C., American Psychological Association, pp. 97–105.

Russ, J. D., and H. R. Soboloff. 1958. A primer of cerebral palsy. Springfield, Ill., C. C. Thomas.

Sievers, D. J., and R. D. Norman. 1953. Some suggestive results in psychometric testing of the cerebral palsied with Gesell, Binet, and Wechsler scales. J. Genet. Psychol., 82:69–70.

Stein, M. 1947. The use of a sentence completion test for the diagnosis of personality. J. Clin. Psychol., 3:47–57.

Strauss, A. A., and L. Lehtinen. 1953. Psychopathology and education of the brain-injured child. New York, Grune and Stratton.

Taylor, M., and H. A. Rusk. 1957. Speech problems of hemiplegics. Public Health Rep. 72:832–35.

Terman, L. M., and M. A. Merrill. 1937. Measuring intelligence. Boston, Houghton Mifflin.

—— 1960. Stanford-Binet Intelligence Scale: manual for the third revision, form L-M. Boston, Houghton Mifflin.

U.S. Office of Vocational Rehabilitation and United Cerebral Palsy Associations of Massachusetts. 1957. Pre-vocational training for the cerebral palsied. Boston, United Cerebral Palsy Associations of Massachusetts.

Wallace, H. M. 1954. New York City's program for the handicapped child. New York J. Med., 54:512–18.

Wright, B. A., ed. 1959. Psychology and rehabilitation. Washington, D.C., American Psychological Association.

—— 1960. Physical disability, a psychological approach. New York, Harper.

Zuk, G. H. 1958. Perceptual processes in normal development, brain injury and mental retardation. Amer. J. Ment. Defic. 63:256–59.

THE LANGUAGE DISORDERS

by JOSEPH M. WEPMAN

STUDY of the language-disordered physically disabled adult almost always poses a problem of extreme complexity both in differential diagnosis and in planning for rehabilitation. Since these patients have all suffered impairment of the central nervous system, the interrelated physical, language, and psychological aftereffects often require a Solomon's judgment to determine the causal factor or factors underlying behavior. So many complex symptoms appear, some of which are directly caused by the neural damage and some by the patient's reaction to his handicap, that frequently the best that can be done is to make a reasonable estimate—an educated guess—of the etiology or the prognosis.

The purpose of the present chapter is to attempt to add some structure to the "educated guess"; to illustrate the role that symptoms drawn from each of the areas affected play in relation to symptoms from other areas; to provide a measure of understanding and objectivity to the multifaceted problems; and, thereby, to increase the probability of psychological prediction in organic psychodiagnosis and rehabilitation.

The emphasis of the chapter is placed primarily upon the language disorders and secondarily upon the physical disabilities and adaptive mechanisms employed by the patients that are most often concurrent with them. It is the language disorder that sets these patients apart from other physically disabled and psy-

Joseph M. Wepman, Ph.D., is Professor of Psychology and Surgery and Director of the Speech Clinic at the University of Chicago.

chologically disorganized patients who have also suffered neural trauma. It is the language disorder that makes these patients so difficult to evaluate and provide for in their search for self-realization.

Whereas not too much is known about these patients that is factual, some clinical evidence and research data are useful in clarifying the concepts held about them. The need for more extensive observation and validated research is pressing. The chapter will sketch the broad outlines while the bibliography should provide a source of useful additional information. Understanding the patient in the light of present knowledge, however, will need to be the continued responsibility of all of the members of diagnostic and rehabilitation teams.

INCIDENCE AND CLASSIFICATIONS. Some observations that have been made in clinical practice on the statistics of the patients who have suffered language disruption after neural disorders may be of interest. First, it has been noted that two of every three such patients show one or another form of physical disability. Since it has been estimated that between 1,000,000 and 2,000,000 adults show some language disorder in this country at all times, the population of physically disabled language disrupted patients is a sizable one. It would be safe to place this estimate at between 1,000,000 and 1,500,000 adults who fall into the category under discussion here.

Second, the broad classification of etiology as central nervous system impairment has its general usefulness, but for other considerations, such as age and incidence, a more specific etiology categorization is more widely used. Three major groups have been defined in this regard: (1) language problems resulting from cerebrovascular accidents like the common "stroke," (2) those resulting from direct, externally induced head injuries, and (3) those resulting from neurological disease and neurosurgical intervention. When grouped by this means, experience shows that, relative to the age of the patients when they come for diagnosis and rehabilitation, the cerebrovascular accidents are most often seen in adults over fifty years of age. The head-injured patients are more often below the age of fifty. The disease and surgery group seem equally divided above and below this age level.

As to the number of patients seen in each of these three groups, experience shows that of every 10 such patients 6 have been caused by "strokes," three by injury and only 1 by disease or surgery.

No relationship has yet been established either clinically or by research between the specific etiology of the disorder and either the type or degree of physical disability, the language disorder, or the psychological impairment.

Localization of function in the central nervous system through attempts to localize damage and to relate the damage to loss of function has found partisans and opponents since the latter part of the last century. For example, it was postulated from clinical experience by the present writer some years ago that no punctate localization for language function could be established from our knowledge of central nervous system organization. However, it was observed that symbolic language disturbances occurred only after left hemisphere involvement regardless of the premorbid handedness or cerebral dominance of the patient (Wepman, 1951). At the present time, additional experience and research data point to confirmation of these observations. Since 1950 additional cases seen and reviewed by the writer have brought the total well above 10,000 in which not a single case of symbolic verbal defect had been caused by right brain damage. In the work of Penfield and Roberts (Penfield and Roberts, 1959) there is further confirmation of this localizing factor. They assert, however, that, when damage to the left hemisphere occurs prior to the development of language, the right hemisphere most likely takes over the language function. This latter finding has been confirmed in part by the writer in studying the language aftereffects of a left hemispherectomized patient who was found to have had left cerebral atrophy from birth and who did, nevertheless, develop and use language undoubtedly through the function of his unimpaired right hemisphere.

Confirmation of a different sort has come from psychometric studies on known brain-injuried patients (Reitan, 1953). In this research it was found that verbal intelligence as measured by the verbal subscales of the Wechsler Adult Intelligence Scales was consistently lower than the results obtained on the performance subscales of the same test battery in patients with left brain damage, while the converse was true of patients who had suffered right brain trauma.

There is evidence of another type for localization, in addition to the noted hemispheric differences. Certain neural pathways do function for singular purposes, for example, the eighth nerve or that part of it which subserves the transmission of auditory signals does only that and nothing more. Equally, however, there are parts of the nervous system which seem to be equipotential and subserve many functions (Lashley, 1929). The reader interested in functional localization in the nervous system is advised to read some of the newer research in neurophysiology and neuroanatomy relating to the reticular system and the association areas that are listed in the bibliography at the end of the chapter (Harlow and Woolsey, 1958).

Goldstein and Scheerer (Goldstein and Scheerer, 1941) have reported extensively on the consistent loss of the ability to abstract by the brain-injured adult. Whereas there has been a wide difference of opinion in the literature on this point, too, it is clinically true that the ability to abstract in language and thought is very often affected and that in place of the abstracting ability comes a type of concreteness of thought and language. It appears to this writer that the widespread difference of opinion relative to the theory of the loss of the abstracting ability after brain impairment has been rather one of definition of what is meant by the terms abstraction and concreteness than a true difference of opinion relative to change after brain injury. There is no question in the writer's mind from his language studies of the aphastic adult that there is more likely to be a concreteness of use and a lessened ability to function with abstract verbal symbols in such cases than in any other type of patient or in the unimpaired.

Finally, it should be pointed out that one of the major distinctions in the language problem after neural disruption that has been confirmed by research is whether it is one affecting conceptual symbol formulation (the aphasias) or whether it is a transmissive language problem affecting a specific pathway of reception or expression (the agnosias or apraxias). So important is this separation of the language disorders into integrative and transmissive categories in the evaluation of a patient that in the following paragraphs *working* definitions of the various language disturbances are presented. These definitions have been established as the result of many years of clinical experience and research that has been reported elsewhere (Wepman, Jones, Bock, and Van Pelt, 1960).

DEFINITIONS OF THE LANGUAGE DISORDERS. Essentially three types of language disorders can be isolated after neural trauma: the transmissive agnosias, the transmissive apraxias, and the integrative aphasias. The separation of the symbolic from the nonsymbolic language problems follows from disruption of the functional roles of the nervous system as presently conceived. Figure 1 shows a schematic model of the input-integrative-output concept of neural function. (For a more extensive discussion of this model, see Wepman, Jones, Bock, and Van Pelt, 1960.) The figure shows the separation of the various roles of the CNS: the specific transmissive input of stimuli; the nonspecific integration of stimuli; the specific transmissive output of motor patterns.

Within this schema the language disorders can be defined according to their symbolic or nonsymbolic roles in the total language act.

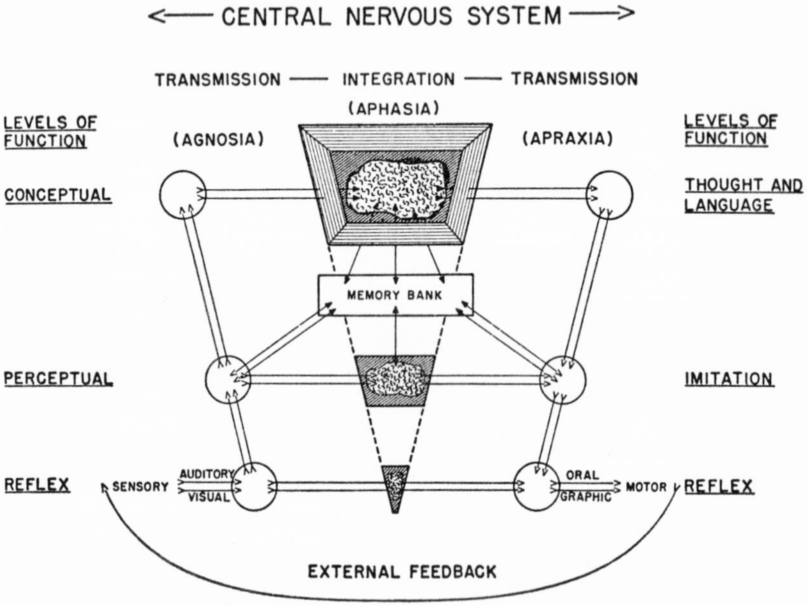

FIGURE 1. *An Operational Diagram of the Levels of Function in Central Nervous System*

Aphasia is defined as any disorder of the abilities necessary to formulate or comprehend verbal symbols that results from organic impairment of the central nervous system. It should be differentiated from speech and language disorders ascribable to dysfunction of the peripheral sense organs, to faulty innervation and ordering of the musculature of speech, or to general mental deficiency.

Aphasias are of five basic types. They may appear independently but are most often seen intermixed, with one type of linguistic disturbance frequently being most prominent. In the order of severity these types can be described as follows:

1. *Global aphasia:* when the patient is incapable of comprehending or functioning with language symbols of any kind.

2. *Jargon aphasia:* when the language output is unintelligible to the listener because it is made up of a meaningless combination of phonemes.

3. *Pragmatic aphasia* [1] when the language product does not relate to the stimulus; contains many neologisms or made-up words as well as many acceptable words that are often meaningless in the context in which they are used.

4. *Semantic aphasia* [1] when the language product is largely made up of the little connective words, the articles, prepositions, conjunctions and pronouns used in proper phrases and groupings, but giving little specific meaning to speech.

5. *Syntactic aphasia* [1] when the language product is made up almost entirely of the substantive nouns, verbs, and modifiers but is lacking the grammatical connective words. (Such speech is frequently called "telegraphic" in style since it consists of single or double word sentences and is not expressed in the usual phrases and groupings of speech.)

Agnosia is the term used to indicate that a language disorder caused by a disruption of reception of verbal stimuli along a specific modality is present. Thus, visual agnosia is produced by a defect in the visual transmitting mechanism and auditory agnosia is producted by a defect in the auditory transmission pathway. It is important to define the agnosias even more closely whenever it is possible for within each modality there can be very specific disorders. In some cases, for example, there is loss of the ability to recognize forms, such as a square, triangle, or other geometric abstraction, while the ability to recognize numbers or letters may be retained; such a disorder would be designated as a *visual form agnosia.* Other patients recognize numbers but not words,

[1] Based on Charles Morris's classification of the semiotic process in his linguistic studies (*Foundations of the Theory of Signs,* Chicago, University of Chicago Press, 1938).

letters but not forms, words but not forms or numbers. Similar fine distinctions can be made within the auditory modality. Circumscribed defects of auditory reception for words, numbers, and specific sounds of the environment have been seen in different patients. The auditory agnosias, like the visual agnosias, need to be defined, then, as carefully as possible since they have such direct effects upon the overt behavior of the patient.

The *apraxias* are caused by defects of the motor transmission pathways which affect language after it has been formulated. They may produce oral defects affecting the manner or speed of expression (called the *dysarthrias*) or graphic defects affecting the coordination of writing (called *motor agraphia*). *Verbal apraxia*, the most serious of the oral transmissive defects, may be so severe that a patient knows exactly what it is he wants to say, but is unable to recall or produce a single correct articulatory movement and consequently is left totally speechless. The dysarthrias, which are in reality only lesser degrees of verbal apraxia, affect the articulation of speech by the distortions in expression that follow the inability to move the muscles of articulation rapidly enough for adequate speech. The agraphias affect writing in much the same way; the patients' efforts are usually adequate but incoordinate and the product may be only minimally intelligible to the reader.

Examinations have been developed and are available that will permit any competent examiner to make the vital distinctions noted above (Schuell, 1955; Wepman and Jones, 1961). Psychological evaluation of a patient should always *follow* the language evaluation and should be made *in terms of the language disorder depicted* for very obvious reasons. If a patient shows a specific agnosia or apraxia, evaluations should avoid the pathway or pathways most affected. If a patient shows an aphasia, the results of any evaluation should be stated in terms of the language ability retained by the patient.

MEDICAL-PHYSICAL ASPECTS OF BRAIN IMPAIRMENT. The most common physical disturbances found in conjunction with language disturbances are listed below. While each of these plays a role that must be considered in psychological evaluation of the patient, space forbids a complete discussion of all of them. To illustrate the relationship between language recovery and the physical disabilities, the first two will be discussed in some detail.

A Partial List of the Physical Concomitants of Language Disorders after Cortical Damage

Hemiplegia (Hemiparesis)	Tinnitus
Hemianopsia	Hearing Loss
Sensory disturbances	Optic atrophy
Epileptiform disorders (Seizures)	Headache
Vertigo	Diplopia
	Palsy

The reader is advised to consult any clinical neurology text (such as Wechsler, 1943) for a more complete list and discussion of the immediate physical affects of central nervous system disruption.

As an illustration of the physical debilities commonly seen in company with language disorders, the paralytic hemiplegias and the vision-limiting field defects are good examples. As discussed earlier, the left cerebral cortex is held to be responsible for the integrative language processes whereas both right and left hemisphere impairment may bring nonsymbolic language disorders in their wake. It follows from this that the most frequent hemiplegias seen accompanying the aphasias affect the right side of the body, the side which in most people is preferred for muscular activity.

When the physical defect affects the leg musculature, the immediate problem presented is one of ambulation. Although this does not affect language directly in any sense, yet it plays a vital role in language rehabilitation. Certainly one of the most important sources of stimulation for the patient is the need to communicate with others. Unless he is ambulatory, his social contacts will often be limited to his family, his therapists, and occasional visitors. Without implying that these people are not important in the recovery process, they nevertheless fulfill very circumscribed roles. They represent a very special kind of social environment, usually a demanding one on the part of the therapist, an over-emotionalized one on the part of most families. The need for interpersonal relationships beyond that provided by these sources is so important that without the ability to make other contacts patients often tend to become depressed, withdrawn, and unmotivated.

Too often the life of the hemiplegic patient is confined to the passive dependency brought on by television, radio, and overconcerned families. Language disordered patients not only must have something to say and the ability to say it, but they must have someone to say it to. The recovery of mobility, of social and goal-directed movement, should always be one of the first goals of all therapy.

When paralysis affects the upper extremities, especially when it affects the hand and arm previously used for writing, one sees a more direct relationship between the physical disorder and a language problem. When the defect is solely in the transmissive motor pathway leading to the arm and hand and does not involve the integrative capacity of the patient, then the language part of the problem is easily offset. Most hemiplegic patients can learn to shift to their unimpaired arm and hand for writing with little or no difficulty. Practice and time will take care of the language problem. The psychological impact of the paralysis, however, is often more far reaching. Patients with global aphasia and upper extremity paralysis have been known to recover completely their previous abilities in speech, reading, and even in writing, yet to remain completely debilitated because of this type of physical limitation. The need to shift to the opposite hand, to become left-handed and remain so, to retain a visible sign of their defect, seems more than some patients can adjust to without assistance. In every instance of brain damage there appears to be some degree of ego weakness and disruption of the self-concept. The psychological problem often becomes all important.

Whereas hemiplegic lower extremities most often recover some degree of usefulness with physical therapy, the upper extremity very often does not recover. (See Bucy, 1949, for a physiological explanation of this.) There is a permanence about the nonfunctional arm—a constant reminder of being different, of being less than a whole man. One patient described this physical problem with singular insight when he spoke of his paralysis as a loss of masculinity, giving him the feeling that he was not a whole man because of his hemiplegic arm.

Physical therapy and language therapy for these patients frequently must become secondary to the need for psychotherapy despite the obvious obstacles involved in this process because of the verbal incapacities of the patient. Insight and understanding of the physical limitations; recognition of the potentials for adaptability to new and challenging vocational possibilities; compensatory activities and adjustments to life that are based upon the reality of the patients' physical propensities—all these need to become the new sources of ego strength. Psychotherapeutic assistance for these patients needs to take on a new and often unusual form. It must rely more on therapist-led discussion, on demonstration, on education, and less on free verbal behavior. The self-concept evolved must be in terms of the patient as he is, facing the reality of his condition and leaving behind the "ghost of the past" that so often haunts him.

The other type of physical disability related to the hemiplegias is the facial paralysis that is not infrequently seen when the paralytic condition is extensive or localized to the facial muscles.

The language defect that results is a transmissive dysarthria due to the inability of the musculature to perform the articulatory acts of speech sufficiently accurately or with sufficient coordination and speed. Direct language training in the speech act, muscular exercise and practice with the affected muscles, slowing the articulatory act until it can be performed accurately, and then by degrees speeding it up again until the flow of language is adequate—these constitute the direct therapy needed. Usually compensatory muscle movement can be brought into play to obviate all but the most severe forms of this type of dysarthria. These articulatory problems are prime examples of the nonsymbolic language disorders. They are the direct aftereffects of the paralysis. They do no affect the integration of language. They are specific to the act of speech and have no counterpart in other muscular acts along other pathways—they are transmissive problems only.

Psychologically the dysarthric patient may present a more serious problem. Whereas his defect in language is admittedly minor compared to the problem of aphasia, the patient is in the position of knowing what he wants to say but recognizes that his speech product is inadequate without being able to alter it. This very often leads to withdrawal and depression. The distortions in speech are easily recognized not only by the patient but by anyone to whom he speaks, and the patient knows this. His defect, in a sense, is audible and, in many instances, visible because of the overarticulation that he must go through as he talks. Accepting and adjusting to this recognizable defect in speech requires careful and thorough working through in psychotherapy. The defect in speech is so often reminiscent of the speech of small children that many adults find it difficult to accept their disability. When such feelings and attitudes are recognized, the need for psychotherapy becomes paramount, replacing in priority the evident need for other therapies.

The hemianopsias or quadrantal visual defects that are not uncommonly seen in the brain-injured patient present an interesting and challenging problem both in therapy and in patient adjustment. The constriction of the visual field may occur in many ways as is shown in Figure 2, dependent upon the location of the lesion along the visual tract.

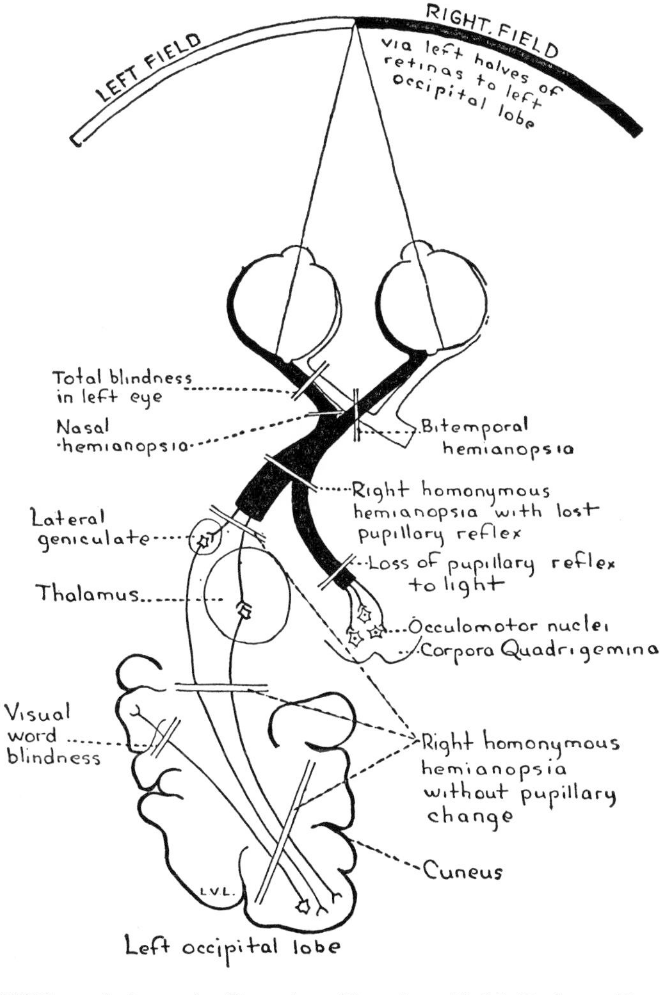

FIGURE 2. *Schematic Drawing Showing Field Defects Resulting from Lesions in Different Places*

From I. S. Wechsler. 1943. *A Textbook of Clinical Neurology*, Philadelphia, Saunders. (Modified from Osler and McCrae).

Homonymous hemianopsia is the most frequently seen type of visual field defect. Vision laterally in the direction of the defect is limited. Uninstructed patients will often complain of a type of blindness. They often ask for glasses to correct what appears to them to be a defect in vision. Such correction is not possible; no external change will produce a restoration of vision in restricted visual fields after brain trauma. For most acts, however, the lateral visual limitation can be offset by an alteration in the position of the head, which again brings much of the lateral field into view since the remainder of the visual capacity is unimpaired. It has always been a matter of concern in therapy to see how difficult it is for otherwise intelligent patients to make the postural adjustment necessary. Without instruction they rarely make voluntary positional changes of the head, and even with instruction it seems very difficult to accomplish for many patients.

In language the only defect caused by hemianopsia is that caused by the limitation of lateral vision. The only correction for the condition is the alteration in head position. For this to be accomplished, however, may take the concerted effort of all the therapists working with the patient, for alteration in head position seems to require relearning for every visual task the patient faces.

The physical problems discussed here are, of course, only illustrative of the symptoms listed at the beginning of the section. They are intended to illustrate the interrelation of some of the physical problems and the total task of rehabilitation these patients face. The diagnostic and rehabilitation teams need to keep them well in mind in company with the problems caused by the other physical conditions, all of which may have a decided effect upon patient behavior and total rehabilitation.

PSYCHOLOGICAL IMPLICATIONS. The list of observed behavioral adaptive mechanisms employed by many patients following brain injury is long and in many ways not distinguishable from the behavior patterns of psychogenically disturbed patients. It need not be said except for emphasis that brain-injured patients are subject to all of the psychological ills of the non-brain-injured, that is, they are as likely to be neurotic or psychotic as anyone else—in fact, they are a little more likely to show psychogenic disturbances since damage to the nervous system often serves as the catalyst for the eruption of neurotic or psychotic behavior previously repressed or previously under adequate control. Man's behavior cannot be separated into neat organic and psychogenic patterns.

With this recognition constantly in mind, however, we can turn to those behavioral manifestations that are either directly or indirectly the result of the interruption of neural control and function. A compilation of the most often observed clinical signs are listed below.

Behavioral Patterns Commonly Seen after Brain Injury

Memory loss (especially immediate memory)
Euphoria
Reduced association of idea
Poor judgment
Tendency to perseverate in both thought and language
Apparent inhibition of internal emotion (sometimes described as the externalization of behavior)
Generalized and specific feelings of inadequacy
Egocentricity
Increased irritability
Tendency to be easily fatigued
Social withdrawal and seclusiveness
Inability to adjust to new situations
Catastrophic behavior
Emotional lability
Reduced initiative
Automatic verbalization
Impulsivity
Regressive, infantile behavior
Fluctuating behavior
Directed anxiety

It should be recognized that these signs are in no sense pathognomonic of brain injury but are the most commonly seen behavioral indications of a readjusting organism. It is also important to recognize that the list cannot be used as a check list to establish, if a given number of signs are present, that there is a greater likelihood of damage or that there is more severe damage if there are greater number of signs.

Some patients, depending on their premorbid personalities, may show many of the signs after relatively little damage, while others may show few or none of them after rather gross damage. Further, no evidence has been validated relative to localization of injury and any of these signs, although some of them do occur more often with damage to certain cortical areas than to others. (Halstead, 1939; Critchley, 1953).

In another context the writer has pointed out that, while these many behavioral signs are frequently seen, the basic personality of the brain impaired patient does not seem to change. In other words, the dynamic personality structure seems to remain the same even when many of the individuals' adaptive mechanisms are recognizably different than they had been (Wepman, 1951). This is true, it is held, since the personality structure of man is formed, according to acceptable psychological theory, during the early formative years, usually long before the occurrence of neural disruptions that cause adult language disorders. Some confirmation of this clinical observation has been reported in the literature. Doehring and Reitan (Doehring and Reitan, 1960) found that on projective tests brain-injured adults showed a variety of personality structures quite in keeping with and indistinguishable from a non-brain-injured population. If changes in personality do occur, they seem to be changes in the sense of exaggeration of the premorbid personality pattern. Outgoing people seem to become more outgoing, while passive dependents become more passive and more dependent.

Quite naturally most of these behavioral signs play an important role in language recovery. To illustrate this, note some of the effects of such factors as memory loss and euphoria upon language disability.

All aphasia—the integrative disorder of language—has been described as a type of memory loss (Wepman, Jones, Bock, and Van Pelt, 1960). In many aphasic patients the problem in language seems to be less a loss of ability than an inability to function with words previously learned but not presently available. In fact, recovery from aphasia is often predicated upon this fact. Recovery from aphasia seems to be dependent upon stimulating the patient to recall—to try to function in language as he did before. It seems much more a matter of the patient's regaining the ability to function with previous vocabulary than it does a matter of new learning. Memory loss then, especially immediate memory, and, specifically, immediate memory for language concepts, has a direct effect upon the patient's language recovery.

Another commonly seen behavioral pattern after cortical impairment that has a major effect upon language recovery as well as upon diagnostic evaluation of the patient is exmplified by the state of well-being called euphoria. The euphoric patient seems quite unaware of his disabilities and unrealistically denies or ignores them. Euphoria seems to serve as a protective defense for the devastation caused by the trauma, acting to keep the person safe until the shock to the system has passed, until the physical and psychological structure has at least started to stabilize. While posttraumatic euphoria may be a fleeting thing in many patients, in others it may last for several months. All self-movement toward recovery is based upon a patient's recognition of the need to change, whereas euphoria represents an acceptance of the *status quo*. Language or psychological evaluation during this period is contraindicated since the results achieved are more likely to mirror the patient's acceptance of his condition and not his potential capacity. Diagnostic evaluation of any kind other than to assess the degree of the euphoria itself is better delayed until the patient begins to recognize the need for change.

Each of the behavioral manifestations listed have their own effect upon language and psychological recovery. The diagnostician as well as the therapist must be prepared to consider the effects, interpret their role in the total behavioral pattern, and plan for their resolution if they seem to be materially retarding recovery and rehabilitation.

The clinically observed behavioral patterns, however, are not the only determinants of the brain-impaired state. Some signs are best discovered through psychometric and projective examinations. Some of the more common patterns found in test protocols are listed below.

Some Psychometric and Projective Signs Commonly Seen on Evaluation of Brain-impaired Patients

Poor attention and concentration
Poor immediate memory
  Auditory
  Visual
  Personal
Poor ability to organize
Poor ability to generalize or categorize
Lowered general intelligence
Differential verbal and performance loss of intelligence
Inability to shift
Psychomotor retardation
Poor productivity
Delay in speed of response
Perplexity (constant questioning of performance)
Impotence (knowing something is wrong but being unable to alter it)
Abstract-concrete imbalance (loss of the ability to abstract in thought or language)

Like the clinically observed signs listed earlier, these too must be recognized as not being exclusively organically determined. They should be seen as adaptations of the total organism to its new limitations.

It is necessary to use the same caution in interpreting the effect of these signs when they appear as is used in considering the clinical observations discussed previously. Neither localization of a neural defect nor extent of damage has been related reliably to any of these signs, nor can the presence of the signs be used to indicate a demonstrable brain impairment. At the same time studies have shown that, when the noted behavior does appear, the likelihood of brain impairment being present is increased (Baker, 1956).

Each of the signs noted have their own effects upon language as well as upon behavior generally. They must be given full consideration in any diagnostic evaluation and due credence in planning therapy and rehabilitation.

It should be noted that both clinical observation and research data bear out the fact that there is a tendency for many of these behavioral manifestations and adaptation mechanisms to disappear with time. Therefore, the evaluator must be cognizant of the length of time that has passed since the trauma since the measurement and assessment of ability will mirror the patient's adaptation to his difficulties as well as his present capacity. When signs such as those listed continue for more than a year after trauma, it is safe to assume that they are permanent and will affect all of the future behavior of the patient.

LANGUAGE AND PSYCHOLOGICAL EVALUATION.

THE DIAGNOSTIC TEAM. The assessment of the language and psychological impairment of patients following neurological insult is somewhat more complex than the diagnostic evaluation of most other physically handicapped adults. The diagnostic team needs to be more extensive, and the findings of all members of the team need to be more thoroughly interrelated. In addition to the usual members of a diagnostic team for rehabilitation problems, there should be included a neurologist or neurosurgeon, a language pathologist, and a psychologist trained in the study of the aftereffects of neural impairment.

The neurologist or neurosurgeon brings with his analysis the specialized laboratory, X-ray, and electroencephalography data that have become such integral adjuncts to neurological diagnosis. Examples of the vital role such medical studies may play in both diagnosis and therapy for such patients are seen in instances where patients are found to be suffering from intractable seizures or incipient brain tumors. Here the neurological diagnoses must control to a large degree all of the corrective procedures that may be necessary before any of the other rehabilitation processes can be brought into play. The medical condition also nominates in a large sense the form and use made of both the language and the psychological examinations.

The language disorders are so important in any over-all diagnosis or therapy that their careful study and fine analysis need to be in the hands of a trained specialist. The evaluation of the linguistic impairment, the distinction between the symbolic and the nonsymbolic types of disorders, and the delimitation of the available transmissive pathways set the limits of all other examinations as well as of later therapy and of the goals in rehabilitation. Any cursory evaluation is likely to miss the very heart of the problem: the effect of the language disability upon the other processes being studied. The success or failure of a diagnostic team may well rest on the establishment of the patient's ability to comprehend or function with language. For example, if an auditory agnosia were not properly defined, the psychological diagnosis might arrive at a completely false estimate of intelligence by asking the patient to perform tasks that he cannot comprehend, while he might succeed if presented with visual tasks that would be clear to him.

The inclusion of a psychologist trained in organic psychodiagnosis, able to function within the limitations imposed by both the physical and language problems, and to develop a useful analysis of the retained intellectual and personality structure, is vital to the success of the entire diagnostic process. Misinterpretations of ability, of behavior, and of the social capacities of such patients is more commonly seen than in almost any other type of handicapped adult. The diagnosis of the retained abilities and the extent of impairment, the capacity of the patient to benefit from therapy and the most useful modalities to explore in therapy, the prescription and performance of psychotherapy when needed, and the establishment of realizable goals in rehabilitation should be the end product of the psychological studies.

The diagnostic team in its entirety needs to be more than a group of well-trained specialists. Each member of the team should be prepared (in his own area of competence and training) to see the deficiencies of the patient. Each one must be, however, equally capable of seeing and explaining the interrelationships between the many-sided symptoms and the recovery process.

THE DIAGNOSTIC EXAMINATIONS. It has been found most helpful to follow a particular order of examinations in arriving at the diagnosis. The first step should always be the medical ones, including the neurological evaluation with its laboratory, X-ray, and electroencephalography findings. These studies should be followed by or include an assessment of the physical disability as well as an evaluation of the patient's ability to utilize his remaining muscular potentials.

The second stage of investigation should be the language studies followed by the psychological evaluation. These should be both diagnostic of the impairment and descriptive of the patient's retained capacity to function. Both the language and the psychological evaluations should be interpreted in the light of the medical and physical disabilities and capacities previously established.

The findings of the language examination should include not only the specific type and degree of language disability but should describe as well any other communication handicap presented by the patient. For example, whether a patient has a hearing loss due to peripheral end organ insufficiency or an unrelated speech defect, such as stuttering, might be of untold value to other examiners as well as to future therapists working with the patient.

Within the language sphere the analysis should not only classify, but provide operational definitions of the communication disability. While technical descriptions using the specialized nomenclature and classification terms relating to the language disorder are valuable, of equal importance is an explanation of what these disorders mean to the patient in such terms as his ability to speak, read, write, and spell. It is very often the case that many therapists as well as most families will find the technical terms only partially explanatory and need to think of their roles related to the patient in the sense of learning constructs rather than pathological ones. In rehabilitation of a particular patient, for example, it might be more important to know that he cannot read than to know that he has visual agnosia with limited comprehension and retention. The need for such operational statements cannot be stressed too strongly.

The language examination should also include an evaluation of the patient's ability to use spontaneous language quite apart from his ability to function with and within the different modalities. At times patients have been known to do better with free unsolicited speech than with response to specific questions.

It has also been found extremely useful for the language evaluation to include a study of the patient's ability to criticize his own language behavior. The present writer has presented in another context the values that may accrue from estimating the capacity of the patient to be self-critical. The self-recognition of errors and the ability to correct those errors has been established as a most likely criteria for prognosis as well as a most useful judgment of the severity of a specific language problem (Wepman, 1958).

Standardized tests for aphasia have been developed that yield scores relating to the impairment of the integrative and transmissive processes in language (Wepman and Jones, 1961). Other tests show the impairment in terms of increasing levels of difficulty in the reception and expression of language (Schuell, 1955). There are also available short screening tests for language disturbances that, while not standardized, do yield useful information if a rapid overview of a particular patient's language ability is necessary (Halstead and Wepman, 1949; Eisenson, 1954; Schuell, 1957).

The psychological studies should be made within the framework of the medical, physical, and language evaluations already completed. The psychologist should adapt his testing and his interviews to the limitations established by these prior studies. Examples of the importance of these limitations are not hard to find. Note, for example, the effect upon the psychological examination of a medical finding that reports an active ongoing neurological process, such as cerebral arteriosclerosis or a progressive Parkinsonism. In cases such as these, the concept of psychological testing would be to define a present condition against which a later study might be undertaken to gauge the rapidity as well as the types of changs the patient is undergoing, rather than to estimate the intellectual and personality characteristics for rehabilitation.

The physical capabilities of the patient also need full consideration in planning the psychological evaluation. Note, here, the importance of a hemiplegia of the previously preferred hand that might well limit the psychological testing to tasks requiring only oral responses or to tasks that do not concern themselves with fine muscular controls.

A recent psychometric study on aphasic adults has shown a comparison of hemiplegic patients' intellectual behavior with and without aphasia on the Wechsler Adult Intelligence Scale. The findings indicated that "left hemiplegic patients without aphasia demonstrated more difficulty . . . than do right hemiplegic patients with or without aphasia" (Hirschenfang, 1960). This, the author felt, might point to a greater problem in rehabilitation with the nonaphasic, left hemiplegic patient than with the right hemiplegic.

The results of the language examinations should be carefully interpreted by the psychologist before he undertakes his own studies. Patients suffering from transmissive language defects should only be evaluated for retained intellectual abilities or personality structure along their least disrupted pathways. Thus, a patient with a specific visual agnosia would most likely demonstrate his best ability when tested by auditory stimuli, while the converse would be true of a patient suffering from a limiting auditory agnosia. On the output side, if a patient is known to have a serious dysarthria or verbal apraxia, it would be fruitless to give him tasks requiring oral expression, just as it would be a false measure of capacity to give paper and pencil or even hand-eye performance tests to a patient who has a motor apraxia or a motor agraphia.

An even greater problem of evaluation exists when the patient has been diagnosed as having an aphasic language disorder of whatever type it may be. There is today a marked difference of opinion about the intellectual capacity of patients who show aphasic disturbances. Some students of aphasia hold that there is always a defect in intelligence (Goldstein, 1948), while others believe that no intellectual loss needs to be predicated by the presence of a language disturbance (Wepman, 1951). Little statistical proof is available on either side. The problem of testing lies largely in the values to be placed on the limited verbalization of the patient. Does the verbal ability actually reflect the intellectual capacity as some claim? Or, oppositely, does the retained language ability merely reflect the specific comprehension and formulation of verbal symbols uncorrelated with other higher mental processes? Whatever side of this discussion one holds to be true will determine the values they place on their psychometric test results. In any case, the results of testing aphasic adults need to be interpreted with great caution.

Certain time limitations should also be noted in studying the aphasic patient. For the most part, rather rapid and spontaneous changes in language deficiencies occur during the first six months after trauma. After that time, an evaluation is more likely to be a true reflection of the retained ability, but, before the six month period is completed, the patient is likely to show day by day changes that deny any statement about the permanent ability. There are real differences in this sense along a time continuum from the actual date of the trauma. The most dramatic changes in ability have been noted soon afterwards, whereas progressive but less dramatic changes may occur throughout the six-month period. A case in point was a patient who, following a stroke, showed a complete visual agnosia and was for all practical purposes completely blind. Within two weeks he recognized light and dark differences. In the following month he could distinguish geometric forms, and in the next two months he recovered the ability to recognize letters and words. Number recognition ability came next, and at the end of the sixth posttraumatic month he had only a limited visual agnosia—limited to the recognition of common life objects and people. For the latter disability he needed very extensive and long term therapy. Evaluated psychologically at different times during the early postmorbid period, he showed an increasing ability to intellectualize from visual stimuli, but certainly none of the tests given actually mirrored his true potential. Tested along the auditory pathway, he showed a retention of high level conceptual ability at all times.

Some aphasic patients can be evaluated by test instruments that call for minimal verbal responses, whereas others seem to do as badly with nonverbal tests as they do with verbal ones. Where the aphasia seems mild and considerable useful language is available to the patient, the only limitation on psychological testing may be in judgments based upon the speed of response. For the most part, the use of power tests rather than speed tests are advised since it is usually true that in the recovering or the recovered aphasic adult the rapidity of function may be the only retained discriminator indicating a previous neurological problem.

Of special note to the neuropsychologist in planning his psychometric battery should be the type of aphasia the language evaluation has shown. The global and pragmatic aphasic patients will most likely not be able to respond to any type of measurement. The jargon aphasic patient may do adequately if he is not assessed in terms of his oral responses. The patients showing any marked degree of semantic or syntactic aphasia will need to be studied with great care since their linguistic disabilities may very well condition the content of their responses. The former, the semantic patient, may appear to be responding with little explicit content simply because the more specific words of the language are the ones he has greatest difficulty with. The syntactic patient, on the other hand, may appear excessively concrete and lose many of the nuances that are added through the grammar of language. The further recognition of the mixed language type so commonly seen during the recovery process needs to be given very careful study even though there is an apparent retention or use of considerable verbal production.

Analysis of personality through projective tests requiring verbalization presents many of the same problems that have been noted in the psychometric evaluations of intelligence. It has been noted, for example, in ongoing research into language usage by aphasic patients using the Thematic Apperception Test that almost no analyzable thema are being produced. The Rorschach test also has limited usefulness when the patient is found to be suffering from limitations of vocabulary or from an inability to relate to a stimulus. This test, however, has a marked value for organic psychodiagnosis when sufficient vocabulary usage has been retained or when the ability to relate to stimuli is not affected (Baker, 1956). The self-report inventory technique represented by the Minnesota Multiphasic Personality Inventory has been used to good effect in one study with patients who could read but had difficulty in oral expression (Doehring and Reitan, 1960).

By and large, the evaluation of personality through the use of any tests has not been overly productive, and the psychologist should be prepared to resort to direct observation of behavior. Discussion of behavior with the immediate family of the patient or with hospital personnel has also been found useful. Very often the immediate reaction of the patient to his disability will be more evident through this method than by any other.

The psychologist should also be aware of the tendency for concreteness of thought and language after impairment. Whereas no good objective criteria for concreteness exists either in thought processes or in language, nevertheless, the observed tendency for reduction of these processes to the most absolute and concrete should be recognized. Frequently, this means applying a clinical judgment relative to behavior that is quite outside the standard scoring principles established for most test instruments. Qualitative evaluation of the language-disordered patient may be more important in many ways than the actual quantitative scores obtained.

From his evaluations the psychologist should be able to assist materially in the diagnosis of organicity, the usefulness of specific pathways for reception and expression of thought processes that are not language-symbol bound, the motivation of the patient for recovery, and the capacity for improvement that all of these factors imply.

Organic psychodiagnosis, while as yet unproven for the most part by the validating procedures of research, is a challenging and often very rewarding study. The organically impaired patient is undergoing widespread study in many centers throughout the country, and the literature is replete with reports of these studies. The neuropsychologist should be in constant touch with the literature for new approaches and validated methods developed through clinical experience and scientific research.

TREATMENT AND REHABILITATION. Other chapters of the present book have stressed the nature of the organization of therapy for the medical and physical disabilities of patients without language disorders. When language impairments are added to the syndrome of posttraumatic behavior, a whole new concept of training and therapy, of rehabilitation and counseling, needs to be similarly added. Recovery from the language disorders frequently needs to be the very core of the over-all recovery process. Other therapies need to be fitted to the need for communication as well as to the capabilities in communication retained by the patient. Through direct language therapy the means of communication may be sought while other therapies provide the opportunity for language usage. Physiotherapy, for example, for increased mobility provides the patient with the means of ambulation so that he can be stimulated socially; occupational therapy provides a source of language through goal-directed action; and recreational therapy provides the outlet for the newly developing ability to communicate. Language remains the coin of all interpersonal relations, and only through language recovery can the patient find maximal readaptation to life.

The organization of therapy for the language disorders has been discussed previously by the writer in a report describing an inpatient center for aphasia under his direction during World War II (Wepman, 1947). The broad rationale of that program would be largely unchanged even today. A typical day's program for many of the patients demonstrates the areas of rehabilitation that seem most important.

A Typical Daily Program Used in an Army Inpatient Aphasia Center

(Adapted from Wepman, 1947)

A.M.	P.M.
Group Writing	Individual Language
Group Spelling	Group Speech and Reading
Individual Reading	Occupational Therapy
Current Affairs	Recreational Therapy
Physiotherapy	Planned Social Activities

Schedules such as these were varied from day to day and from patient to patient depending upon the individual need at the time. For some patients this meant it was necessary to substitute individual and group psychotherapy for some of the educational activities. For others manual arts therapy and additional physiotherapy were substituted for occupational therapy. The program employed all of the adjuncts to rehabilitation that were available. At different stages, for example, both vocational and avocational counseling took the place of many of the educational activities as these were found to be less necessary or beyond the level of the patient. Social service was employed broadly in exploring with the families of the patients the future programs that might be utilized as the patients faced discharge from the hospital.

It is unfortunately true that, excluding the Veterans Administration, resources capable of providing intensive and extensive inpatient therapy for the general population, such as those provided at the army hospital described above, are few and far between. The government at both the federal and state levels has recognized this and through the Office of Vocational Rehabilitation in the United States Department of Health, Education, and Welfare is constantly seeking to increase and extend services to the handicapped. Private resources are being developed as are many semiprivate rehabilitation and convalescent centers.

The need, however, remains great and is only partially being met.

There is also a great need for research in the benefits to be derived from such concentrated inpatient services as compared with the relative values of outpatient therapy. The present tendency is to consider a comparatively short period, three to six months, of highly organized inpatient therapy as a valuable precursor to the two to three years so often necessary in the total program of recovery. As the need is recognized and if it is confirmed by research, more and more physical resources should become available.

Outpatient therapy for the language disorders and their concomitant physical and psychological debilities is by far the most frequently employed approach. Here, too, a regular order of events seems most productive. During the early stages a patient needs most often the combined attention of physical therapy, language and psychological therapies, and social counseling. As the physical problems become less intense or become at least partially resolved through compensation and adaptation, vocational and avocational counseling with the patients and their families needs to become more active. Not infrequently the occupational therapies are used as precursors to vocational training, and this is followed whenever possible by vocational placement. Because of the length of time involved in language therapy and psychotherapy, these frequently need to continue right to the point of rehabilitation to either vocational or independent living goals.

Resources for outpatient therapy, including all or most of the elements described, are constantly on the increase. Most colleges and universities today have speech clinics that provide some language therapy, and many provide in addition the other therapies needed. Where a decade ago it was difficult to secure the services of anyone trained in this basic area of rehabilitation, through the attention given the problem by the American Speech and Hearing Association and by institutions of higher learning some kind of language therapy can be found in most communities. There has been too little done in relating the language needs to the physical and psychological needs of the patients perhaps, but here, too, there seems to be a movement in the right direction.

Such service oriented organizations as the National Society for Crippled Children and Adults and the United Cerebral Palsy Association with their widespread local organizations provide assistance to this much needed ever-increasing outpatient population. The previously mentioned Office of Vocational Rehabilitation provides training support for rehabilitation workers of many disciplines who will add to the growing potential for total programs. The trend is a good one; it should not be permitted to falter. The need for facility and personnel is a constantly growing one.

It should be added that the field of psychology has also lately seen the need for training in the psychological aspects of disability. A relatively short time ago it was almost impossible to find a psychologist trained or even interested in organic psychodiagnosis or psychotherapy with the brain-impaired. Now, however, a whole division of the American Psychological Association (National Council on Psychological Aspects of Disability) is made up of psychologists devoted to these interests.

In research, as well, great strides have been made. The National Institutes of Health, the National Science Foundation, the Office of Vocational Rehabilitation, and a great number of other governmental, private and semiprivate philanthropic foundations provide support for research in the area of the neurologically impaired. Aphasia has become the focus of studies by students of language, human engineering, cybernetics, behavioral science, and the educational sciences. The trend here, too, is good, but the amount to be done, the questions to be answered by research, is still far greater than the knowledge at hand. One of the important aspects of recent research has been the standardization of evaluation methods for the language disorders. This will provide in time a standardization in nomenclature and classification that will markedly increase communication among the many disciplines interested in aphasia and its kindred disorders.

The varied members of the rehabilitation team should be on the alert to the wide variety of publications in the field of aphasia. From the present writer's work in this area has come a recently developed bibliography of important studies, including several hundred entries. This listing of research and clinical reports from all over the world is available to anyone interested in following the developments in rehabilitation and research for the language disordered patient (Wepman, 1961).

The problems presented in the present chapter are admittedly complex, yet, with all of the ramifications of the syndrome described, the most noteworthy conclusion that can be drawn is that these patients are amenable to therapy. They do improve with assistance, stimulation, and understanding. The time spent in diagnosis, in therapy, and in rehabilitation will be found to be most rewarding and well worth the concentration of research and training necessary. The lawyer returned to his practice, the shoemaker to his last, the young to their school books and their future, the old to an improved capacity for independent living—all these make rehabilitation with the language-disordered, psychologically disorganized, and physically handicapped patient worthwhile.

REFERENCES

Baker, G. 1956. Diagnosis of organic brain damage in the adult, in Klopfer, B., and others. Developments in the Rorschach technique. Yonkers, N.Y., World Book Co., pp. 318–75.

Bucy, P. 1949. Organization of central nervous system control of muscular activity. Chicago Med. Soc. Bull. 51:836–66.

Critchley, M. 1953. The parietal lobe. London, Arnold.

Doehring, D. G., and R. M. Reitan. 1960. MMPI performance of aphasic and non-aphasic brain-damaged patients. J. Clin. Psychol. 16:307–9.
Eisenson, J. 1954. Examining for aphasia: a manual for the examination of aphasia and related disturbances. Rev. New York, Psychological Corporation.
Goldstein, K. 1948. Language and language disturbances. New York, Grune and Stratton.
Goldstein, K., and M. Scheerer. 1941. Abstract and concrete behavior: an experimental study with special tests. Psychological Monographs 53, No. 2. Washington, D.C., American Psychological Association.
Halstead, W. C. 1939. Behavioral effects of lesions of the frontal lobe in man. Arch. Neurol. Psychiat. 42:780–83.
Halstead, W. C., and J. M. Wepman. 1949. The Halstead-Wepman aphasia screening test. J. Speech Hearing Dis. 14:9–15.
Harlow, H., and C. N. Woolsey, eds. 1958. Biological and biochemical bases of behavior. Madison, Wis., University of Wisconsin Press.
Hirschenfang, S. 1960. A comparison of WAIS scores of hemiplegic patients with and without aphasia. J. Clin. Psychol. 16:351–52.
Lashley, K. S. 1929. Brain mechanisms and intelligence. Chicago, University of Chicago Press.
Morris, C. W. 1939. Foundations of the theory of signs. International encyclopedia of unified science: Foundations of the unity of science, Vol. 1, No. 2. Chicago, University of Chicago Press.
Penfield, W., and L. Roberts. 1959. Speech and brain mechanisms. Princeton, N.J., Princeton University Press.
Reitan, R. M. 1953. Intellectual function in aphasic and non-aphasic brain injured subjects. Neurology 3:202–12.
Schuell, H. 1955. Minnesota test for differential diagnosis of aphasia. Minneapolis, University of Minnesota Printing Dept.
—— 1957. A short examination for aphasia. Neurology 7:625–34.
Wechsler, I. S. 1943. A textbook of clinical neurology. 5th ed. Philadelphia, W. B. Saunders.
Wepman, J. M. 1947. The organization of therapy for aphasia: I. The inpatient treatment center. J. Speech Hearing Dis. 12:405–9.
—— 1951. Recovery from aphasia. New York, Ronald Press.
—— 1958. The relationship between self-correction and recovery from aphasia. J. Speech Hearing Dis. 23:302–5.
—— 1961. An aphasia bibliography. Chicago, Language Research Associates.
Wepman, J. M., and L. V. Jones. 1961. Studies in aphasia: an ap-

proach to testing. Chicago, Industrial Relations Center, University of Chicago.

—— 1961. The language modalities test for aphasia. Chicago, Industrial Relations Center, University of Chicago.

Wepman, J. M., L. V. Jones, R. D. Bock, and Doris Van Pelt. 1960. Studies in aphasia; background and theoretical formulations. J. Speech Hearing Dis. 25:323–33.

Whorf, B. 1956. Language, thought and reality. Cambridge, Mass., Technology Press.

CANCER

by BEATRIX COBB

ALTHOUGH physical restoration and vocational adjustment are major problems in cancer, the real challenge for rehabilitation lies in the area of personal counseling. Too often, the role of the counselor in cancer is a limited one. If he is brought into the treatment team at all, it is usually only to arrange for physical restoration services, including surgery and irradiation, or to supply the prosthesis indicated, following loss of eye, limb, or organ. Perhaps because of the high mortality rates in the disease, it is seldom that a change in vocation is mandatory. And yet, if we accept the concept of psychological resistance to cancer introduced to medical thinking through recent research (Gengerelli and Kirkner, 1954), the potential of the counselor in the course of the disease is a crucial one.

Simply stated, the concept of psychological resistance to malignancy raises the following questions: Are there definable psychological factors operating when a patient lives on against medical odds? Are these factors related to the seeming control, or regression, of the neoplasm? Can these factors, or attitudes, be engendered, encouraged, and sustained through counseling in such a way as to contribute to the ultimate control of the cancerous growth? If these questions can be answered in the affirmative, certainly the role of the psychological counselor in cancer becomes crucial, and the implication is that such counseling

Beatrix Cobb, Ph.D., is Director of Counselor Training Programs at Texas Technological College.

skills should be brought into the treatment team at the time of definitive diagnosis of cancer.

Even if the questions raised cannot be categorically answered in the affirmative at this time, the implications for the need of emotional support on the part of the patient seems implicit on two counts. First, if the patient survives the onslaught of the cancerous growth, he requires assistance toward an emotional acceptance of the disease and the threat it involves to his life and happiness, and consequent adjustment to disabilities or limitations. Second, if the patient succumbs, early or late, the ironic goal reversal arising so often in cancer is indicated wherein the counselor's purpose becomes one of assisting the patient toward an emotional acceptance of the sure approach of death and the separations and adjustments this event portends.

Inasmuch as cancer is many diseases and the medical aspects voluminous and inasmuch as vocational evaluation and placement would be practically identical to those employed in any chronic illness, this chapter will limit its scope to a discussion of the challenging factors highlighted above as they relate to the role of psychological counseling in cancer. First, then, the history of the theory of psychological or host-resistance to cancer will be reviewed, and the implications pertaining to the responsibility of the counselor pointed out. Second, adjustment counseling in cancer will be described from the background of case materials collected over a period of some eight years of work with these patients. Finally, some suggestions for counseling for acceptance of death will be summarized as they pertain to the responsibility of the counselor.

PSYCHOLOGICAL RESISTANCE TO CANCER. Physicians, nurses, social workers, and counselors working with cancer patients over the years have witnessed a strange inexplicable phenomenon wherein an individual who to all medical intents and purposes should die remains alive and productive over a period of years, while another person with the same disease goes into a rapid decline and succumbs. The medical picture in both cases seems the same. The stage of the disease seems similar. The basic physical condition of the two patients is comparable. But some indefinable something sets one apart for life against odds and marks the other for early death. This enigma has been called various things, "the will to live," the "fighting spirit," and many other vague epithets.

It was not until the early 1950s that careful research observations were made of this phenomenon in an effort to delineate its characteristics and to evaluate its power in psychological resistance or acquiescence to the cancerous growth. At the Veterans Administration Hospital in Long Beach, California, West and Ellis (West, 1954) initiated an intensive study of cancer patients in 1948. At this time, the autonomous nature of cancer had been successfully challenged by Huggins (Huggins and Hodges, 1941) so far as prostatic cancer was concerned. It had been demonstrated that alteration of the endocrine balance of the host by administration of female sex hormones sufficed in many cases to arrest, or produce regression, of prostatic cancer. Around this time, also, nitrogen mustard had been found effective in reversing the course of Hodgkin's Disease. These successes had alerted the medical world to a careful surveillance of even the minutest changes in the patient following administration of hormones and nitrogen mustard in an attempt to elucidate the interaction in terms of a possible "cure" for cancer.

It was, perhaps, owing to this medical alert, that West and Ellis first became aware and started systematic observation of psychological resistance to the onslaught of cancer. They were involved in research in which nitrogen mustard was being used. Each patient entering the research project was given a screening interview and followed carefully under treatment. It was not long before they observed that often a dose of nitrogen mustard would put one man back on his feet for months, or even years, in apparent good health; whereas, under the same dosage, another patient in a seemingly comparable stage of the same disease would fail rapidly and die. Soon, they found themselves involved in predicting whether or not a patient would respond to the treatment or go into decline as they entered the treatment ward. So high was their predictive success that they began to analyze the cues upon which the predictions were based. Upon realization that they were mostly psychological clues, having to do with personality and attitudes of the individual patients, the researchers called upon the services of a psychiatrist and several psychologists for collaboration. An exploratory research was begun in an effort to delineate the nebulous, but potent, clues differentiating the resisting and acquiescing patients.

In 1953, a symposium was held and the proceedings published wherein the results of the preliminary survey were reported. In that symposium Blumberg (Blumberg, 1954) reported on his study of fifty patients in which he attempted to clarify through psychological testing the differences evident between patients who resisted and those who acquiesced to the disease. His data indicated that those who resisted the growth of the malignancy were less defensive, displayed less anxiety, and were more able to release tensions through motor discharge activities than those who rapidly succumbed to the disease. These characteristics needed further elucidation. Unfortunately, the following year the research team working in California dissolved as a group, and the further delineation of this exciting finding fell perforce to other researchers or to individual members of the team. To date no further systematic research has been reported from this auspicious beginning.

At the University of Texas M. D. Anderson Hospital in Houston, Texas, however, the problem of host resistance and acquiescence was approached in an elaborate Giant Metabolic Study initiated by Dr. J. B. Trunnell, head of Experimental Medicine (now Dean of Home and Family Life, Brigham Young University, Provo, Utah). This study was begun in an effort to record the biochemical processes in the patient with cancer of the prostate as the disease progressed from initial stages, through crises, successful responses to chemotherapy, and eventual collapse and death. Some twenty-three biochemical indices were recorded daily in a rigorous intake and output regimen.

This study had been under way for some time when psychologists were drawn into the research. The tentative plan called for a pilot experimentation during which the psychologists would develop more objective measures for the psychological data than the techniques utilized in the Blumberg Study. The major reason for this was that the techniques used did not lend themselves to repetition from day to day or week to week. Lansing, a physiological psychologist, was added to the Medical Psychology Staff to do research of his own design, but with the understanding that he would also participate in the Metabolic Study. A laboratory was designed and put into operation wherein all central nervous system and autonomic nervous system data could be obtained over the course of the disease with the same sort of systematic observations as those given the biochemical. A pilot study of patients with thyroid disorders was undertaken in order to perfect procedures.

Simultaneously, Damarin started collaboration with Lansing and Trunnell in developing a series of psychological tests that could be repeated from week to week and would also give the essential psychological knowledge desired. These procedures and tests were to have been transferred the following year to the study of the prostatic cancer patients collected simultaneously with the Metabolic Study.

In the meantime, Damarin was also collaborating with Trunnell in an effort to establish a statistical procedure whereby the psychological, central nervous system, autonomic nervous system, and biochemical data could be concurrently analyzed following their collection. At this point in the investigation, the research team at M. D. Anderson Hospital was disbanded, scattering to all parts of the country as they reported to new endeavors. The Metabolic Study data was moved with Trunnell and Damarin, and they have been working on its evaluation periodically since. In a recent communication, Trunnell states the progress of the statistical and medical analysis to date.

> The Giant Metabolic Study cannot yet be said to shed light upon the psychosomatic side of cancer of the prostate. . . . Nevertheless, the analysis has proceeded far enough to permit certain surmises about stresses in general, and about the alleviation of stresses, in terms of course of the disease. These surmises are still in accord with our preliminary view that psychologic stresses work in favor of the disease and against host defenses, whereas relief from stress has the opposite effect. [Personal correspondence with author, November, 1960.]

Trunnell also observed that often, when prostatic cancer patients were hospitalized, and prior to initiation of treatment, "precipitous falls in levels of serum acid phosphatase, rises in serum alkaline phosphatase and urinary glucuronidase 'humps' [from the graphed data], all signifying clinical improvement" were noted. He states:

> We have labeled the seemingly spontaneous remission which accompanies relief from stress, "psychosoteria." The literal meaning of this word is "psychic refuge." And, the relapse which follows either planned or naturally-occurring stress we have referred to as "psychoporia," meaning "psychic-up-against-it-ness." [Personal correspondence with author, November, 1960.]

A planned psychologic stress investigation was conducted in a pilot study by Dr. John I. Wheeler, Jr., psychologist at the University of Texas M. D. Anderson Hospital (now in private practice in Houston), and Trunnell. Wheeler devised a simple projective task for the patient to accomplish.

> Calling the patient to his office, he would explain that as part of the study, the patient would need to take some tests. After the patient had started to comply with his directions, Wheeler would express mild dissatisfaction with the slowness [whether actually slow or not],

content of the answers, etc., and would contrast unfavorably the patient's performance with that of other patients on the ward. Without exception, increases in serum acid phosphatase were found following as little as 15 minutes of such stress.

Even under such rigorous research procedures utilizing biochemical measures of the course of the disease, it would seem that the data from the Texas study is concurring with the results of the California investigation. Much more work is needed in order to gain definitive answers, but the evidence accumulating from this initial attempt to collate biochemical-physiological-psychological indices as they interact in the course of cancer is in favor of the implications of psychological resistance to cancer.

To summarize, then, in both the California and the Texas studies strong indications are evident favoring the concept of psychological resistance to the onslaught of cancer. Implications are that patients who are able to cope successfully with the emotional stress involved in the diagnosis and treatment are more likely to live longer and more productive lives following the diagnosis of cancer. Those who succumbed rapidly seemed less able to cope with this stress effectively. These facts seem to be self-evident when we recall that certain biochemical, metabolical, and hormonal activities are accepted as significant for the development of cancer, and when we recognize the influence of mental process on some of the hormonal steroids as taking place through the intermediation of the hypothalamus. It is not unreasonable, then, to conjecture that psychological factors may affect cancer through the elaboration, or suppression, of certain hormones through this pathway.

ADJUSTMENT COUNSELING IN CANCER. Adjustment counseling with cancer patients is both provocative and complex because of the intricate array of knowledge with which the counselor must be armed as he goes into the counseling relationship. First, he must know much about the disease itself. Inasmuch as cancer has been called many diseases, he must constantly review pertinent information concerned with the particular type of malignancy from which the patients suffer. Second, treatment for cancer is varied and severe, and he must, therefore, keep informed in this area. Third, the counselor must work closely with the physician on the case. He must learn the latter's customary procedures, the way he wishes his patients handled psychologically, and his own feelings and approaches to cancer itself, because the counselor must become an extension of the physician to the patient and an interpreter of the patient to the doctor. Finally, the counselor must be adept at handling the anxieties of family members to the end that he may convert their fear into the foundation of emotional support for the patient throughout the ordeal ahead. The skilled counselor learns that the most effective support comes from the natural figure of succor—a member of the family group. Often a few hours of counseling with a family member results in continued and continuous emotional support for the patient that is much more effective than that offered by the counselor, and relieves his time for others in need as well.

The basic emotion with which the counselor must deal in working with the cancer patient is anxiety. This anxiety is deep, realistic, and debilitating because it has its roots in the threatening "unknowns" surrounding the disease and its treatment. In cancer, perhaps more so than in any other disease, the patient experiences the full gamut of fear, springing from the devastating connotations of body mutilation, long illness, and eventual death. Often, too, it is irrationally associated with the idea of punishment for past wrong-doing, and hence bears a connotation of guilt. All these feeling tones combine to produce a heavy weighting of grim uncertainties that constitute a vicious threat to the individual from within and without.

In light of the concept of psychological resistance to cancer, the counselor's task is to combat the ravages of this anxiety in order to free the energies of the patient for coping with the onslaught of the cancerous growth. The antidote for the fears of each individual must be developed out of the basic emotional needs and perceptions of that person as he surveys himself and his situation following diagnosis. It has been found in a study reported from the University of Texas M. D. Anderson Hospital (Cobb, 1953) that "hope through intelligent coping with facts can conquer fear" in most cases.

The question arises: "How may one cope intelligently with the threatening facts of cancer?" Research utilizing a population of some two hundred patients seems to indicate some pertinent guide lines for the counselor to explore with the patient in attempting to plant the seeds of hope in troubled hearts. First, a knowledge of the personal meaning of cancer to the victim is a beginning toward correction of misconceptions and the foundation of correct information upon which hope may be built. Second, the psychological meaning to the individual of the organ involved by the malignancy is often a key to understanding secret fears debilitating the patient. Third, the strange new "horizontal" world of the hospital with its baffling procedures and enforced dependency may be responsible for dissipation of energy needed to rebel against the disease. With these facts at hand, the counselor may then turn to his major role of providing emotional support during treatment and convalescence, or until death. Each of these factors will be reviewed in terms of case histories and counselor experiences pertinent to the establishment of insights for the new counselor as he approaches adjustment counseling with a cancer patient.

THE INTIMATE MEANING OF CANCER. Cancer is a devious disease surrounded by half-truths and unknowns. The diagnosis of cancer precipitates a person into a state of biologic defenselessness against danger that is difficult to tolerate. The anxiety this engenders must be coped with, or it will sap the energy the patient needs to resist the physiological invasion of the malignancy. We know that each individual handles anxiety in accordance with the basic personality pattern developed through the years. The first step in counseling, then, is to get to know the individual—to become aware of his unique method of reacting to stress and to know first hand what the diagnosis of cancer means to him.

Research has demonstrated that cancer means many things to different people. One investigation (Cobb, 1959) of cancer patients disclosed that to 12 percent of that group the diagnosis meant only that they had a "bad disease"; they were not really aware of the real meaning of cancer. Another 10 percent had an intelligent, controlled fear of cancer because they did know much about it, the treatment to control it, and to a great extent their own realistic chances for survival. This left 78 percent for whom the diagnosis of cancer was synonymous with dire events.

Twenty-six percent of this number had a vague, diffused fear of cancer, but they could not really focus their concern. It was a "horrible thing," it meant long-drawn-out suffering, it connoted guilt and punishment for wrong-doing, or it might even have meant a mark of shame and social disgrace. But, to 52 percent of the total group, cancer meant simply *death*. It would seem, therefore, that the psychologist's first task in counseling with the newly diagnosed cancer patient is to determine just what having cancer means to the individual. With this knowledge as his guide, the psychologist then proceeds to work through these feelings, dispelling erroneous, preconceived notions, building a basis for hope, and establishing an intelligent, controlled fear in place of the unreasoning anxiety. Controlled fear is desirable in a cancer patient because it becomes a motivating force that keeps the patient cooperative, expending his energies toward fighting the disease.

Sometimes undue anxiety has been engendered because of strange visualizations patients have of what is going on within their bodies. One young lady was so restless that sleep was impossible for her. She had cancer of the thyroid, which is usually amenable to treatment, with subsequent return to normal living. While the counselor was working through with her the meaning of cancer, it was discovered that she had the following visualization of what was going on in her throat:

> Well, to me it is just like a grey seaweed floating around there in my body juices and it has lodged here in my throat. It is clingy and slimy and sometimes it seems to be growing by leaps and bounds, and I can't breathe because it is filling my neck and my nose and the oxygen won't go through. I know it will soon have all of my body filled up, and I'll die.

A picture of the thyroid was secured, and the invasion described. The doctor was called in to explain actually what was going on in her throat. The patient heaved a sigh of relief, and most of the nervousness and difficulty in breathing cleared up.

Once the counselor knows what the patient visualizes is going on inside him, the counseling process can begin. Correct information may be supplied. Working through the feeling tones and setting the stage for hope may then pave the way for the intelligent, controlled fear enabling the patient to expend his energy toward the goal of combatting the malignancy.

THE ORGAN INVOLVED. The meaning to the individual of the organ involved is also critically important information. The loss of a breast, for example, is always a deep ego blow to a woman. Our culture has emphasized the value of the curvacious feminine figure. As a result, many patients are highly traumatized by such loss and do not allow their husbands to behold them disrobed. They feel they are no longer desirable as women.

In such cases the counselor often works best with the marriage partner. If the husband knows the secret fears and doubts of his wife, if he is able to make her feel *his* acceptance of the loss and his love for her, the anxiety soon dissipates. Sometimes the husband needs to talk through his own feelings about this loss to the point that he can view it without deep feeling before he attempts to reassure his wife. With some insight and a real desire to work through this crisis, most couples are able to overcome the despair involved and develop a deeper relationship than ever before.

There are times, however, when the husband is not mature enough to accept this change in his wife, and here the skill of the counselor is really challenged. Emotional support, reassurance, and understanding of the husband must all come from the counselor as the patient assumes the supportive role to the partner. It is often surprising to the counselor how magnificently some of these women do respond, the nature of the insights they achieve, and the role they are able to play in understanding the deep feelings of repulsion their husbands may experience. Despite these odds, they are often strong enough to win the husband back. One courageous woman, sensing her husband's rejection, asked for the best prosthesis available, worked hard at getting to handle it, and went home from the hospital with the same—outwardly—beautiful figure with which she came. Utilizing all her charm, and wearing the prosthesis day and night for the most part, she was eventually able to overcome her husband's feelings of repulsion, and today they have a closer relationship than in the early days of their marriage.

This is not an area of trauma restricted to the female sex. Men have similar painful experiences. One charming gentleman of some sixty summers came into the hospital for surgery for prostatic cancer. He was told that he had every right to expect rapid recovery and a long life to follow. His wife did not understand his deep depression, despite this prognosis, as he went into surgery. She came to the counselor's office as they took the husband to surgery. As she disclosed her fears, she described the husband's behavior and her own bafflement when it was her understanding that he was going to be all right. The counselor reviewed with the wife the operation the husband was undergoing and the high rate of complete recovery. While doing so, it was mentioned that sometimes there was a loss of libido for a while—and sometimes permanently. The wife looked up with a glow of understanding on her face and exclaimed: "That is what he has been trying to tell me. That's what is bothering him! It never occurred to me, and it doesn't make any difference anyhow. I just know that's what it is." When the patient returned from the recovery room, he kept mumbling something about "half a man." The wife, now realizing his meaning, reassured him of her love and understanding of his fear. Together they worked through his anxiety, and today, seven years later, he is hale and happy.

Facial disfigurement resulting from cancer of the skin is an area for special consideration by the counselor. The trauma of seeing a hole in the face where the nose was, of seeing unsightly scars and discolored skin over the face, of losing an eye or an ear, all of these experiences sear the ego. Often exploring these hurts, getting them out in the open, and ventilating them means the difference between continuing to live with people or withdrawing into a darkened corner to hide some portion of the disfigurement. One woman, who suffered through an invasion of one eye, her nose, and finally half of each cheek, continues to interact with her friends, and to work at her job as a clerk in a variety store, with a plastic prosthesis over the gaping hole in her face. She is aware of the curious stares, but she has accepted the challenge that she was left alive for a purpose, and chooses to live the years left to her in courage and cheerfulness. The counselor played only a minor role in this case. The patient's chief support came from her understanding husband and empathic physician.

Plastic surgery may often do a miraculous job of repairing such damage when the cancerous invasion is really arrested. On the surgery ward one sometimes sees a strange assortment of regrowths of parts of the face in process. One patient is well remembered because he was the first viewed by the counselor. He was going from office to office speaking loudly and always drawing attention to his large nose. The counselor did not understand because the nose seemed far too large and a bit misshaped to her. Sensing her puzzlement, the patient paused in her doorway and said,

> You see, when you've gone around without a nose for six months, and then you go around with what looks like the snout of an elephant [the skin transplant where the patient grows more skin from which the new nose is formed looks a bit like a snout] for that much longer, and then suddenly you have a nose again and look almost human, well, I just want to go around sticking my old nose in everybody's business, and say, "Look, I've got a nose too!"

Needless to say, the counselor made it her business to learn about the process of plastic surgery immediately. Quite often this hope for reconstruction holds out to the patient the straw that keeps psychological resistance to the disease intact.

THE HORIZONTAL WORLD. In this sophisticated age, the counselor may sometimes be startled at the reaction exhibited when an adult is hospitalized. Those of us who work in hospital settings often forget that, to the uninitiated, hospital procedures are often very strange and frightening. Here we see an erstwhile independent adult precipitated in to a state of enforced dependency most difficult to tolerate. Many have never been a patient in a hospital. Before this, they have always been the ones looked up to for protection and comfort in times of family stress. Now they find themselves in a new role, in a new world, the horizontal world of the ill. Strange deviant behavior often results as patients resist or accept this world.

They may become contrary, uncooperative, and management-problems simply because they do not understand what is going to happen, or because of the indignity with which they feel themselves treated. It is difficult to be cooperative and placid with a tube in every orifice of the body, and prey to roving technicians with test tubes and needles throughout the day. To the male patient, the nurse may become a threat rather than a comfort because of the embarrassment engendered from the indignity of having a woman care for him. Everything going on around him may become tinged with his personal frustration, and his realistic and imagined fears of the strange new world in which he finds himself.

Others may settle too far back into dependency. Such patients become demanding and anxious when a nurse or doctor is not hovering near. They utilize the threat implied by the diagnosis as a weapon with which to bludgeon constant attendance from hospital staff and family members much as an infant wrests attention from frantic parents when he is ill. Here, the deep personal meaning of the necessity for hospitalization and the strangeness of the horizontal world has pushed the individual into a regression toward infantile behavior.

Of course, a good number of patients enter the hospital with the same intelligent, controlled fear with which they accept and cope with their diagnosis. They are able to adjust to the limitations of the horizontal world, to cooperate with the nurses and physicians in the procedures prescribed with a minimum of anxiety. Hospitalization, with all its stress, is viewed as a means toward the end of recovery. With the same flexibility they display in meeting other crises in life, they adapt to the horizontal world and its demands in order to make a speedy return to the freedom of active living.

Still others shift from mood to mood, now reacting hostilely and the next moment becoming dependent and wheedling favors. It is a challenge to the counselor to find out the cause for such behavior and to assist the patient toward an accurate knowledge of his surroundings, toward an acceptance of the limitations of his horizontal world for the moment, with hope that through cooperation he may soon once again be a member of the perpendicular world of work for which he yearns.

THE COUNSELOR'S INTERPRETIVE ROLE. The inhabitants of this horizontal world—the physicians and the nurses—become most important to the new patient. Often the decision to come to the hospital was tantamount to admission that death was imminent. Whether or not this was a realistic deduction has nothing to do with the feeling tones the decision activated. The actions and attitudes of the nurses and the physicians, then, become the equivalent of hope for life or acceptance of doom to the victim. In any severe illness, the need for a humanistic doctor is great. When that disease is cancer, the need is intensified. Sutherland says: "A good patient-physician relationship . . . is the patient's best guarantee against the development of crippling beliefs and their expression in unnecessary restriction of activities" (Sutherland and Orbach, 1953).

It is important, then, for the psychologist to know the psychological needs of the patient in the doctor-patient relationship, and also to know the physician and his philosophy in this critical interaction. Often, the counselor finds himself in the role of the middleman, interpreting the patient to the doctor and the physician to the patient. Again, this complex relationship must be approached each time as a unique case with individualized needs. Research has indicated three rather common needs of patients in this interaction. First, in an unpublished study by A. B. Cobb (data in process of analysis), it was found that 87 percent of a population of 100 patients wished their physicians to have a warm, friendly personality. They wanted to feel that he was approachable, that he was genuinely interested in them as persons, not just as "another case." The indication was that, if the doctor was such a man, the patient could then relax and let him carry some of the burden of anxiety. If the doctor did not radiate this personal interest, the patient remained tense, alarmed, and questioning all along the way; because he was not sure his treatment reflected all the skill the doctor had to give.

Second, the need for communication was urgent for these patients. This was a two-way street as they saw it. They wanted the doctor to talk with them, to tell them what he was going to do, why, and how he was going to do it. This information seemed to make the ordeal of treatment less terrifying. They also wanted the doctor to listen, to hear out their concerns, and in the telling some of the sharpness of the anxiety diminished. Communication was nonverbal as well as verbal between the doctor and his patient. Communication at the nonverbal level expressed the attitudes of doctors and nurses that were sometimes transmitted to the patients in unsuspected ways and were often erroneously interpreted by the patients.

An example of this sort of misunderstanding concerned a very ill male patient who had related closely to a sympathetic nurse on the floor. She always visited him before she went off duty, to smooth his bed and prepare him for the night. He looked forward to this attention and interpreted it as part of the magic that kept him from death, despite his alarm over the diagnosis. One morning, the counselor found him much worse, running a temperature and in deep depression. Upon probing, it was revealed that the nurse had been preoccupied the night before as she tucked him in. She had then "rushed off with a barely civil 'good night.'" The patient had brooded over this and felt rejected, and real fear reared its head because he truly believed he would have died long before had this nurse not cared enough to "pull him through." When the counselor discussed the patient with the nurse, it was found that she had an early date that evening, was a bit late, and was hurrying. Had she just thought to share this information with the patient, perhaps he would have understood and the "bad night" been avoided.

The third need expressed by the research population of patients in the doctor-patient relationship was that of action, of doing something about the illness. When the patient understands the flow of activity around him or the reasons for "no-action," he can cooperate more effectively and with better peace of mind.

The counselor's role in interpreting this need for action to the physician and the nuances of that action or no-action to the patient again becomes a challenging one. It becomes a matter of preparing the patient for what is to come. For example, a young girl was referred to the counselor by a physician because of uncooperative behavior. She had yanked the needle out of her arm and refused a blood transfusion. The girl reviewed the incident as follows:

> Well, I'm nineteen years old, and I have a right to know what they are fixing to do to me. They just come in, start setting up the treatment cart to do something. All those vicious old needles and things make me nervous. Then they just grab my arm, roll up my sleeve, and start jabbing. Well, I just made up my mind that the next time, I'd show them! And, I did!

The counselor listened, and then tried to explain the necessity for the blood transfusion, and the way the technicians and nurses went about setting up and administering such an order from the doctor. It was pointed out that to the nurses and technicians this was just another routine of the day, whereas to the patient it was intimate and vital. The patient was able to accept this view but insisted that she had a right to know what was to be done before it was done. In this feeling, the counselor concurred. Returning to the physician, the counselor learned it was inadvertently forgotten that the patient had not been informed of the procedure. Once this oversight was brought to attention, careful preparation was made before any further treatment or diagnostic procedure, and the patient cooperated beautifully.

Preparation of the patient, then, becomes a counseling challenge. Preparation for the unknowns of treatment is imperative if the patient is to cope with the impending crises with intelligence and understanding rather than grim, disintegrating fear. Preparation involves repeated explanations as phases of the disease and concurrent treatment progress; teaching positive facts again and again; discussing possible and expected reactions to treatment and developments of the disease, as these possibilities arise in the thoughts of the patient; and discussion of side effects of the drugs administered or the treatment prescribed. Large dosage of hormones produce personality and emotional changes in patients that may be disconcerting even if they are understood. For instance, androgens have proven effective in the control of cancer of the breast, but it has also been demonstrated (Wheeler, 1955) that continued consumption of this hormone tends to activate a strong sex drive in the woman. One widow of some ten years, confided her fears that she was "going loco." She had come to the point that she was literally afraid to trust herself alone with the elderly man whose housekeeper she had been for years. She thought she had become immoral and "sex-mad." When the treatment was explained and the side effects discussed, she heaved a great sigh of relief. She found she could handle the increased sex drive once she understood it, but as long as she did not understand why she had suddenly reacted this way, she was frantic.

X-ray treatments, and especially the use of cobalt and betatron machines are often quite frightening to patients. One patient was returned to the ward in hysterics because there was an occasional clicking noise in the X-ray machine administering her treatment. She was placed in the treatment booth, which was sound proof. This alone often proves frightening, for there is a sense of pressure and strangeness in such rooms. The attendant then withdrew; the heavy door was closed, leaving as her only contact with the outside world the half-face of the technician as he peered through the tiny window during treatment. Suddenly a sharp clicking sound started in the machine. It was not constant, but to the uneasy patient it could mean many things, among them that the machine was broken and that she was receiving lethal dosage of X-ray. The noise was a customary one in the machine, but to the patient it constituted a threat to life. Careful preparation for such treatments often reduces the side effects of nausea and fright following irradiation.

Radioactive iodine is another procedure little understood by patients and their families. The imaginative patient can conjure up many harrowing possibilities as to what is going on in his body, if he is not prepared. The family of one young woman scheduled to receive radioactive iodine for treatment of thyroid cancer was told not to come into the room the day following the treatment but to chat with her from the doorway. It was explained that this was to protect them from irradiation by contact with the patient during the time of peak radioactivity. The family had recently read a magazine article on the results of radioactivity on fish. They panicked. They visualized the patient lying abandoned in a room, with radioactivity playing all around and within her body. So obvious were their fears that these were transmitted to the patient, and she threatened to refuse the treatment. However, explanations from the physician and counselor made the treatment something to look forward to as an added precaution against recurring malignancy rather than a mysterious added threat to the patient and her family.

Drastic surgery, often mandatory in cancer, needs careful preparation. If a patient knows he is to lose a leg when he goes to surgery and if he also has at his command the availability of crutches or an artificial limb, he can concentrate on these hopeful factors rather than the loss of the important member of his body. Careful preparation and realistic understanding of the loss to be incurred as well as the hope for rehabilitation often makes the difference between rejecting surgery and acceptance.

The role of the psychologist, then, in this new horizontal world of dependency and threat, as he works with the patient and the physician, is one of interpretation, communication, preparation and, in all of these, emotional support. The psychologist works as a vital member of the doctor-nurse-counselor team and must study the physician as well as the patient. He must learn to interpret this man to the patient and the patient to the physician. For, when the patient knows what he is fighting and what the odds are, he gains confidence so long as he retains hope. Most cancer patients are able to build surprisingly positive worlds, if they are given the blocks of *truth* and *hope* with which to work and supportive understanding when the pattern becomes a bit obscure.

When the basic needs of the individual indicate that shielding from the full impact of knowledge is essential, he may still be assisted toward achieving mental health and hope by skilled counseling through preparation, communication, and action as prescribed by his doctor. Nothing calms panic more than the simple quietness and secure actions of the doctor into whose hands the patient has tendered his life. No other one person can give him so great a sense of security and hope.

This is a serious responsibility, for the doctor is human too. The very nature of malignancies constitutes a frustration to his medical skill. He may think it is best to steel himself and the patient for the worst. He may wish to avoid the patient, not because he is not interested but because he is unable to solve the problem and he cares too much. He may assume an unwarranted optimism. Whatever his actions or attitudes, the patient senses the finest nuances of his doctor's reactions and responds to them. For the mental health of both, it is most important that the doctor be aware of the psychological effects of cancer upon the patient and upon himself as well. The psychologist has a grave responsibility to both the physician and the patient in this matter; here again, he finds himself in the role of the insightful interpreter through virtue of his training in human behavior and his hours of counseling focused around understanding the meaning of cancer and the horizontal world to the individual patient.

COUNSELING FOR THE ACCEPTANCE OF DEATH. Paradoxically, the most devastating and at the same time the most rewarding experience of working with cancer patients comes from the relationship leading to an acceptance of the inevitability of death. It is devastating because no sensitive person can work with the deep emotional problems of another human being in the process of preparing for death without reeling at times under the impact of stark separation trauma. It is rewarding because there is never a greater need for emotional support, for empathic understanding, even for moments of diversion, than one finds in the patient getting ready for death. Between devastation and reward, it takes courage, tenacity, and humility to maintain a counseling relationship when the goal is acceptance and adjustment to the finality of death.

The psychologist is likely to panic when he first finds himself involved in such a relationship. His inclination is to withdraw. This is a defense mechanism set into motion by his own ego. He rationalizes that he can no longer be of real assistance, that he might even say or do the wrong thing. Unfortunately, the same defenses are often utilized by the patient's physician, family members, and friends. This leaves the patient to face the most traumatic experience of a lifetime alone. One would not physically walk away from a man dying in a carwreck, nor should one "walk away" emotionally from a person dying from cancer.

Counseling with a person preparing to die is not unlike counseling for life in many respects. The goal is still to give emotional support to the point that the client may gain insights, face his problem, work it through, and arrive at some semblance of peace within and without. The ultimate purpose is reversed—from adjustment to life to adjustment to death. Just as in counseling for life, the patient must face his problem in his own characteristic way. The skilled counselor will soon sense the basic needs of the client in this situation as quite similar to those he has displayed heretofore. If he has always been a fighter, he is likely to go down fighting. One husky, active man kept quoting the following lines from Robert Browning's "Prospice" to the counselor:

> I was ever a fighter, so—one fight more,
> The best and the last!

And he did go down fighting, without ever admitting the possibility that he might die.

A gentle woman, who verbalized her knowledge of impending doom but deep in her heart rejected the idea as impossible, hesitantly requested of the physician, "Now, if I am going to die, I want to know. There are some things I might need to do." Knowing that her house was in order and that her husband would care for any business essential, the understanding physician replied,

> Now, Mrs. X, you know that only God really knows when a person's time to go has come. You are responding to the medication we are giving you, and if you should cease to respond, we will just start something else.

She would have been miserable for her remaining days, had she been told. As it was, she lived fairly happily and content to within a week of her death.

On the other side of the ledger, another woman, mother of two children, asked the doctor:

> I know I am not responding to treatment as well as I should. I have two girls at home. My husband and I divorced ten years ago. I don't even know where he is. I have no family. If I am going to die, I need to know so I can arrange for the girls. A family at home will adopt them; I need to make the arrangements.

The doctor told her she had approximately six weeks to live. She went home, made the arrangements for her children, returned to the hospital, and within six weeks had indeed passed away.

The psychologist often questions just what to do or say under such circumstances. Certainly, this is an area where nondirective counseling would seem indicated. Perhaps the basic principle to keep in mind is that the patient should always lead the way—with the counselor only lending support when needed. If the counselor listens, the deep needs of the patient will soon become evident; in the meantime, talking about it lends catharsis. If the patient prefers not to see the approach of death, if he needs to hold on to hope of recovery, certainly the counselor should not feel it necessary to tear this false hope from him. If the patient seems to feel an urgency to explore the possibilities of his demise, this he should be allowed to do, without the counselor's feeling he must interrupt to reassure him falsely he will live. This does not mean that the counselor must agree with him in his hopelessness. As the doctor pointed out in the case reviewed above, hope is always present, and the counselor can give realistic reassurance based upon persistent efforts to turn the tide of the disease. Although each case must be explored as an individual entity, intensive work with cancer patients have indicated three general rules applicable to the successful interpersonal relation with the person facing death.

First, the counselor can listen. Quite often, all the patient really needs is a sympathetic listener as he works through his own feelings about his illness, the treatment received or not received, his doctor, his family, and, finally, if he has the courage, his death. Many times all these feelings have been cooped up within the patient because he does not wish to add to the strain he knows his family members are experiencing. A good listener, reflecting an occasional feeling as he senses need for further exploration, may lift a heavy burden from the patient.

Second, the counselor can supply correct information that will ease many of the fears and anticipations of the patient. At times the patient wishes information related to his illness, his current treatment, what is going to happen if he does not respond to it, the reassurance that the staff is not giving up and that there will always be action to combat the disease. Sometimes he wishes information about religion. The counselor not only assists by listening but also, with the consent of the patient, by inviting a clergyman of the individual's faith to come by to see him. Many times restless, uncooperative behavior is due to a secret desire to "get right with God," and, when this is accomplished, the patient becomes a changed man.

At times, the patient really wants to talk about death. One man who had gone through intensive pain for a period of some eight years said one day to the counselor, "What do you have to do to die? I've been so near to it and pulled out, and the pain was so terrific, that it scares me. I just don't believe I can stand to die." When the counselor explained that death was not necessarily extremely painful, that often death was a peaceful release from pain, that many persons actually drifted away in their sleep with no struggle at all, the patient relaxed. The counselor was deeply grateful that, when this man's time came, he just breathed a little more loudly than usual and fell asleep.

Finally, the counselor can "stand by" physically and emotionally. This is a time that the patient often feels alone and lonely. The counselor is a warm, human contact with life. Through his presence, and his words, he can assure the patient that he is actually not alone, that "we [the doctors, nurses, counselor, and family members] are always here to help in any way we can. You have only to call, and we are here." Often patients yearn for physical contact, and a touch on the hand or shoulder soothes and reassures the weary wanderer between two worlds.

The psychologist might also ask: "What are some of the things we can expect as far as behavior is concerned?" In cancer, with the advent of new drugs and treatments that often seem literally to drag one back from the brink of the grave to a few more months, weeks, or days of fairly normal living, there seem to be two categories of basic behavior alternating according to the course of the disease. First, there are episodes of false hope. With remission of the disease following chemotherapy, surgery, or irradiation, the spirits are buoyed by the seeming return to health. Patients begin to feel that a miracle has happened and cure is inevitable. Eventually, this high hope must be supplanted by sure despair as the disease becomes rampant once more. When this happens, usually the second phase sets in. This is a period characterized by rebellion and bitterness, a rebellion against an inexorable tide sweeping them toward "nothingness," against a God who would permit it, and a bitterness that this lot is theirs. The fortunate—and mature—grow into a calm acceptance as they eventually recognize the "handwriting on the wall" and, with humility and dignity, go to meet death with poise and peace.

How do patients really feel about this? and what does a counselor actually say or do? Perhaps some of the patients could answer such questions better than a counselor. One young mother of four small children, who fought a brave battle against bitter emotional odds—her husband and mother both rejected her because they could not stand to see her suffer—for three critical years, spoke in her last month of life:

> Every time I felt better, I'd build up false hopes. Really I know they [the doctors] can't cure me, but we all look for miracles, I guess, and, when you have been so low so often and when they pull you out, you just can't help thinking—maybe. And, I guess, it's best because when I'd get better and could go home to the children, I'd be able to live almost normally and enjoy them, and that was better for them. Then, each time the old lumps would start growing again [she had Hodgkin's Disease] and I'd start downhill again, I'd feel bitter and afraid. Looking back though, I guess the hope and bitterness and the fear all helped me to get ready for what I know must happen. You get so weary of fighting, you know at last that you can't really get well and strong again, so you say, "Let me live as long as I can for my children, but Thy will be done," and most of the time you are content.

Sometimes, in trying to bear up and be brave, family members succeed only in making the patient feel they are indifferent. A husband who had maintained strong cheerfulness in the presence of his dying wife appeared suddenly one day in the counselor's office. He pushed into the room, said not a word, lurched into a chair, and burst into sobs. The counselor remained quiet until the flood had subsided, then tendered a Kleenex box as she said: "I do understand just how frustrated and heartbroken you feel, but I know nothing anyone can say really helps the pain." He nodded and lapsed into a heavy silence. After some time had passed, the counselor tried again: "Would it help to talk about it?" After a moment of hesitation, it came out that his wife had flared up at him, saying: "You don't love me at all, or you couldn't be so gay when I am dying." This broke his heart for he had kept his composure before her at great emotional cost to himself. But, in just telling of his own hurt, he came to some understanding of hers and realized that his cheerfulness could have appeared to be indifference to her as she struggled wearily with the disease and pain. Soon, he straightened his shoulders, set his jaw, and marched back to her bedside with the gentleness and concern that carried her through her final days with the full knowledge of his love now discernible to her. The counselor had actually asked one question and expressed concern that she could not really help, but she did understand. So often it is not anything the counselor may say—or not say—it is just being there, just communicating to the family member, or the patient, that you understand, that you care, and want to help, that gives him courage to do the things that must be done.

These examples, in many ways, are the exceptions. These people were aware of what was happening, and they coped with the situation. Many others simply cannot accept the fact that the end is near, and their anxiety is expressed in defiant behavior, such as whining, demanding, and complaining. What they really want is somone to understand their unspoken fears and to give them some reassurance. Often, just a chat about nonessentials or just interested listening as they explore their aches and pains serves to lend some semblance of calm to their day.

As they meet life, each individual must also face death in his own way. The psychologist must study the individual, allow the leading cards always to be in his hands, and then follow through when and if he can lend emotional support, warm understanding, or information that may ease the anxiety of final separation as death descends.

REFERENCES

Abrams, R. D., and J. E. Finesinger. 1953. Guilt reactions in patients with cancer. Cancer 6:474–84.

Bacon, C. L., R. Renneker, and M. Cutler. 1952. A psychosomatic survey of cancer of the breast. Psychosom. Med. 14:453–60.

Bard, M. 1952. The sequence of emotional reactions in radical mastectomy patients. Public Health Rep. 11:1144–48.

—— 1953. The use of dependence for predicting psychogenic invalidism following radical mastectomy. Unpublished PH.D. dissertation, New York University.

Bard, M., and A. M. Sutherland. 1955. Psychological impact of cancer and its treatment. IV: Adaptation to radical mastectomy. Cancer 8:656–72.

Blumberg, E. M. 1954. Results of psychological testing of cancer patients, in J. Gengerelli and F. Kirkner, eds. The psychological variables in human cancer. Berkeley, Calif., University of California Press, pp. 30–61.

Blumberg, E. M., P. M. West, and F. A. Ellis. 1954. A possible relationship between psychological factors and human cancer. Psychosom. Med. 16:277–86.

Bozeman, M. F., C. E. Orbach, and A. M. Sutherland. 1955. Psychological impact of cancer and its treatment. III: Adaptation of mothers to the threatened loss of their children through leukemia, Part I. Cancer 8:1–19.

Cobb, B. 1952. A social psychological study of the cancer patient. Unpublished PH.D. dissertation, University of Texas.

—— 1953. Mental health of cancer patients. Texas Trends 10(2).

—— 1954. Why twenty patients went to quacks. Med. Econ. 32(2): 123–25, 225–29.

—— 1956. Nurse-patient relationships. J. Amer. Geriat. Soc. 4:690–97.

—— 1957. A review of the highlights of a decade of psychological research in cancer. Year Book of Cancer, 1956/57, pp. 534–57.

—— 1959. Emotional problems of adult cancer patients. J. Amer. Geriat. Soc. 7:274–85.

Cobb, B., R. L. Clark, C. McGuire, and C. D. Howe. 1954. Patient-responsible delay of treatment in cancer: a social-psychological study. Cancer 7:920–26.

Cobb, B., with F. Damarin, A. Krasnoff, and J. B. Trunnell. [n.d.] Passivity, dependency, and aggression in prostatic cancer patients. To appear in Psychosom. Med.

Ellis, F. W., and E. M. Blumberg. 1954. Comparative case summaries with psychological profiles in representative rapidly and slowly progressive neoplastic diseases, in J. Gengerelli and F. Kirkner, eds. The psychological variables in human cancer. Berkeley, Calif., University of California Press, pp. 72–82.

Fisher, S., and S. Cleveland. 1956. Relationship of body image to site of cancer. Psychosom. Med. 18:304–9.

Gengerelli, J., and F. Kirkner, eds. 1954. The psychological variables in human cancer. Berkeley, Calif., University of California Press.

Greene, W. A., Jr. 1954. Psychological factors and reticuloendothelial disease. I: Preliminary observations on a group of males with lymphomas and leukemias. Psychosom. Med. 16:220–30.

Greene, W. A., Jr., L. E. Young, and S. N. Swicher. 1956. Psychological factors and reticuloendothelial disease. II: Observations on a group of women with lymphomas and leukemias. Psychosom. Med. 18:284–303.

Huggins, C. B., and C. V. Hodges. 1941. Studies on prostatic cancer: effect of castration, of estrogen and of androgen injections on serum phosphatases in metabolic carcinoma of prostate. Cancer Res. 1:293–97.

Krasnoff, A. 1956. Personal counseling as adjunct to medical therapy with cancer patients. Unpublished PH.D. dissertation, University of Texas.

LeShan, L., and R. Worthington. 1955. Some psychologic correlates of neoplastic disease: a preliminary report. J. Clin. Exp. Psychopath. 16:281–88.

—— 1956. Personality as a factor in the pathogenesis of cancer, a review of the literature. Brit. J. Med. Psychol. 29:49–56.

Meerloo, J. A. M. 1954. Psychological implications in malignant growth. Brit. J. Med. Psychol. 27:210–15.

Orbach, C. E. 1953. Psychological management of the patient with incurable cancer. Geriatrics 8:130–34.

Orbach, C. E., A. M. Sutherland, and M. F. Bozeman. 1955. Psychological impact of cancer and its treatment. III: Adaptation of mothers to the threatened loss of their children through leukemia, Part II. Cancer 8:20–33.

Renneker, R., and M. Cutler. 1952. Psychological problems of adjustment to cancer of the breast. J. Amer. Med. Ass. 148:833–38.

Reznikoff, M. 1955. Psychological factors in breast cancer; a preliminary study of some personality trends in patients with cancer of the breast. Psychosom. Med. 17:96–108.

Richmond, J. B., and J. A. Waisman. 1955. Psychological aspects of children with malignant diseases. Amer. J. Dis. Child. 89:42–47.

Shands, H. C., H. W. Miles, and S. Cobb, eds. 1951. The emotional significance of cancer. Amer. Practit. 2:261–65.

Stephenson, J. H., and W. J. Grace. 1954. Life stress and cancer of the cervix. Psychosom. Med. 16:287–94.

Sutherland, A. M. 1952. Psychological impact of cancer surgery. Public Health Rep. 67:1139–43.

—— 1955. The psychological impact of cancer and its treatment. Med. Social Work 4:57–68.

Sutherland, A. M., and C. E. Orbach. 1953. Psychological impact of cancer and cancer surgery. II: Depressive reactions associated with surgery for cancer. Cancer 6:958–62.

West, P. M. 1954. The origin and development of the psychological approach to the cancer problem, in J. Gengerelli and F. Kirkner, eds. The psychological variables in human cancer. Berkeley, Calif., University of California Press, pp. 17–26.

Wheeler, J. I., Jr. 1955. Psychological alterations following administration of male sex hormones to women with malignant tumors of the breast. Unpublished PH.D. dissertation, University of Texas.

FACIAL DISFIGUREMENT

by RICHARD MADAN

IT IS INTERESTING that despite the attention given almost all other types of physical disability, facial disfigurement has been studied but rarely. Investigations of the face have focused upon its expressive aspects, the "personality" features, but only occasionally have the facially deformed been shown attention. While this neglect is in part a result of factors such as the question of whether facial disfigurement is strictly a physical disability and the diversity of conditions covered by this title, it is wondered whether the neglect might also be a type of avoidance. In other words, do similar feelings exist among psychologists that have tended to repel investigators from work with the facially disfigured just as the public feels repulsion when in the presence of disfigurement?

The paradox of the situation becomes even more striking when we acknowledge that the face is the most important part of the body as far as representing who we are. As such, it is given more attention, pampered more by us, and valued more by far than other parts of our body. Certainly this aspect has not escaped the attention of the beauty industry, which bombards us daily with advertisements, constantly reiterating that beauty plus a pleasing personality are the keys to success. So, we avoid the facially disfigured person. His pain may be intense as he perceives himself an atypical member of society. While he

Richard Madan, M.A., is a Clinical Psychologist at the Institute of Reconstructive Plastic Surgery, New York University Medical Center.

may suffer from no physical disability (sensory or motor defect), his anguish may be great owing to the intensity of the social and psychological forces that react within and upon him.

INCIDENCE AND CLASSIFICATIONS. The number of persons seeking remedy for their deformities has greatly increased during the years following World War II. That conflict, with its many wounded, has been instrumental in bringing on significant advances in surgical procedures. Our highly industrialized society with its many accidents is a present contributor to the patient population. We also find many more persons coming for treatment because of their improved standard of living, which enables them to obtain help when formerly it was beyond their financial means. Lastly, increased medical facilities have aided many who could not meet the costs of private treatment.

Because the facially disfigured represent a group that covers a multitude of possible conditions and are treated in many different institutions, there are no available statistics pertaining to the incidence of the condition in the general population. (There is no national organization that carries on such work.) However, to give the reader some idea of the number of disfigured in the United States let us look at the figures given for cleft palate and/or lip. This congenital condition makes up only a relatively small percentage of the patient load, and yet the figures are surprisingly high. Olin reports that in the United States there are "approximately 190,000 to 200,000 individuals" with this condition and that it occurs in "approximately 1:750 to 1:800 live births" (Olin, 1960, p. 9). It takes little imagination to realize how many of our fellow citizens are disfigured, or believe themselves to be so.

The inherent difficulty in dealing with such cases stems from the overwhelming importance of the social and psychological factors. Persons may think themselves disfigured when in reality they fall within normal limits of facial structure. Thus, to define what is truly meant by facial disfigurement is exceedingly difficult. A discussion of the classification of such cases will clarify the problem more fully.

There are three primary ways in which disfigurements of the face are classified. These are used in combination with one another so as to give as full a picture of the condition as possible. First, the deformity is categorized as to type: which part of the face is involved. There are eight areas or types: nose, eye, jaw, ear, lip, facial paralysis, birth marks and scars, and combinations of the preceding seven. Further refinement of the type can be made by ascertaining whether the defect is present in the soft tissue or bony structure of the face. Of course, there are variations in the degree of deformity within each type. A defect of the nose could cover either a simple hook or complete absence of the nose due to disease. Similarly, an ear defect might be a case of protruding or lop ears or congenital absence of almost the entire external ear.

To handle the problem of degree of deformity, the type of condition is usually rated along a continuum ranging from simple or mild deformity to severe or gross defects. This classification is arbitrary as there have been no standard groupings ever made within the field. Each installation handling the disfigured devises its own rating scale and decides who will be the judges. They have to keep in mind factors such as the social and psychological importance of one part of the face as contrasted to another and the ease or difficulty of surgery. An idea of the confusion existing in this classification category can be seen by the use of the word "cosmetic." Some authors use it to refer to cases of mild disfigurement, yet recently an author used it in the title of a book that was a text on plastic surgery in general. Broadly speaking, all plastic surgery is "cosmetic" in nature.

Finally, after labeling the deformity as to its location and severity, it is classified as to its etiology. There are two broad categories: congenital (present at birth) and acquired. This would, on the surface, appear to be the simplest of the three categories of classification, but in reality it, too, has its problems. Complications arise because congenital conditions are not always apparent at birth. For example, the nose does not develop its final shape until puberty, so that a familial nose (congenital condition) will not appear until relatively late in life. Nevertheless, congenital cases can be further divided into physical irregularities where shape or size is involved or conditions where there is gross distortion or absence of part of the face. Acquired conditions may result from accidents, previous surgery, or disease.

No discussion of classification should fail to take into account the cultural dimension. A condition of the face that one culture or society views as a defect may be seen by another as a positive status symbol. Facial scars are seen as marks of immorality by some peoples and as a sign of manliness and bravery by others.

The preceding discussion of classification has pointed up the problems that exist in dealing with and "diagnosing" facial disfigurement. The absence of objective means and standards of classification stems primarily from the fact that at least half, and possibly more, of the patient population is only mildly or moderately disfigured. This means that they are not, for the most part, physically disabled. They come for treatment because they subjectively believe themselves disfigured. Consequently, two persons with essentially similar facial structure would not necessarily both be classified as disfigured. The psychological factor becomes all important in such cases. It is a simple step then to imagine that complaints of disfigurement may cover any possible condition of the face. It may be simple acne, a slight, almost unnoticeable scar, slightly protruding ears, or even, as in one case, a man complaining that he wanted his lips corrected so that he would have a more permanent and prominent smile. With such a multitude of possibilities it is little wonder that the facially disfigured present such problems of treatment.

MEDICAL ASPECTS. Since we are dealing with not one but many different types of conditions or illnesses, there is no one consistent course of the condition. Specific etiological factors are as numerous as there are types of disfigurement. They may range from suspected racial factors in the case of keloidal growths, to inherited familial tendencies in the case of cleft lip and/or palate, to a severe burn suffered in an accident. The conditions remain stable, but, if the deformity is caused by disease, then, of course, it may worsen if not treated.

Most instances of physical disability occur in patients with severe or gross deformity. Facial paralysis can interfere in the normal development of half the face. Microtia, "a developmental anomaly characterized by abnormal smallness of the ears" (as defined in *Dorland's Illustrated Medical Dictionary*), usually means not only deformity of the outer ear but an impairment in hearing, too. Similarly, defects of the outer eye area may be connected to impairment of sight. Defects of the jaw usually are associated with dental problems, and the actual bite of the patient may be defective, causing eating problems. Even in cases with a simple or mild disfigurement, as are most nasal defects, the breathing of the patient is frequently faulty.

The primary medical treatment for disfigurements is plastic surgery. Almost any complaint voiced by a patient is amenable to this form of surgery. Any medical textbook dealing with this specialty lists and describes the procedures necessary for treating the many conditions. For the most part, the surgery is as serious as is the defect. A simple scar may only require skin abrasion, with the patient leaving the doctor's office in a matter of hours. Nasal deformities require at least one operative procedure and perhaps more, with hospitalization being necessary. In the case of ear reconstruction it may take years, there being, in some instances, over one dozen different operative procedures involved.

The proper time of surgery has to be ascertained. In the case of young children it is advisable to carry on the surgery before the youngster enters school and is subjected to the pressures inherent in such competition. At times this is not possible as it may be necessary for the part of the face in question to develop further before treatment can be undertaken. Cleft palate and lip are repaired quite early, in most cases, to enable the child to develop as normal speech as possible. A child with a malformed jaw may have to wait till adolescence before an operation can be undertaken. In the latter instance, orthodontic treatment might be started before the final surgical procedure takes place.

The plastic surgeon may need the services of other allied medical specialists in order fully to plan and carry out the course of treatment. Such services as the ophthalmic surgeon, the orthodontist, the cephalometrician, the prosthodontist, and even the medical artist are often required. In short, the treatment may call into use a gamut of medical services just as it may not require any of these.

In planning surgery the doctor has to assess the situation and determine if the patient's complaint adequately pinpoints the deformity. For example, a young girl came to a surgeon requesting that her nose be altered as she believed herself to be ugly. Upon examination it was observed that, although her nose was somewhat large, the appearance of her face was really marred by a receding chin. Thus, the initial complaint actually became secondary in the treatment.

Once surgery and recovery are completed, it is rare that the individual requires further medical care. Since most disfigurements are not the result of disease, there is little possibility that a recurrence or complication will take place. Success in surgery (from a purely technical standpoint) is quite good. Almost all kinds of facial defects can be handled by the surgeon. The great strides made in this field have made it possible for almost anyone with a deformity to look forward to improvement in some degree. As in other areas of medicine, constant research and exploration are going on, facilitating even greater advances. Anyone who is disfigured and desires improvement can now be helped.

PSYCHOLOGICAL IMPLICATIONS. As with all others who suffer from physical disability, the facially disfigured finds himself a deviant. He is (looks) different from others. Because of this fact alone, he is regarded by people as being alien and consequently is viewed with suspicion. We certainly are aware of the emotions stirred up within groups when a stranger enters their midst. But the disfigured is under an even greater burden than just being deviant. The very nature of his deviation compounds the social attitudes toward him. For as long as we know, people have regarded the structure of the face as being the mirror of the personality, and the disfigured suffer from this belief. They are regarded as deviant not only in looks but also in personality. Because of this attitude they may be singled out as scapegoats, be objects of jest (the clown with the big red nose), or be regarded as being inferior in some way to the nondisfigured.

Perhaps even more devastating to them is to be left out of the main stream of their culture. As already mentioned, the unusually intense quest for the physically beautiful in the United States makes them even greater outcasts. They certainly cannot conform to the accepted norms of beauty, and the need to conform in all areas of our life is apparently at an all-time high. This need to conform on the part of the disfigured is a very real pressure in those that come for surgery.

We are all aware to some degree that the disfigured person is regarded hostilely and discriminated against either in an open manner or in more subtle ways. He may be regarded as a gangster or a person of questionable moral character. A flattened nose along with its brother, the cauliflower ear, can suggest the stereotype of the punchdrunk fighter. Puffed eyelids or a red bulbous nose may bring to mind excessive drinking. The disfigured is questioned as to how he received his defect. Frequently a member of a minority group will find that he is not believed when he gives an explanation for his condition. A Puerto Rican woman who was scarred in an automobile accident was viewed with skepticism by both fellow Puerto Ricans and native-born Americans. If the defect was received in a socially honorable manner, however, the deformed may find himself the object of sympathy, bordering on pity. War wounds are regarded with far less antipathy than similar disfigurements received in accidents or from congenital causes. Certainly the most insidious discrimintaion stemming from deviation of looks lies in racial and religious prejudice. Persons find themselves not wanted and indeed reacted against because their appearance is supposedly characteristic of members of a minority group. The flat nose of the Negro, the slanted eyes of the Oriental, and aquiline nose of the Jew are all facial characteristics that are stereotyped by the bigot.

Not surprisingly then, we find the same irrational, illogical beliefs present in the parents of children who are born deformed. These beliefs follow many of the same lines as those found in parents of children with other physical disabilities. Fathers may believe it was something the wife did during pregnancy; mothers may attribute it to some behavior of the father. Even more "primitive" explanations are listed by Macgregor (Macgregor, Abel, Bryt, Lauer, and Weissmann, 1953, p. 67) such as incestuous parentage, or sins of the fathers. At its mildest, giving birth to a disfigured child is often felt to be a social stigma.

Not only do the disfigured suffer from these social attitudes but they share the same problems in the vocational field as their fellow disabled. Employers may believe that they will not be tolerated by either fellow employees or by customers. If employed, they may be relegated to a back area and in a sense isolated from others. They may be offered jobs below their abilities and, even worse, may seek out such jobs, feeling that, because of their defect, they cannot qualify for a position that they want and can fill. Conversely, a deformed individual suffering from a motor or sensory defect may strive to obtain a job for which he is not physically qualified.

The child in school may find himself the object of the same type of discrimination. We are familiar with the teasing and cruelty with which some children deal with others. The facially deformed do not, however, present an educational problem as do certain other disabilities since there is no physical nor mental impediment to learning.

Having seen how social attitudes affect the disfigured and influence their lives, let us now turn to the individual himself and see what he really is like. The few studies done with such patients have concentrated upon those cases that would be classified as mild or moderately disfigured. This group forms the majority of the patient population and, in addition, offers interesting material for investigation. It includes persons who fall within the normal limits of facial beauty. The displacement they make upon their "disfigurements" as a cause of their poor life adjustment is due primarily to psychological factors. The social attitudes and vocational problems already mentioned apply only slightly to them. Further, they are primarily adolescents and adults, easier to study than children, and again a greater part of the patient load.

The studies have shown that the incidence of emotional disturbance is unusually high in the mildly disfigured. Edgerton, Jacobson, and Meyer (Edgerton, Jacobson, and Meyer, 1960) found that 70 percent of such patients were assigned a formal psychiatric diagnosis. Hill and Silver (Hill and Silver, 1950) state that, "the actual consultation of the plastic surgeon by the patient, for reasons other than trauma, should be considered as an overt symptom of neurosis." Finally, Linn and Goldman (Linn and Goldman, 1949), in observing cases of rhinoplasty (plastic surgery of the nose) said: "With few exceptions the patients . . . were ill from a psychiatric view. This illness varied from minor neurotic disturbance to overt schizophrenic psychoses." In addition, Edgerton makes the observation that in cases of males seeking cosmetic surgery the incidence of emotional disturbance is greater than in females. The reason for the latter finding seems to be that these men are ignoring social pressures against surgery more strongly than women and thus are more disturbed.

Such people have been found to have difficulties in dealing effectively with life both socially and vocationally. They have generalized difficulty in heterosexual relationships, in finding or maintaining jobs. Frequently they are members of a minority group and are first or second generation Americans. Often they are the products of broken homes or ones where there was abnormal tension between the parents. They are reported to be above average in intelligence, but this finding may be a result of the selectivity of the researchers. In brief, this group of mild or moderately disfigured persons shows as diverse a variety of personality pictures as might be found in an exclusively psychiatric population. The diversity of personality corresponds to the diversity of physical conditions.

The mildly disfigured were found by Abel and Weissmann (Macgregor, Abel, Bryt, Lauer, and Weissmann, 1953, pp. 130–65) to be less productive in their use of imagination and less likely to respond to others and to show their emotions than the average person. They could not accept themselves, nor did they expect others to accept them. They had some awareness that their disfigurement was not entirely a realistic one. Bryt (Macgregor, Abel, Bryt, Lauer, and Weissmann, 1953, pp. 166–207) in the same study found that the "complainers" were predominantly the mildly disfigured. They were more spontaneous in their complaints and believed their deformity was more of a liability than did the severely disfigured.

Still further differences between the sexes were observed in a study done at the Johns Hopkins Hospital. The investigators found relatively clear-cut dynamic formulations for each sex (Meyer, Jacobson, Edgerton, and Canter, 1960; Jacobson, Edgerton, Meyer, Canter, and Slaughter, 1960). The men had great difficulty in childhood and adolescence in identifying with their fathers. This failure in identification hindered the male patient in mastering intense ambivalent feelings in relationship with the mother. The investigators found that, as a result, the request for surgery was part of an active struggle by the patient to free himself from his ambivalent relationship with women and his identification with the mother.

The women, on the other hand, were found to have identified strongly with their fathers in childhood and to have had a weakened identification with the mother, thus hampering the development of the feminine role. Later in life these women wished to function more effectively in their feminine roles and found the earlier male identification to be a disturbing element. The conflict was shown with most of them in a preoccupation with a sense of nasal deformity and the wish to eliminate this physical manifestation of their masculine identification. Both sexes said their deformities resembled their father's facial structure.

The severely disfigured exhibited similar personality pictures to their moderately deformed counterparts. However, definite differences were observed. Abel and Weissmann (Macgregor, Abel, Bryt, Lauer, and Weissmann, 1953) report that the severely disfigured are in a sense more resigned to nonacceptance by others and are more repressed and withdrawn than those less afflicted. On the other hand, the grossly deformed can more easily accept the connection between their emotional difficulties and their defect. Bryt found that the severely deformed appeared to be less emotionally disturbed than the moderately disfigured and that the latter considered their defects more of a social and economic liability than did the former. The severely disfigured included patients who were more often afflicted in adulthood in contrast to the moderately disfigured, who more frequently were marked since childhood.

In his interviews with parents of children who were disfigured, Bryt (Macgregor, Abel, Bryt, Lauer, and Weissmann, 1953) described five main patterns of maternal behavior concerning the handling of the child: avoidance, hiding, denying, undoing, and normal. Some mothers, "avoided any situation which could have exposed them to questioning." Others hide the deformity behind special clothing, gestures, or postures (for example, the mother who put a hat on her child even in the hottest weather to hide her child's ear defect). Still others denied the defect by entering into situations where such questioning might very easily take place and thus symbolically attempted to minimize the deformity. There was a group of parents who by saying the defect was "cute" attempted to undo the deformity. And lastly, there were those mothers who handled the child's condition in a normal manner. They did not hide their concern and discussed the child with others in order to obtain advice.

Those mothers who adhered to the first four patterns exhibited neurotic characteristics. They dealt with the child's deformity much as they dealt with any other anxiety-producing situation, always having in mind the reduction of the conscious anxiety and not seeking its source. As a consequence, when the children were operated upon, the mothers were interested in the degree of perfection that could be obtained and they had little concern or even grasp of the fact that their anxiety would in some way affect their children. All such mothers experienced considerable guilt and resentment toward their offspring that was primarily unconscious. The conscious manifestation of such emotions was oversolicitousness and overprotection of the child.

Thus, as Bryt says, a vicious cycle was set up: guilt brought on the overprotectiveness, which in turn engendered the resentment, which in its turn brought on more guilt.

SPECIAL CONSIDERATIONS IN PSYCHOLOGICAL APPRAISAL. Psychological appraisal of the facially disfigured does not present any intrinsic problems. The absence of any definite physical disability eliminates the necessity of developing special interview techniques or instruments to handle the problems caused by sensory or motor defects. Occasionally such defects may be encountered, but the incidence of such cases is small. Naturally, in those cases appropriate measures should be taken.

The diagnostic team, too, consists of the standard personnel employed in purely psychiatric settings, that is, the psychiatric social worker, clinical psychologist, and psychiatrist. It may be necessary in some cases to call upon the services of a vocational counselor. (The medical aspects of the case are covered by the disciplines already mentioned in the section on Medical Aspects.) The referral of the patient by the medical team to the psychosocial one is a delicate task. Since many of these patients have spent years in developing defenses against the acknowledgment of emotional problems—indeed, the seeking of surgery may be the manifestation of the defense—the referral may engender much anxiety within the patient. However, the medical team, if they are enlightened as to emotional factors involved and the services offered by the psychosocial team, can make the referral a relatively smooth one. Fortunately, in this instance, most plastic surgeons are aware of the strong emotional overlay present in their cases.

Case history and interview should concentrate on several areas in addition to the standard ones studied in psychiatric examination. These areas are as follows:

1. When and how the disfigurement occurred.

2. Why does the patient seek surgery at this particular time? Is it a personal desire, or does he come at the urgings of some other party? How long has he thought of surgery?

3. What results are anticipated by the patient in himself and others? The expectation that there will be great change in others as a result of surgery has been found to be a sign of severe psychopathology.

4. Patients' questions and doubts about surgery.

5. How the patient believes his disfigurement has handicapped him in life.

6. Presence of deformity in other members of the family, and how the family members reacted to the patient's disfigurement. In this area it is useful to know which member of the family the patient believes he resembles.

Observations of the patient should be made with special attention given to the way he holds his body and how he dresses and, with women, the way they use cosmetics. Many patients have adopted bodily postures to compensate for their disfigurements, such as tilting the face to compensate for lack of symmetry or showing only one side of the face to hide a defect on the other side.

Psychological testing should, of course, follow the main lines of the entire evaluation. Since the emotional life of the patient is all important, there should be a concentration on the projective techniques. Special consideration should be given the defensive structure of the personality, the attitudes toward the self, the reaction to and relatedness toward others, and the primary sexual identifications. Of especial importance in psychological testing is an evaluation of the presence of and degree of emotional disturbance; that is, an evaluation has to be made as to whether the patient may be too emotionally disturbed to undergo surgery at that particular time. In reality most patients are able to undergo the stress of the surgical experience regardless of psychiatric diagnosis. Psychotic individuals can most definitely benefit from surgery despite the fact that their initial complaint is highly unrealistic. Those patients however, who are in the midst of an acute emotional state may not be able to handle the stress adequately. Testing can also help in assessing the patient's reactions to the surgery. Paranoid patients can be a threat physically as well as legally if they believe the surgical results have not been satisfactory. Such patients will more likely than not be highly critical of the surgical result.

Unfortunately, research in the area of psychodynamic appraisal is sparse with this type of patient. They have been studied so rarely as to make the formulation of certain key areas of investigation difficult. The presence of psychosocial evaluations in plastic surgery units is almost unheard of. Thus, our present knowledge stems from the few reports that have been primarily theoretical in nature. Nothing is present in the literature concerning the everyday handling of patients in such units. Practical suggestions, typical cases, and so forth have yet to be formulated.

REHABILITATION. The problems of rehabilitation with the disfigured are in some respects similar to those of other physical disabilities. But just as this group differs in many respects from others, so do the problems. For example, it is generally taken for granted that vocational problems are paramount in this group, but such is not the case. As mentioned in the section on Psychological Implications, such problems do exist, primarily with the severely deformed. They are the ones who need vocational advisement. The majority of the cases, however, do not need vocational help per se. Their problems in vocational adjustment are part and parcel of their greater emotional disturbance. In the author's experience it is rare to find patients who attribute their lack of vocational progress to their disfigurements. There is one group that does—those who aspire to the theatrical profession. In such jobs physical beauty is a major factor. Yet, even these patients exhibit far more serious problems of living than vocational adjustment. Their seeking careers in the performing arts is, in many cases, an outgrowth of their emotional upset. Frequently, such people do not have the equipment to be successful in such jobs.

Certainly, the major problem area concerning rehabilitation of such cases is plastic surgery. It is difficult to predict, on the basis of our present knowledge, just who will benefit from surgery. There are patients who are initially greatly satisfied with the results only to become dissatisfied when the changes they had anticipated do not occur. Sometimes minimal physical restoration will be viewed by patients as a wonderful occurrence in their lives. There are those that, despite an excellent surgical result, will be dissatisfied. There are the "complainers" already mentioned. Occasionally patients cannot even recall what they looked like before surgery and are unsure of their change. There are those who after surgery is completed do not feel it was worth the pain, money, and emotional stress to achieve what they then look like. Young girls with ear defects fall into this category. They could easily hide the defect behind their hair, but frequently they undergo a course of surgery that lasts literally years only to have a surgical result that still looks "deformed." In simple terms, those persons who do not acknowledge that changes in their adjustment will only come about with a change within themselves rather than on their "surface" are poor risks for this rehabilitation. They are the ones who seek magical cures for their poor interpersonal relationships.

On the other hand, those patients who have discussed their expectations and have a realistic idea of what surgery entails and what results they may expect adjust more easily to the final appearance. In cases where there has been improvement of some physical defect, such as breathing, there appears to be much satisfaction. Many of these patients do not stress physical appearance as being a major factor in their seeking surgery.

In dealing with such a diverse group the question of psychiatric screening takes on special importance. Plastic surgeons have found much practical help by collaboration with the psychological team. If the surgeon feels that psychological services will benefit his patient, then the patient will accept such help more willingly. Almost all patients undergoing cosmetic surgery can benefit from some type of counseling where they can air their expectations, fears, and hopes. Sometimes dramatic changes take place in appearance even before surgery has been undertaken. The patient institutes such changes as a result of someone being interested in his problems.

The question of psychotherapy for such patients has been little explored. They seem, as a group, unsuited for such a course of action. For the most part, their defensive structure rules out such referral. However, in some cases they can be guided toward seeking such help. Group psychotherapy might be a more ideal setting for such people, but, again, little has been done in this area.

PUBLIC EDUCATION. There is a definite lack of public information in the area of facial disfigurement. Despite the presence of facilities for such cases, many persons do not avail themselves of the services. Most large hospitals have plastic surgery units, and yet people are unaware of their existence. Plastic surgery still suffers from the belief that it is only available to the financially comfortable. An attitude that some patients express is that it is almost immoral of them to contemplate altering their physical appearance. Many such persons could be helped if they believed this type of surgery was publicly accepted.

A more destructive consequence of the lack of public education is in the prejudice felt toward such persons. All professional persons connected or coming into contact with the disfigured could help them immeasurably if they disseminated information about such cases. Then, perhaps, the deep rooted attitudes present in society and directed against the deformed could be altered. In this respect there is not one national organization that devotes itself to the problems of the disfigured. Much more can be done to help these handicapped persons. Research is needed both in the medical and psychological fields concerning their problems. Perhaps the fact that such persons are neither fish nor fowl (that is, neither purely medical nor purely psychiatric problems) accounts in part for the neglect that they have borne.

REFERENCES

Edgerton, M. T., W. E. Jacobson, and E. Meyer. 1960. Surgical-psychiatric study of patients seeking plastic (cosmetic) surgery. Brit. J. Plast. Surg. 3:136–45.

Hill, G., and A. G. Silver. 1950. Psychodynamic and esthetic motivations for plastic surgery. Psychosom. Med. 12:345–55.

Jacobson, W. E., M. T. Edgerton, E. Meyer, A. Canter, and R. Slaughter. 1960. Psychiatric evaluation of male patients seeking cosmetic surgery. Plast. Reconstr. Surg. 26:356–72.

Linn, L., and I. B. Goldman. 1949. Psychiatric observations concerning rhinoplasty. Psychosom. Med. 11:307–14.

Macgregor, F. C., and B. Schaffner. 1950. Screening patients for nasal plastic operations. Psychosom. Med. 12:277–91.

Macgregor, F. C., T. M. Abel, A. Bryt, E. Lauer, and S. Weissmann. 1953. Facial deformities and plastic surgery. Springfield, Ill., C. C. Thomas.

Meyer, E., W. E. Jacobson, M. T. Edgerton, and A. Canter. 1960. Motivational patterns in patients seeking elective plastic surgery. Psychosom. Med. 22:193–203.

Olin, W. H. 1960. Cleft lip and palate rehabilitation. Springfield, Ill., C. C. Thomas.

AUDITORY DISABILITY

by EDNA S. LEVINE

THE DELICATE mechanism that makes hearing possible has been described as "perhaps the nearest to perfection of any human attribute" (Kleinfeld, 1953, p. 1). Situated for the most part in the temporal bone of the skull, it plays a critical role in the conversion of certain vibratory disturbances called sound waves into their heard equivalents. Through this role, the diminutive auditory structure takes on giant psychological proportions; for, in its capacity to help transpose sound waves into spoken language, the hearing apparatus represents man's strongest line of communication with the world in which he lives.

When the line of communication breaks down, psychological integrity is threatened. If the break occurs in early childhood, the avenue for learning spoken language is blocked, and the child is thereby deprived of a vital stimulus for mental, social, and emotional development. When the break occurs in later life, complex problems of readjustment commonly arise that require deep understanding for rehabilitation management. Sometimes the line breaks down under the pressure of psychic stresses. Such cases emphasize the many unknowns that have yet to be solved concerning the role of hearing in human development.

Although the psychodynamics of hearing is still a matter for research (Knapp, 1953; Isakower, 1939, 1954), we have after

Edna S. Levine, Ph.D., is a Consultant in the Department of Educational Psychology at New York University.

many centuries of groping finally come to understand something of the impact of impaired hearing upon the human organism (Hodgson, 1954). It may be that a clearer understanding of impaired hearing will ultimately disclose the full story of man's unique dependence upon the sense of hearing for psychological survival (Huizinga, 1954). If so, it will not be the first time that knowledge of dysfunction has led to an understanding of function. With this thought as well as rehabilitation goals in mind, the following summarizes a number of important aspects of orientation for psychological practice and investigation in the area of auditory disability.

DEFINITIONS AND INCIDENCE. In this discussion, persons with auditory disabilities are those who are handicapped in communicative efficiency because of deficits or disorders in the reception and/or interpretation of sound, or in response to sound. According to current estimates, there are better than 12,000,000 adults and 3,000,000 children in the United States with some kind of auditory defect. About 4,500,000 are seriously handicapped by the condition, and approximately 760,000 of these are totally deaf (Masland, 1960).

At one time, it was common practice to call all persons with auditory defect "deaf." Or if the loss of hearing were severe enough and its onset early enough to interfere with the development of speech, the terms "deaf and dumb" or "deaf-mute" were used. But when the feat of teaching "deaf-mutes" to speak was achieved, it became evident that these rough definitions had lost their main discriminative advantage and were in fact completely inadequate to cover the wide variation that exists among persons with impaired hearing.

The operational benefits of defining the component subgroups in the vast and heterogeneous parent body are obvious. But the traditional problem has been to establish the criteria for forming mutually exclusive groupings. The difficulties involved are illustrated by the many efforts of the United States Census Bureau to enumerate the deaf (Levine, 1956, b). The efforts finally ended in defeat, and after the 1930 census the Bureau gave up the task altogether.

Nevertheless, the problem of definition and classification was not dropped. Factors other than enumeration were (and still are) involved that make classification an essential base of reference for workers in the field. Educators and rehabilitation personnel in particular need to know the main characteristics and differentials of the kinds of hearing impairment they are expected to deal with so that adequate programs of service can be set up.

The next major effort to classify the hearing-impaired population was made by the White House Conference on Child Health and Protection in 1930 (White House Conference, 1931, p. 277). The Conference began the job by sweeping out a confusing assortment of terminology that had been cluttering up the field, such as semi-mute, semi-deaf, deaf and dumb, partially deaf, partially hearing, etc., and then proceeded to divide the population into two main groups—the deaf and the hard of hearing—based upon whether or not impaired hearing interfered with the natural (or near-natural) learning of language and speech. However, there were those who complained that in the resultant definitions too much stress had been placed on speech and not enough on hearing loss. To correct the situation, a special committee on terminology was appointed by the Conference of Executives of American Schools for the Deaf, and in 1937 the following definitions were submitted by the committee and accepted by the Conference:

The Deaf: Those in whom the sense of hearing is nonfunctional for the ordinary purposes of life. This general group is made up of two distinct classes, based entirely on the time of the loss of hearing: (*a*) the congenitally deaf—those born deaf; (*b*) the adventitiously deaf—those who were born with normal hearing but in whom the sense of hearing becomes nonfunctional later through illness or accident.

The Hard of Hearing: Those in whom the sense of hearing although defective is functional with or without a hearing aid. [Conference of Executives of American Schools for the Deaf, 1938, pp. 1–3.]

These have been the accepted classifications until very recently, with the hard of hearing comprising the large majority of the group and the deaf variously estimated as numbering from about 100,000 to 250,000 persons throughout the country.

There are, however, a number of inadequacies in the 1937 classifications. One of the most outstanding is the fact that the categories fail to take account of other types of auditory disorder than the straight deficits. To be sure, it is only within the past two decades that these other conditions have gained field prominence; but, now that they have, a more timely classification scheme is required. An auspicious beginning has been made along this line by Davis and Fowler (Davis and Silverman, 1960), and the terminology used by the author in this chapter as well as in the following classification has been guided largely by their proposals.

CLASSIFICATION OF THE HEARING-IMPAIRED POPULATION

1. *The Hypacusic or Hard of Hearing:* those whose hearing loss is not or has not been severe enough to prevent the natural learning of language and speech either with or without a hearing aid. To distinguish persons with usable residual hearing from those whose hearing is no longer functional, the term "deafened" is conveniently applied to the latter.

2. *The Anacusic or Deaf:* those with irreversible deafness since birth or childhood severe enough in the speech range to prevent the natural learning of language and speech even with the help of a hearing aid.

3. *The Dysacusic:* those with disorders in the synthesis and/or interpretation of acoustic stimuli (including spoken language) that are not due to loss in auditory acuity but may exist in the

presence of unimpaired (as well as impaired) hearing ability. Persons with such conditions as auditory agnosia or word deafness fall into this category.

4. *The Psychodysacusic:* those with disorders of hearing or of response to acoustic stimuli (including spoken language) that are due to the action of psychic mechanisms. Persons with such conditions as functional, psychogenic, or hysteric deafness fall into this category.

The preceding categories are not mutually exclusive, and various etiological factors involved will be considered subsequently.

The major attention of the present discussion centers upon the hard of hearing and the deaf who together constitute the largest segment of the hearing-impaired population, and about whom relatively definitive information is available. The dysacusic are currently under intensive research study (St. Joseph's School for the Deaf and Department of Otolaryngology, Columbia–Presbyterian Medical Center, 1960); and the psychodysacusic are largely a psychiatric research and treatment problem (Ruesch, 1957) with significant assistance from audiology (Johnson, Work, McCoy, 1956).

In regard to incidence, here, too, a change seems to be taking place (Ronnei, 1955), with the number of hearing-impaired persons in the population apparently on the increase. Medical advances have made significant strides in decreasing infant mortality, in lengthening the life span, and in the successful "wonder drug" treatment of previously morbid diseases. But at the same time, these advances have resulted in a higher incidence of impaired hearing among the infants saved as well as among the aging whose life span has been extended and among those treated with certain "wonder drugs" that have been found to have ototoxic effects (Dunlop, 1960). In addition, technological advances have introduced the menace of noise and blast in industry and military activities (Fox, 1960), and this adds further to the number of hearing impaired in the population. And finally, more extensive hearing conservation programs (American Academy of Ophthalmology and Otolaryngology, 1959) and finer diagnostic techniques in the assessment of auditory acuity (Hirsh, 1957; Hoople, 1957) are disclosing the presence of hearing defects that would otherwise have remained undetected.

MEDICAL-ACOUSTIC ASPECTS. Fundamental to an understanding of the psychological problems and management of persons with impaired hearing is some basic familiarity with the sensation of hearing in terms of (1) the process of hearing (Pierce and David, 1958; Stevens and Davis, 1938); (2) the anatomy and physiology involved (Fowler, 1939; Wever and Lawrence, 1954); (3) the pathology (Mygind, 1952; Ballantyne, 1960); and (4) measurement (Watson and Tolan, 1949; Hirsh, 1952; Lawrence, 1957). Highly abridged summaries of these follow.

THE PROCESS OF HEARING. Before sound is heard, it exists in the form of acoustic forces called sound waves. These are longitudinal vibrations that speed through the air at a rate of 760 miles an hour from an oscillating source of energy and move with accordianlike ripplings of alternating compression and rarefaction. The human ear is generally sensitive to waves that come in a series of from about 20 to 20,000 alternations of pressure (cycles) per second (cps). For hearing to take place, the mechanical energy of these waves must first be analyzed into its acoustic equivalents (pitch, volume, timbre, etc.), and then transposed into corresponding patterns of nerve impulses for transmission to the auditory cortex in the temporal lobe of the brain where the sensation of meaningful hearing takes place.

The initial phase of the total process is carried out by the combined operation of what are termed the three ear parts: the outer, the middle, and the inner ear. Some of the critical structures involved in the operation are so small that microscopic enlargement is required before they can be described in detail. However, detailed description not being the present aim, the following sketch of the process of hearing and the accompanying diagram (Figure 1) are presented for general orientation.

When sound waves reach the ear, they are gathered up by the outer ear and conducted inward to the tympanic membrane or drumhead (commonly called ear drum) which represents the external boundary of the middle ear. The sound waves strike the tympanic membrane and cause it to vibrate in a corresponding pattern. The pattern is picked up and amplified in the middle ear by a jointed chain of three tiny bones or ossicles—the malleus, incus, and stapes—which spans the middle ear from the tympanic membrane, attached to the malleus on the one side, to the membrane covering the aperture to the inner ear (the oval window), attached to the footplate of the stapes on the other. Vibrations passing from the tympanic membrane along the ossicle chain are transmitted to the fluids of the inner ear (or labyrinth) by a pistonlike rocking of the stapes against the oval window membrane. The pattern of fluid vibrations thus set up in the inner ear arouses selective excitation of certain sensory cells (hair cells) in the essential organ of hearing. This is the organ of Corti which is found in the cochlea of the inner ear. Excitation of the hair cells of the organ of Corti serves: (1) to analyze the mechanical energies of the fluid vibrations in terms of their acoustic attributes; and (2) to transform the pattern of mechanical energy into a corresponding pattern of nerve impulses. The latter is accomplished by stimulation of fibres of the auditory nerve with which the hair cells are in contact; but the exact way in which this stimulation is effected is not yet known, although there are numbers of interesting theories on the subject (Kietz, 1958). Minute bundles of these auditory nerve fibres group together to form the auditory nerve which passes through the internal auditory canal to the cochlear nuclei in the brain stem and then proceeds upwards as a decussating auditory lemniscus or pathway (bilaterally) to the auditory cortex in the temporal lobes of the brain where the sensation of hearing takes place. The whole of this complex operation is practically instantaneous.

The preceding manner of conduction of sound waves to the organ of Corti is called air conduction, with the conductive apparatus being the outer ear, the middle-ear ossicle chain as well as the tubelike opening of the middle ear into the nasopharynx (called the Eustachian tube), and the fluids of the inner ear. But sometimes the air passage for sound vibrations is blocked because of damage, obstruction, or disease. When this is the case, sound waves can still stimulate the fluids of the inner ear through vibrations in the bones of the skull. This route is known as bone conduction. Although it is not as efficient as the air route, it serves a highly important function when the air passage cannot be used.

PATHOLOGICAL CONDITIONS. The delicate auditory apparatus is vulnerable to damage from many sources throughout the whole of its chronological span from the prenatal period through senescence. The wonder is not that there are so many people with impaired hearing but that there are so many who escape. In escaping, these persons are spared the numerous psychological problems associated with the different types of auditory defect. As orientation for subsequent discussion of some of these problems, the main characteristics of important pathological conditions of the ear and of hearing are summarized in this section.

In the outline that follows, hearing impairments have been categorized under the two main headings: "deficits" and "disorders," according to whether the major involvement under consideration is simply decreased hearing sensitivity or whether it represents another type of dysfunction altogether that may or may not be accompanied by decreased hearing ability. As recommended by Davis and Fowler (Davis and Silverman, 1960), the term "dysacusis" is here used to refer to these latter conditions. Although they have been grouped separately from the

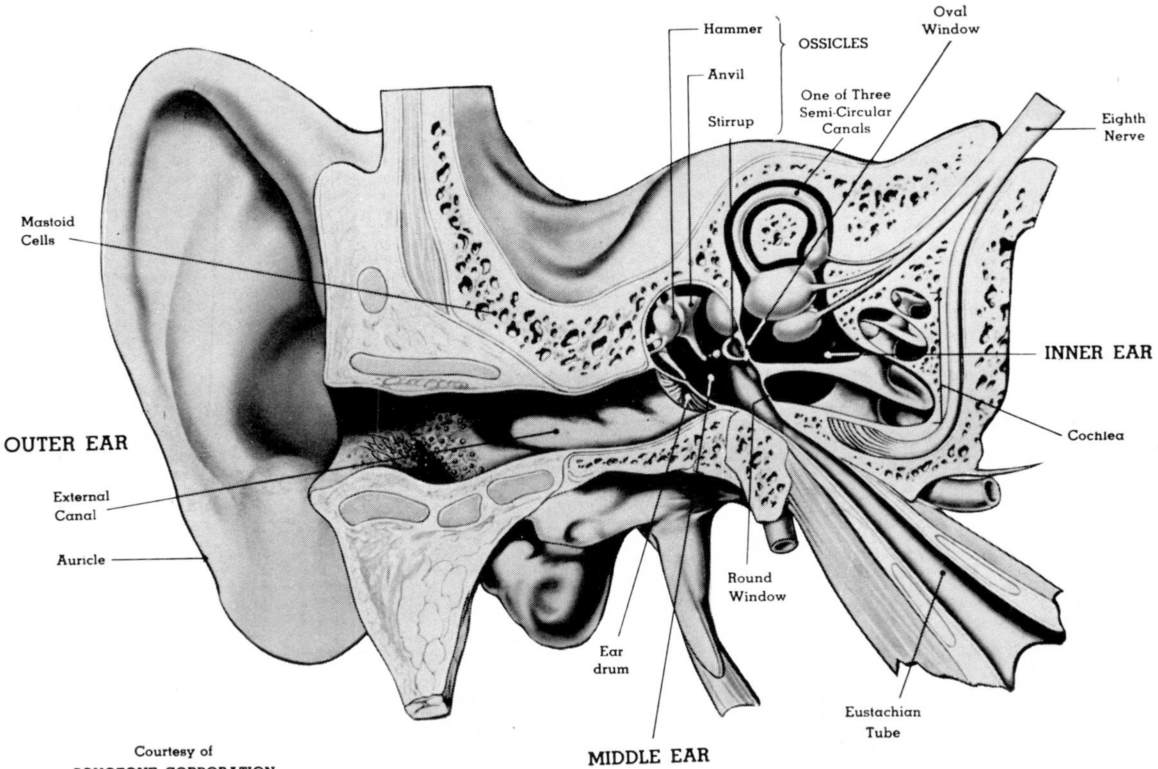

Courtesy of
SONOTONE CORPORATION
Manufacturers and Distributors of Hearing Aids
Elmsford, New York

FIGURE 1. *Sectional Diagram of the Human Ear*

deficits for ease of classification, dysacusias and deficits are not mutually exclusive clinical conditions. They may exist together in the same patient as a "combined hearing impairment" (Davis and Silverman, 1960, p. 556). Also included in the following outline are some of the alternate terms the reader is likely to find in the literature for the impairments here mentioned.

Types and Causes of Hearing Impairment[1]

I. *Auditory Deficits* (decreased hearing ability; loss of sensitivity of hearing)

A. Peripheral Impairments (those outside the central nervous system)

1. Conductive Impairment (also referred to as Conductive, Obstruction, or Impedance Deafness): results from interference with the passage of sound vibrations to the inner ear. Found mainly among the hard of hearing.

a. Common Causes

(1) Outer ear: malformation; impacted wax or other foreign body; inflammation (otitis externa); injury to tympanic membrane

(2) Middle ear: inflammation (otitis media); serous otitis; fixation of the stapes as a result of otosclerosis (bone invasion of the bony capsule surrounding the inner ear usually involving the oval window)

(3) Eustachian tube: blockage by lymphoid tissue overgrowth; infection due to head colds

b. General Prognosis: "Conductive hearing loss, especially in its early stages, can often be arrested, improved, or circumvented" (Davis and Silverman, 1960, p. 91). Hearing aids can be used to great advantage with this type of impairment.

2. Sensory-neural Impairment (also referred to as Nerve or Perception Deafness): results from injuries to, degeneration of, or developmental anomalies of the sensory-neural structures of the inner ear or of the auditory nerve. This type of impairment is characteristic of the deaf.

a. Common Causes

(1) Prenatal: hereditary, developmental or degenerative defects of the auditory nerve or the organ of Corti;

[1] The author is grateful to Louis Kleinfeld, M.D., F.A.C.S., for his valuable assistance in reviewing this outline.

maternal infections in early pregnancy (rubella, mumps, influenza); Rh incompatability of the maternal and fetal blood

(2) Paranatal: anoxia; prematurity; birth injuries; neonatal jaundice

(3) Later acquired: infectious diseases (meningitis, measles, mumps); hyperpyrexia especially in early childhood; noise exposure and blast injuries (acoustic trauma); head injuries; ototoxic drugs (dihydrostreptomycin; quinine); neural atrophy as a result of aging (presbycusis); acoustic tumors; acute vascular occlusion of cochlear blood supply

b. General Prognosis: "Neural hearing loss, which implies degeneration of delicate but essential elements of sense organ or nerve, can rarely if ever be improved by medical treatment" (Davis and Silverman, 1960, p. 91). Hearing aids are considerably less effective here than with conductive impairment.

3. Mixed Impairment: refers to conductive and sensory-neural impairments in the same ear and can be found among both the deaf and the hard of hearing.

B. Central Impairments (those affecting the auditory pathways within the central nervous system): hearing loss resulting from some impairment in the auditory pathways. Where the impairment also involves brain tissue, as it often does, signs of dysacusis are present.

1. Common Causes: diseases of the brain affecting the auditory pathways, such as cerebral tumor or abscess, arteriosclerosis, cerebral hemorrhage, multiple sclerosis

2. General Prognosis: depends upon the amenability of the etiological condition to treatment, and upon the amount of irreversible damage done to the central auditory structures

II. *Auditory Disorders or Dysacusias* (hearing impairments other than decreased auditory sensitivity and which may or may not be accompanied by loss in hearing sensitivity)

A. Peripheral Impairment: Sense-Organ Dysacusis—results from faulty function of the auditory sense organ and usually involves the sensory mechanism of the inner ear that deals with the perception of movement, gravity, and balance (the vestibular apparatus)

1. Cause: not known

2. Symptoms: vertigo, tinnitus (head noises), diplacusis (double hearing). These symptoms are classically found in Ménière's disease.
3. Prognosis: sometimes amenable to medical treatment or may improve spontaneously

B. Central Impairment
1. Congenital or Developmental Auditory Imperception (also termed Developmental Word Deafness, and Idioglossia): refers to an inability to understand spoken language, despite normal mentality and adequate hearing ability, and is present since birth or early childhood. The condition may also coexist with lessened hearing sensitivity. In such cases, the difficulties in learning verbal language and in auditory training are out of all proportion to the amount of auditory deficit present.
   a. Presumed Cause: injury to or developmental defect of auditory cortex
   b. General Prognosis: "There is a tendency to improvement and most authorities state that training is helpful. The outlook would seem to depend upon the severity of the defect and the child's intelligence" (Ford, 1948, p. 259).
2. Auditory Aphasia (also termed Word Deafness, Verbal Dysacusis, Auditory Agnosia): a type of receptive (sensory) aphasia that represents a basic disruption of an individual's already developed patterns of speech and language and is manifested by imperceptions in the meaning of sounds and/or spoken language even though clearly heard (Longerich and Bordeaux, 1959)
   a. Cause: lesions in the cortex and association paths of the brain pertaining to comprehension, concept formation, and symbolization through audition
   b. General Prognosis: depends upon the kind and extent of the lesion, the amenability of the etiological factor to medical treatment, the age and vitality of the patient, and the functioning capacities retained in other sensory areas that can be used for reeducation
3. Senile Verbal Dysacusis or Phonemic Regression (Davis and Silverman, 1960, pp. 117–18): disability in understanding spoken language out of proportion to the amount of hearing loss that may be present, and due to the degeneration of brain cells as a result of aging

C. Psychogenic Dysacusis (also termed Functional, Nonorganic,

Hysteric, Psychogenic Deafness) includes the feigned deafness of malingering; the "apathy" deafness that may be found in certain psychotic conditions and depressive states; etc.: refers to disorders in the perception of and/or in response to sound and spoken language due wholly or in great part to the action of psychic mechanisms

1. Common Causes: personality inadequacies generally associated with neuroses, psychoses, or secondary gains
2. General Prognosis: depends upon the nature of the psychic disturbance and the patient's responsiveness to psychotherapy

THE MEASUREMENT OF AUDITORY ACUITY. Besides familiarity with the various types of hearing impairment, an important clinical guide through the maze of associated psychological problems is knowledge of the nature and amount of hearing loss sustained by a patient. Certain basic facts involved in such appraisal as well as the interpretative application of the results are briefly summarized in this section.

Procedures and Rationale. The two aims in measuring hearing ability are: (1) to find out how well an individual's hearing serves for communicative purposes, especially in regard to language and speech development, speech retention, and psychosocial-vocational adjustments; and (2) to see what can be done for the individual in the line of optimum aural rehabilitation. To accomplish these requires, among other things, the examination of a number of different aspects of hearing, such as: the ability to discriminate pitch and loudness; the ability to hear and to understand speech; sensitivity to increase in loudness; the ability to tolerate loudness; the possibility of functional or central impairment; etc. A considerable number of instruments and techniques are available for such examination, but the present discussion shall have to be limited to a brief consideration of the classic precision testing instrument: the electric pure-tone audiometer.

This instrument is designed to measure auditory acuity in

terms of response to pure tones, i.e., sounds derived from simple sinusoidal vibrations uncompounded with other sounds, and is calibrated to measure the amount of amplification required for a listener to hear the test tones. The total range of pure tones produced by most audiometers is from 125 cps to 10,000 cps in octave or half-octave steps, with the critical range for speech sounds extending from about 250 cps to 4000 cps.

The unit for measuring the amount of increase in sound energy required to make a test tone audible to a subject is called the decibel (db). The decibel may be roughly defined as the smallest perceptible change in loudness that can be detected by the human ear. Actually, the decibel is an expression of the logarithmic ratio of loudness differential, so that a 20 decibel increase means an increase in sound energy of 100 *times*. In referring to the amount of increase necessary to make a sound just perceptible (the threshold response), the number of decibels required is commonly termed the hearing-impaired patient's "decibel loss." The substitute term "hearing level" has recently been introduced by Fowler (Davis and Silverman, 1960). Hearing level can be audiometrically measured for both air and bone conduction.

Pure-tone audiometric readings are recorded on graph-charts called audiograms, with the numbers on the base line representing the pitches of the various test tones, and the numbers on the vertical axis representing the number of decibels required to make a test tone just barely audible to the patient. Different symbols are used in recording left (>) and right (<) bone conduction results and left (x) and right (o) air conduction readings. The resultant audiogram represents a graphic profile of an individual's auditory acuity for pure tones. (See Figure 2.)

For those able to interpret audiograms, the profiles provide valuable and often essential information. Some types of hearing impairment have characteristic audiogram-profiles and are used as diagnostic aids by otologists. A competent reader can tell from an audiogram what a patient's speech and hearing problems are apt to be and what kind of aural rehabilitation services he may require. Audiograms are valuable aids in school placement, vocational training, and occupational planning. Often critical information is provided by hearing tests and audiograms in prob-

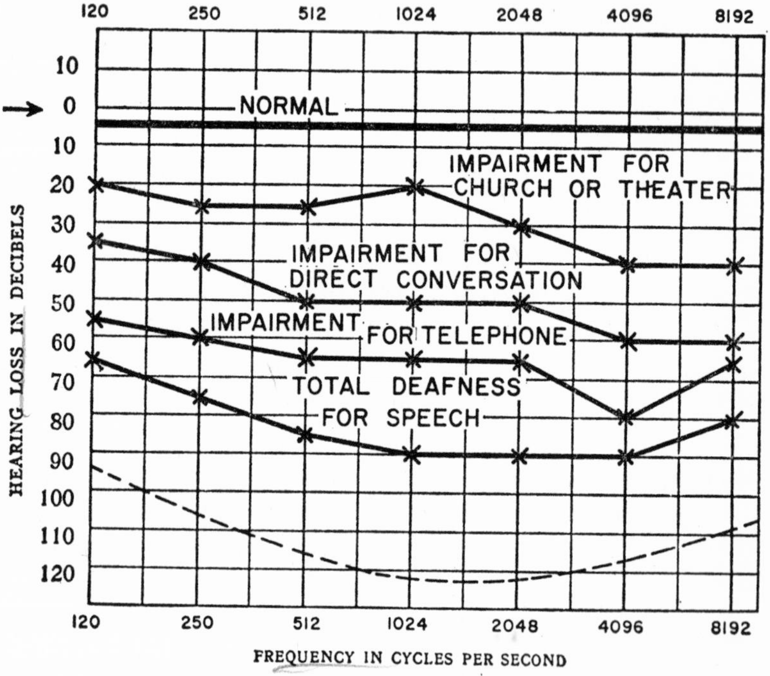

FIGURE 2. *Example of an Audiogram*

Reproduced by courtesy of the American Hearing Society from *Orientation Training for Vocational Rehabilitation Counselors,* American Hearing Society, 1956.

lems of differential diagnosis (Fournier, 1958). Of particular benefit to the child psychologist is the fact that increasingly reliable results are being obtained in the audiological examination of very young children (Meyerson, 1956; Haug and Guilford, 1960).

The specialist in whose province the testing of hearing falls is the audiologist. The relatively new discipline of audiology has made remarkable strides in the past decade. In the opinion of the writer, psychologists can derive valuable insights about a patient by observing him in audiological examinations.

Practical Significance of Hearing Level. What hearing level means in terms of everyday hearing experiences is graphically illustrated in the accompanying audiogram (Figure 2).

PSYCHOLOGICAL IMPLICATIONS. The psychological implications of auditory disability reach into every life area in which normal or near-normal hearing are essential for learning, for development and maturation, for interpersonal relations, social participation, occupational satisfaction, recreational pursuits, and for personal assurance and fulfillment. The universe of implications is extremely broad. But, as previously noted, within this universe is found considerable variation in type and degree of hearing impairment, and this in turn creates corresponding variation in the psychological reactions, the problems, and the needs of persons with auditory disability.

To do justice to all the psychological aspects of the disability within the space of one chapter is not possible. The plan therefore is to center the major attention upon the auditory deficit types of hearing impairment as exemplified by three different kinds of onset-and-amount-of-loss situations—sudden, severe nerve deafness in adulthood, progressive hearing loss, and profound congenital deafness; and to consider the respective implications in terms of the following factors: (*a*) effects upon the human organism of the acoustic environments created by the deficits; (*b*) individual reactions; (*c*) attitudes of society and the occupational world; and (*d*) compensatory communicative measures.

EFFECTS OF ACOUSTIC ENVIRONMENTS CREATED BY IMPAIRED HEARING. We stand today in general agreement concerning the critical importance of the environment in psychological development and adjustment. As summed up by Fenichel: "There is no 'psychology of man' . . . in a vacuum, as it were, but only a psychology of man in a certain society and in a certain social place within this concrete society" (Fenichel, 1945, p. 6). That this is so is readily conceded. However, the clinician usually approaches the subject of man's adaptation to the environment in terms of inner-drive motivations and tends to pay scant attention to certain more basic factors such as perception, the structure of the environment, and the "meaning" attributes of sensory experience. There is no great blame attached to shying away from the awesome body of perception theory or from the weighty hypotheses put forth to answer the classic question of perception: why things appear as they do (Allport, 1955; Heider, 1959). But neither can a clinician afford to entirely ignore the bond between perception and behavior in environmental adaptation, especially in work with the sensorially disabled.

Striking evidence of the strength of this bond has come to us by way of the investigations of Hebb (Hebb, 1955) and others (Solomon, Kubzansky, Leiderman, Mendelson, Trumbull, and Wexler, 1961). By subjecting physically normal subjects to drastic environmental deprivation, Hebb was able to demonstrate the extraordinary dependence of the human organism "on a normal sensory environment for the maintenance of its psychological integrity" (Hebb, 1955, p. 829). It is surprising that the relevance of Hebb's findings to situations in which the normal sensory environment has undergone drastic deprivation as a result of sensory disability has escaped general notice. In an entirely pragmatic and descriptive way, therefore, the abnormal environments created by auditory deficits are briefly explored at this time in order to learn something of their nature as well as of their effects upon the human organism.

Sudden Severe Deafness. When an adult experiences sudden severe deafness, it is as if all the vigorous, energizing forces of his environment were abruptly switched off, leaving nothing behind but the "silence of the tomb." Some readers may be familiar with the sensation. It happens when a normally hearing person steps into a completely sound-isolated room such as is used in audiometric testing. Suddenly he finds himself suffocated in silence. His ears feel as if they are stretching forth to grasp for the comfort of whatever small sounds may break through. He holds his breath lest he miss them. And when none come, he nervously produces vocal utterances of his own to dispel the almost physical discomfort of the sensation of soundlessness. Many people are obliged to fight down rising panic, and they generally end their visit by beating a hasty retreat with the traditional comment, "Let's get out of this mausoleum." Lucky the ones who are able to leave the cubicle when anxiety becomes intolerable.

The victim of sudden profound nerve deafness is not one of them. The soundless cubicle is the new environment created by his disability. He cannot run out and leave it behind. It is his for life.

For a person who has been created by and for a hearing world to find himself thus suddenly trapped in silence can be a shattering experience (Allan and Gordon, 1952). As a rule, terror, panic, and disorientation are the first reactions: terror at being cut off from the world; panic at being out of touch with reality; disorientation at being caught in a place with neither acoustic substance nor auditory structure. The individual feels himself trapped in nothingness.

After the initial shock has somewhat abated, the individual finds himself faced with a host of new ones. Not only have familiar, everyday objects lost their sound identities and practical usefulness, but—even more important—their ego-supportive values. For example, the alarm clock no longer arouses a deafened person to his *importance* in the world's work. The doorbell no longer informs him he is a *wanted* member of the community. The telephone no longer shrills its friendly demand for *his per-*

sonal attention. There is no familiar household bustle to welcome him and wrap him in its warm security; no outside sounds to keep him attuned to his environment. He is alone in his cocoon of silence.

Former outlets cannot ease his grief and mourning. Radio, the TV, music, the theatre—none of these old reliables can comfort him with their magic. Even his body has joined the rank of soundless things that surround him. He talks, and he cannot hear his own voice. He coughs, and there is no sound. He walks, and there is no accompanying footfall. He is a creature detached even from himself.

But even worse than this eerie sensation of a soundless body-image and self-concept is the individual's abrupt isolation from others. Where life had once been filled with the warmth of the human voice conveying all its myriad moods, information, and messages, there is nothing now save depressing gaps of empty silence. We on the outside talk pretty glibly of "accepting disability." To accept sudden severe deafness is to accept the abrupt transition from pulsating life to the isolation, unreality, and flatness of a soundless world while at the same time straining to keep up with the demands of a hearing one. In Knapp's study of war-deafened servicemen (Knapp, 1948), numbers of his profoundly deafened subjects did not consider it worth the struggle and withdrew instead into isolation. The strongest deterrent against such capitulation was the healthy predisability personality.

Progressive Hearing Loss. Difficult though the adjustment is to sudden deafness, there are those who claim that adjustment to an environment that is becoming increasingly muted is even more taxing. In the former case, environmental change is over and done with in one telling blow, and the individual is forced to take rehabilitation measures; but, in progressive hearing loss, acoustic damping takes place slowly, sometimes erratically, and often begins with changes that are so small as to escape notice altogether.

Nevertheless, the signs that something is wrong with the individual break through. They show up in terms of behavioral inconsistencies. As Berry describes the situation in regard to children, "The father thinks Tom is inattentive; the mother calls it preoccupation; the teacher suspects stupidity, his comrades think he does not care or that he is queer or self-centered" (Berry, 1933, p. 1599). As many different roles are assigned the child as there are misinterpretations of his behavior, with each inflicting its own particular form of ego-insult.

Hunt relates something of what the otologist sees when such a child grows to manhood:

> Now the man is grown. In spite of his unacknowledged handicap, he has forced from life the things he most wanted—a good job, marriage, family. He has arrived at the otologist's office—why? Because he has everything the normal man wants out of life and he is in mortal fear of losing every bit of it.
>
> The otologist who examines this patient and writes on his record card, "Progressive deafness," has only made superficial diagnosis. The record might more accurately read: "Diagnosis: fear."
>
> Fear of failure, fear of ridicule, fear of people; fear of new situations, chance encounters, sudden noises, imagined sounds; fear of being slighted, avoided, made conspicuous—these are but a handful of the fears that haunt the waking, and even the sleeping hours of the sufferer from progressive deafness. Small wonder that, at best, he tends to live in an atmosphere of despondency and suspicion. Small wonder that, at worst, he may not particularly want to live at all. [Hunt, 1944, p. 230.]

But since neither deafness nor its associated environmental deprivations "show," the man in the street wonders what there is about the disability to lead to such catastrophic reactions. If it were only possible for him to step into the environment created by progressive deafness even for a brief time, he would know. In this environment, the acoustic attributes do not diminish in an orderly or predictable way; on the contrary, they usually inflict erratic patterns of acoustic anomaly upon the sufferer not only from day to day, but sometimes from hour to hour. On certain days, all the environment is muted and distant, while on others the world suddenly comes through relatively loud and clear, thereby leading the patient into surging hopes that the condition is improving or has at least abated—only to have him find that this is just a pause before hearing resumes its steady if erratic decline. Nevertheless, as long as some serviceable hearing remains, the patient typically clings to the hope that it will improve or at least get no worse. He bolsters himself in the hope by denying there is anything seriously wrong. But deep inside he is torn by the fear that there is. He wonders if others have noticed anything and if they are discussing it among themselves. Since he cannot hear the comments, he cannot know. But he suspects. And so he begins each day in a state of tension and anxiety wondering what sounds will be missing from life today and whether he will succeed in covering up.

At the same time, problems arise in the individual's perception of his own voice and speech. Not hearing these effectively means that they cannot be monitored effectively. And so he undergoes added torments, wondering how *he* sounds to others, and if *he* will be understood. In many cases of progressive deafness, the receding acoustic environment is rendered even less intelligible by head noises (tinnitus) that can assume wracking pitch and volume, and through which the individual must learn to listen in order to get to the sounds "outside." In other types of impaired hearing, attacks of vertigo occur in which the environment suddenly begins a mad whirling about the helpless victim, disrupting both his physiological and psychological balance (i.e., Ménière's disease).

In short, the acoustic enivornments created by progressive hearing loss do not spare their victims. At best, it is like "living in a blur—like trying to get a radio talk through static" (Murphy, 1954, p. 11). At worst, it leads many patients to pray for the relief of total deafness or wish they had been born without any hearing at all rather than have to endure such perceptual confusion. However, it is a moot question whether 'tis better to have had and lost or never to have had at all. And this brings us to the last of the acoustic environments to be considered here, that of the profound congenitally deaf who represent the never to have had at all.

Profound Congenital Deafness. The singular environment created by profound congenital deafness is as barren psychologically as it is dead acoustically. It is often referred to as the "soundless world" in which the only acoustic forces that break through are experienced as noises. What does *not* break through is the sound of the voice; and herein lies the basic deprivation of a soundless world. When the voice is not heard, neither are words nor language. When words and language are not heard from birth on, they cannot be learned in the natural way. If they remain unlearned, normal contact with the world suffers stark disruption. Something of what this means is described in the following analogy:

> If I had the power to forbid you to communicate; forbid you to listen, to speak, to read or to write, I could reduce you in one stroke to intellectual slavery. I could reduce your environment and social structure to that of an animal. I could completely stop the teaching-learning process. I could lock your intellect. [Welling, 1954, pp. 1–2.]

With the wealth of special educational facilities for the deaf in this country today, we seldom see the human results of such deprivation in their pristine state. However, the field literature contains ample descriptions of the status of the deaf in the times preceding special education (Best, 1943). During those long dark ages of their history, uneducated deaf-mutes were considered witless, uneducable, fools or idiots, doomed souls, and the like. Observers of the day found them self-willed, melancholy, suspicious, treacherous, and cruel.

Even when it was discovered that the deaf were educable, they were still considered a class apart. Teachers in the first permanent schools for the deaf in this country in the nineteenth century entered upon their work with the zeal of missionaries bringing light to minds "wrapt in the impenetrable gloom of silence, sorrow, and despair" (Best, 1943, p. 407).

Thanks to advances in special education, these minds are no longer wrapt in gloom nor the hearts in despair. In fact, the deaf today are described as an exceptionally cheerful group (Best, 1943). Never having experienced the sensation of hearing, the congenitally deaf do not mourn the loss in the way other hearing-impaired groups do. Nevertheless, the results of a soundless developmental environment show up in other ways. They show up mainly in developmental lags and gaps; for even special education is limited in its ability to open the door to the verbal world quickly enough to keep pace with a deaf pupil's informational needs and experiential requirements.

The work of "artificially" verbalizing minds born into silence is slow, painstaking, memory-taxing. Since hearing cannot be used as the major sensory avenue of learning, vision and touch are substituted. This is a very long way around. Then the pupil must be specifically taught, and he must remember the correct meaning or meanings and the correct usage or usages of every one of the things called words with which, if born deaf, he has never had any previous contact. And the task does not end with vocabulary building. The pupil must also be taught how to use his growing store of verbal language for mental development, emotional maturation, social participation, vocational adjustment. But since it is virtually impossible to get the necessary language skills to an average congenitally deaf pupil in pace with his maturational needs, a lag arises between what the pupil knows and has experienced, and what he should know and should be experiencing for his age. It is this lag that constitutes the major psychological handicap of a life-long voiceless environment.

The hearing world is prone to look down upon the deaf as somewhat odd, peculiar, or backward. Underdeveloped they often are; but far from being peculiar, the congenitally deaf individual represents as unique a phenomenon as is known in the annals of human development. He represents the forced cultivation of a human being in the absence of all auditory contact with the civilized world.

Summary. A sampling of the effects upon the human organism of three different types of acoustically deprived environments has been briefly noted. When an individual's auditory relationship to his environment is abruptly destroyed, the impact is one of psychology's most traumatic events. When the muting process takes place in increasing increments, it can lead to chronic emotional instability. And when a child is born into a soundless environment, he encounters one of the greatest developmental obstacles known to man. The major problems a psychologist is apt to encounter in the two former groups are associated with emotional disturbance; in the latter group, with communicative interchange, with developmental lags and retardations, and with disturbances induced largely by these developmental handicaps.

INDIVIDUAL REACTIONS. Turning now to individual reactions, we find that the responses of a particular person will vary not only with the type and amount of acoustico-environmental deprivation, but also with other acoustic determinants as well as with the host of factors commonly responsible for individual differences. Those of particular importance in work with the hearing impaired are listed in the section Special Considerations in Psychological Appraisal.

In real life, of course, these factors and determinants operate as global influences and give rise to global reactions on the part of the individual. The reactions may remain more or less fixed as permanent patterns and attitudes, or they may vary from period to period either as the individual progresses toward ultimate adjustment or regresses in the opposite direction. Drawing on her personal experiences with hearing loss, Warfield (Warfield, 1957) describes a typical course of reaction to progressive impairment as beginning with anger, living through fear and insecurity, and finally seeking the help needed for rehabilitation.

A common obstacle in reaching the many who need such help is their tendency to deny there is anything wrong. Fowler has noted that this tendency is particularly pronounced in cases of otosclerotic hearing loss, with many patients inclined "to ignore or deny the first indications of deafness, [to display] aversion to consulting an otologist, and even to resent suggestions that the hearing is not 'perfectly all right,' [to voice] persistent objections to using a hearing aid or studying lipreading, until long after these are clearly indicated" (Fowler, 1951, p. 255). So common and prolonged is this tendency despite the wide psychological differences among the persons who do the denying as to suggest that it represents a succession of grief and anger reactions for each progressive increment of loss that occurs.

Another reaction that is commonly mentioned in connection with hearing-impaired persons is "suspicion" or "a paranoid trend." However, cautious diagnostic interpretation should be exercised before an assumption of psychopathology is made. On the basis of broad psychiatric experiences, both Knapp (Knapp, 1948) and Zeckel (Zeckel, 1950) agree that suspicion is frequently present but, as Knapp states, "often with cause, for people do avoid them, exploit them, and talk about them" (Knapp, 1948, p. 220). These authorities do not therefore consider it the suspicion of psychopathology. In this connection, Altshuler and Rainer (Altshuler and Rainer, 1958) report no preponderance of paranoid symptoms among the subjects of a psychiatric study of schizophrenia in the deaf.

As to neuroses among the hearing impaired, here are to be found the whole armamentorium that exist in man's defense against anxiety. None are unique to persons with hearing loss, nor does impaired hearing create neuroses. It only precipitates what was already there (Zeckel, 1950). It is pertinent at this time to emphasize that many hearing-impaired persons attain ultimate adjustment. The compensations they employ are summarized in the section on Rehabilitation.

Misconceptions concerning hard of hearing children have been noted previously. Here too, common reactions on the part of the children are resentment against being different and denial. These are manifested in a variety of ways depending upon which best "suits" the child's psycho-constitutional make-up, his previous experiences, and the situations in which he finds himself. The child may become overly aggressive and demanding; he may withdraw into phantasy, take to clownish, attention-getting behavior, develop patterns of deceit, become overly compliant and "good" or stubbornly negativistic and "bad." But whatever the manifestation, underneath is the familiar triad of reactions commonly encountered among the hard of hearing: fear, shame, and anger.

child behav

With the congenitally deaf child we face a different situation. Here there are no predisability personality characteristics so to say since the condition is present since birth. Individual reactions are therefore determined to an exceptional extent by the behavior of the two major figures in the small deaf child's sparsely populated world: parent and educator. Where their influences have been optimal (and all else is equal), the deaf child can emerge from his silent world a psychologically healthy youth. But where the course of child development is hampered by overanxious, overprotective, rejective, or domineering parents, and inadequate educational experiences, the results are manifested in such permanent reactions as: passive indifference; excessive dependency; inability to assume and carry out responsibilities; hostile attitudes toward the hearing world; emotional immaturity; excessive scholastic retardation, experiential limitations, and factual ignorance. In short, parents and educators acquire unusual influence in the development of children who cannot hear what the rest of the world has to say. It is their influence rather than the condition of deafness that is the major determinant of individual reaction and adjustment.

ATTITUDES OF SOCIETY AND THE OCCUPATIONAL WORLD. To the world at large, impaired hearing is an irritating block to quick, easy communication. If there is to be contact with the person behind the block, a barrier needs to be negotiated. But this takes patience and understanding—a patience to which modern living is not geared, an understanding which society has not yet attained.

Although considerable progress in understanding has been made since the dark ages in the history of the deaf, remnants of early misconceptions still persist. There are, for example, many parents of deaf children who find it hard to believe that such children are "normal," who consider the disability a mysterious affliction, an hereditary taint, a "punishment from above," who count on miracles. There are numbers of hard of hearing persons who consider their lot a sign of Divine displeasure, a punishment for some thoughts or actions of the past, a trial sent to test them.

Such attitudes on the part of persons directly involved in the problem reinforce similar misconceptions held by the public at large. In addition, society commonly reacts with aversion to physical deviation, especially to such a mysterious one as impaired hearing which does not "show." And at the other extreme is society's naive faith in the magic of lipreading and the hearing aid to effect complete restoration, and the suspicion that ensues when the magic fails to produce the expected results in a given case. That there must be something worse wrong with the person is the public verdict. But possibly the cruelest attitude of all is the "comic figure" stereotype so frequently attached to hearing-impaired persons.

The special section of the general public known as the occupational world carries the same body of misconceptions and attitudes into an area of critical importance in rehabilitation—the area of employment. When these attitudes are reinforced by hearing-impaired job applicants who are still in the throes of personal disturbance or who have been misdirected vocationally, they become fixed misconceptions in an employer's mind. As a result, job opportunities suffer considerably greater limitation than is warranted by the nature of the disability. As summarized by Ronnei:

> It is not nearly so difficult to locate suitable employment possibilities as it is to place a hard of hearing person on the job. Unless the prospective employer is prepared by a counselor to accept the client's handicap, a hard of hearing job hunter may lose his chance to prove his worth before the interview begins. He may knock on the door and fail to hear "Come in." [Ronnei, 1955, 284.]

The same applies to the deaf as well except that there are even fewer doors that will open to them (Lunde and Bigman, 1959). The need in occupational placement of hearing-impaired workers is for comprehensive programs of vocational preparation, knowledgeable vocational counseling, and consistent employer education and assistance.

COMPENSATORY COMMUNICATIVE MEASURES. It is obvious by now that the basic problem of deafness is one of communication and that many of the difficulties of hearing-impaired persons are offshoots from this basic problem. Where communicative efficiency cannot be restored to any significant extent, these offshoot problems remain and multiply. Therefore, the task of repairing the lines of communication damaged by loss of hearing is of high priority in the rehabilitation of the hearing impaired.

Where hearing loss is irreversible, the following compensatory measures are used to initiate, restore, and maintain communicative efficiency:

Language development: the initiation and/or development of vocabulary and connected verbal language through highly specialized techniques with individuals born deaf or severely deafened in early childhood (Groht, 1958).

Speechreading (lipreading): the skill of understanding spoken language by watching the movements of a speaker's mouth (lips, teeth, tongue), face, and facial expression (Deland and Montague, 1931). Speechreading helps many hard of hearing people understand what they hear with a hearing aid. Instruction in this skill is recommended for irreversible losses of 20 to 30 db or more in the speech range of the better ear. What the factors are that make for facility in speechreading is still a matter for research (Lowell and Taaffe, 1957), but it is generally agreed that intelligence does not play a major role in its acquisition.

Hearing aid: a device that amplifies the sounds an ear is still capable of responding to but cannot hear loudly enough (Ballantyne, 1960). Hearing aids are recommended for losses of 25 to 30 db or more in the speech range of the better ear.

Speech therapy: the training or retraining of a person with defective speech (Travis, 1957). Depending on the therapist's competencies, speech therapy may include: (1) speech retention, preservation, or insurance, which is speech therapy for adults with basically well-developed speech patterns but who experience (or will eventually experience) difficulties in monitoring voice and speech as a result of impaired hearing; and (2) speech development, which is the initiation and development of speech in congenitally deaf children and children with early severe deafness (New, 1949).

Auditory training: a means of educating or reeducating whatever hearing ability is left (residual hearing) in order to develop the greatest possible acuity in the perception and interpretation of acoustic stimuli (Whitehurst, 1947).

In addition to the foregoing are the manual methods of communication that are commonly used by deaf persons:

Finger spelling: verbal communication based on forming the letters of the alphabet by designated positions of the fingers through which means words and sentences are spelled out in straight language (Long, 1949). Habitual finger spellers generally possess proficient verbal language, which they use in written communication with those who cannot "read" finger spelling.

The Sign Language: a nonverbal method of communication in which words and ideas are graphically expressed by various established gestures, and conventional positions and movements of the hands, arms, and body (Long, 1949). Deaf persons whose *main* means of communication is the sign language generally lack verbal proficiency and their written communications are sometimes barely comprehensible to the uninitiated. With deaf patients who communicate mainly through the sign language, interpreters are used when the worker is unable to communicate in this medium.

SPECIAL CONSIDERATIONS IN PSYCHOLOGICAL APPRAISAL. In clinical practice with hearing-impaired patients, a psychologist must be "set" for an unusual heterogeneity of problems, situations, and individuals. This has been stressed previously. To offer generalizations on such a disparate population would be dangerous; but to enter into specifics in one chapter would not be possible. In this section therefore the aim is to offer practical guides and references to special factors in the diagnostic appraisal. (More detailed discussion is found in Levine, 1960.)

THE DIAGNOSTIC TEAM. Naturally not all hearing-impaired patients referred to psychologists require full diagnostic evaluation; but, where such appraisal is required, the discussion thus far is enough to alert the psychologist to the fact that the undertaking is neither a one-man job nor a one-specialty operation. The psychologist functions as a member of a diagnostic team that includes a number of other specialists as well as the patient and his family. Each represents a source of special information needed to fill in and interpret the psychological picture, as for example:

Family physician: health and medical history; presence of other disabilities.

Otologist: diagnostic, treatment, and prognostic information concerning the hearing defect; protective cautions; patient's acceptance of the medical facts.

Audiologist: audiometric analysis of hearing; desirability and effectiveness of hearing aid; patient's attitudes.

Social worker: personality, social, and cultural factors that impair individual's functioning and influence family attitudes; availability of community resources.

Special educator: educational history; analysis of scholastic and communicative strengths, weaknesses, disabilities, potentials; school adjustment; parent-school relations; parent-child relations.

Special therapists: evaluation of individual's potentials, performance, and attitudes in regard to speech therapy, speechreading, auditory training, hearing aid.

Vocational counselor: vocational training and occupational history; analysis of individual's potentials, adjustments, attitudes, and problems in finding, holding, and/or progressing in an occupation.

Patient: attitude toward disability, family, the hearing world; self-concept; motivations; plans and aspirations, pre- and post-disability; insight and judgments; personal evaluation of problems; potentials and attainments.

Patient's family: family history; other hearing-impaired members; family aspiration level; family attitudes toward patient and his problems; patient-family relations.

In ideal situations, the psychosocial disciplines are regularly represented on the diagnostic team which functions as an integrated unit. Where this is not the case, the psychologist is obliged to assemble the required data from wherever the primary sources happen to be, and from the data and his own contributions produce an up-to-date account of the patient's problems, the diagnostic impression, and appropriate treatment recommendations.

THE PSYCHOLOGICAL EXAMINATION. The cornerstones of comprehensive appraisal of hearing-impaired patients are the same as with the hearing (Thorne, 1955), namely: the case history, interview, observation, and psychological testing. The kinds of problems that commonly call for such appraisal among the hearing impaired are:

1. At the preschool and school-age levels
   a. Differential diagnosis of communicative disorder to establish whether a sign of auditory deficit, mental defect, psychogenic dysacusis, developmental dysacusis, or any combination of these.
   b. Differential diagnosis of behavior, adjustment, and attitude disorders.
   c. Evaluation of appropriate special educational techniques and placement.
   d. Scholastic retardation out of proportion to abilities, intelligence, and age of beginning school.
   e. Rejection of school, communicative aids, special teaching, etc.

f. Special disabilities in acquiring communicative skills.
g. Parent-child tensions.

2. At the youth and adult levels
   a. Psychological handicaps out of proportion to amount of hearing loss.
   b. Rejection of communicative aids and rehabilitative measures.
   c. Persistent difficulties in psycho-social-vocational adjustment.
   d. Excessive and prolonged grief and mourning reactions.
   e. Neurotic conflicts and psychotic disorders.
   f. Differential diagnosis of auditory disability to establish whether a deficit, a disorder, or a combination of these.

These problems are of course only samplings, and the lists could be expanded considerably. Since the basic techniques involved in their diagnosis are part of a psychologist's competencies, they need not be repeated here. Attention will center on the special factors.

Case History. A major function of the case history with hearing-impaired patients is to help the psychologist establish (*a*) the circumstances surrounding the onset of the given problem particularly in relation to auditory disability; (*b*) whether the resultant psychological handicap was and is in reasonable relation to the amount and type of disability; (*c*) the manner of "spread" of psychological handicap into the major life areas; (*d*) the factors in the affected areas and in the individual that serve to advance or retard this spread; and (*e*) appropriate treatment.

Special lines of inquiry that are of particular importance in disclosing the relevant facts include: (*a*) type, amount, cause, and age of onset of impaired hearing; (*b*) psychological impact of the onset on patient and family; (*c*) presence of other hearing-impaired persons in the family; (*d*) patient's major modes of communication and the problems arising from communicative limitations; (*e*) changes brought about by the disability in the patient's social, educational, occupational, recreational, and domestic situations; (*f*) patient's behavior, attitudes, achievements, and aspirations pre- and post-disability; (*g*) history of diagnostic experiences and rehabilitative measures, including special education; (*h*) attitudes, motivations, and problem-solutions offered by family friends, community; (*i*) presence of other disabilities, especially visual defects, and organic brain damage; (*j*) health and medical problems.

The context in which these special lines of inquiry are followed is the full case history. (A case history form designed for use with the hearing impaired can be found in Levine, 1960, pp. 128–37.) The team sources from which pertinent information is obtained have already been noted, and the underlying rationale has been described in the section Psychological Implications or are easily inferred from the context.

Interview. Ordinarily, interview presents an exceptional opportunity for seeing life through the eyes of the patient himself, and for making direct contact with his feelings, attitudes, self-concept, preoccupations, judgments and insight, values and aspirations. But with the hearing impaired, interview can become a highly frustrating experience unless the psychologist is prepared to handle the various problems of communication he is apt to encounter. A number of suggestions and cautions for the interviewer are briefly summarized:

1. Interviewing speechreaders
    a. Make certain mouth and face are clearly visible at all times
    b. Speak clearly and naturally (no mouthing, shouting, slowdown)
    c. Use nontechnical language and uninvolved sentences
    d. Watch for signs of lipreading fatigue (drop in lipreading ability, restlessness, fidgeting with hearing aid, irritability, exhausted appearance)

e. Have pad and pencil handy to write key words or expressions

2. Interviewing non-speechreaders

a. Poor or non-speechreaders with good speech and verbal language proficiency: The pad and pencil will have to be used for questions and comments, and the patient, of course, communicates in speech; or, if deaf, through manual communication if the interviewee prefers and the interviewer is able.

b. Non-speechreaders with incomprehensible or no speech and with verbal language deficiency: Such patients are generally found among the deaf who communicate almost entirely in the sign language. Unless the interviewer is familiar with the sign language, an interpreter will be needed. (Psychologists specializing in work with the deaf will themselves have to master manual communication.) For obvious reasons the interpreter should not be a member of the patient's family. State associations of the deaf, religious organizations for the deaf, and schools for the deaf can be of assistance in locating interpreters.

In all instances, the interviewer must guard his own actions and behavior, for, as Wright cautions:

> Remember that the deaf and the hard of hearing are very observant. (They have to be!) The way you stand or sit, the way you shrug your shoulders (perhaps in impatience) the way you walk from your desk to the door tell a great deal to a keen observer. Your manner, your poise, your smile, the expression in your eyes and on your face, the way you use your hands, all tell a story of indifference, or understanding. [Wright, 1956, p. 19.]

Finally, to make sure a hearing-impaired patient has got the important points of the interview, it is best to have him review them before leaving.

Observation. To a psychologist experienced in work with the hearing impaired, a perceptive eye and ear can render significant diagnostic assistance. In addition to the clues ordinarily observed in appearance, manner, and behavior, the following are examples of special kinds of information that can be detected through observation:

1. *Type of auditory deficit:* Among the hard of hearing who have not availed themselves of speech and voice therapy, those with substantial conductive loss tend to speak in lowered voices, sometimes so faint as to be scarcely audible, because they hear themselves with disproportionate loudness (through bone conduction) and hence are under the impression they are talking too loudly. On the other hand, persons with sensory-neural impairment have trouble hearing their own voices and, being under the impression they are not talking loudly enough, tend to speak in raised and often raucous tones. The speech of deaf persons (deaf speech) is characteristically mechanical, hollow-sounding, and monotonal and often requires getting used to before it is readily understood.

2. *Acceptance of disability:* If there is evidence that a patient could have profited from aural rehabilitation, and his voice, speech, and indifference to using a hearing aid indicate that he has not, the psychologist should be alerted to the possibility of nonacceptance of disability.

3. *Auditory malingering:* If a patient's voice and speech are in strong contraindication to his claimed history of auditory deficit and hearing aid benefits, the psychologist should be alerted to the possibility of malingering. Where malingering is suspected, the psychologist notes the patient's reactions to certain classic test tricks used in such detection, as for example: giving helpful but low-voiced suggestions to a patient while he is concentrating on a difficult test task; calling the patient's attention (again in a low voice) to the omission of an important detail while he is filling out a record form; injecting low-voiced observations and warnings while the patient is busily occupied such as: "Your pen is leaking"; "Your watch crystal is broken"; "Is

that a paint stain on your pants?"; "Is that your mother coming down the hall?"; etc. Naturally, the ultimate diagnosis requires team evaluation, but the tricks are used to confirm an impression calling for such evaluation.

4. *Significant signs in differential diagnosis:* With children in particular, observation is the technique above all for detecting signs as well as types of clinical conditions in a context of communicative disability. However, effective observation requires unusual competencies. It requires familiarity with: normal child behavior; the behavioral signs of impaired hearing in childhood (Gesell and Amatruda, 1947); the signs of childhood psychopathology (Strauss and Lehtinen, 1947; Harms, 1953; Strauss and Kephart, 1955; Hoch and Zubin, 1955; Bender, 1956); and clues to childhood psychogenic and developmental dysacusis (Kastein and Fowler, 1954, 1960; Myklebust, 1954; Wood, 1959). Observation of children needs to be conducted in as wide a variety of situations as possible and should always include observation of parent-child relations. (The latter obtains not only for young children but also for parent-ridden youth and adults.)

Finally, a considerable aid in the use of observation with the hearing impaired is the fact that the classic signs of psychopathology are the same here as with the hearing at both child and adult levels.

Psychological Testing. For lack of an adequate supply of tests designed for hearing- and communicative-handicapped groups, verbal tests standardized on the normally hearing are almost routinely used at the youth and adult levels, and often at the school-age level. Sometimes their use presents no problem of validity; but more often it does. Whether or not such problems arise depends largely on (*a*) the attribute to be tested; (*b*) the amount of deviation from normative development and experiences associated with impaired hearing in a given case; and (*c*) the amount of deviation from normative language proficiency.

As a rule, persons with mild hearing loss or with severe loss in conversational hearing ability beginning in adulthood present few if any special testing problems other than the cautions in communication previously noted under Interview. But where conversational hearing ability has been deficient or absent since childhood, the likelihood is that language deficiencies and experiential limitations are present which would invalidate the results of tests based on a normative range of language comprehension and background of experiences. This possibility must be borne in mind in the case of persons with deficient conversational hearing ability dating from childhood, even though there may have been enough hearing to "get by." The likelihood is strongest in the case of the deaf. Guides in the test selection, administration, and interpretation for these two groups are summarized as follows:

1. *Test selection and administration:* Since the level of language proficiency plays such an important role in the selection of psychological tests for patients with hearing and communicative handicaps, this level should be ascertained early in the test proceedings. Any good reading and language achievement tests can be used for the purpose, providing (*a*) the grade range covered by the test is in keeping with the patient's attainments as revealed by the case history and in interview; and (*b*) the test directions are fully understood by the patient even if this requires extra sample tasks and the simplification of the language of the test directions. But when it comes to other school subjects (with the exception of arithmetic computation), such as social studies, literature, arithmetic problems, etc., great care in selection and use must be exercised, for if the language of the test questions is beyond the patient's comprehension the examiner cannot be sure if an incorrect answer was due to lack of knowledge or lack of language comprehension. It happens not infrequently that correct answers are obtained when the test langauge is simplified.

In the case of adults, a reading comprehension achievement

score below the fourth or fifth grade automatically invalidates a great many if not all of the verbal self-administering types of group tests of intelligence, personality, interests, and aptitudes. In such instances, an examiner relies heavily upon case history and interview for diagnostic information; and where testing is possible upon the use of individually administered nonlanguage, nonverbal, or performance tests, selected projective techniques, and such verbal tests as the Wechsler tests with their simple vocabulary and common-sense appeal. The following illustrative sampling is taken from Levine's comprehensive listing of tests and batteries for the hearing impaired (Levine, 1960):

Intelligence: Army Beta Revised; Arthur Point Scale of Performance Tests; Wechsler Full Scale Intelligence Tests (for adolescents and adults)

Personality: Figure Drawings; House-Tree-Person Technique; Rorschach Test

Special Clinical: Bender Visual Motor Gestalt Test; Benton Visual Retention Test

Motor Skill, Aptitudes, Coordination: any good tests requiring actual task performance

Vocational Aptitudes and Interests: largely pictorial test tasks such as the Knieval adaptation of the Factored Aptitude Series (Knieval, 1954) or the Geist Picture Interest Inventory presently being revised for the deaf

In testing deaf adults with language comprehension levels below the fifth grade, the examiner should not be surprised to find substantial numbers with average and even above average intelligence. What went wrong in their scholastic development is for the psychologist to find out. In regard to testing, however, the examiner will find such persons remarkably alert to pantomime directions or to verbal instructions that have been sufficiently simplified to fit within their range of comprehension. Most effectively used, of course, is manual communication. If the examiner is not familiar with such communication, an interpreter can be of great assistance in test administration as well as in reporting the patient's responses to some of the projective techniques or verbal tests that may be used. The interpreter should be strongly cautioned not to give cues or pass judgments either in the course of communication or through facial expression.

The latitude of test selection broadens in proportion to increased language proficiency; but even where language skills compare favorably with hearing norms, the examiner must be alert to items in hearing-standardized tests that are inapplicable to a hearing-impaired person's life situation and experiences (Heider and Heider, 1941; Levine, 1960). Also to be borne in mind is the fact that many hearing-impaired individuals have two "sets" of reactions and behavior: one when in the company off their hearing-impaired peers and another with hearing groups. Thus, when a test question is intended to probe behavior in a particular setting, it is often necessary to find out which situation the patient had in mind when he answered the question. In short, test selection for hearing-impaired persons requires careful screening not only for language but also for situational content.

With children who are deficient in conversational hearing ability, verbal psychological tests are not recommended (except for language proficiency). Many hard of hearing children in this category demonstrate enough hearing to get by. What they do not demonstrate is how much they do *not* get. The latter is more readily seen with deaf children. In either case, even though word recognition achievement scores may compare favorably with hearing norms, this is no indication that the children are equally proficient in the comprehension of connected language, and it is in connected language that test questions are asked. Preferred tests for these children are performance and nonlanguage tests exemplified by such intelligence scales as Merrill-Palmer or Randall Island Performance Tests for the preschool level, and for the school-age range the Grace Arthur or Pintner-Paterson Performance Scales, and the following scales that were either standardized on deaf pupils or specifically designed with the deaf in mind—Ontario School Ability Examination, Hiskey-Nebraska Test of Learning Aptitude for Young Deaf Children, and the Chicago Nonverbal Examination. Other tests for preschool children and for children with cerebral defects that can also be used with the deaf are discussed by Haeussermann (Haeussermann, 1958) and Taylor (Taylor, 1959).

In the evaluation of child personality, the importance of observation has already been mentioned. In addition, the Vineland Social Maturity Scale, figure drawings, and various play technique tests such as the Make-A-Picture-Story (MAPS) test can often provide helpful information. Finally, with older pupils, the Brunschwig Adjustment Inventory (Brunschwig, 1936), devised specifically for deaf pupils, performs a useful clinical function.

Whatever tests are used, the examiner must make sure the subject fully understands what he is expected to do. The importance of meaningful test administration with the hearing impaired cannot be stressed too strongly. The manner of communicating test directions depends upon the *patient's* (not the examiner's) communicative skills and preferences and takes the forms outlined under Interview plus the use of pantomime where necessary.

2. *Test interpretation:* Judging whether the scores and norms of tests standardized on the normally hearing obtain for a hearing-impaired patient rests with the clinical wisdom of the examiner. Where scores and norms cannot be used, certain tests may nevertheless perform highly useful qualitative functions and should be used as clinical probes rather than measures. Whatever the situation may be, careful thought should be given the following guides in testing the deaf and the severely hard of hearing and in the interpretation of the test results as formulated by the First Institute for Special Workers for the Aural Disabled (Institute for Special Workers for the Aural Disabled, 1950):

(*a*). The test results based upon tasks involving verbal concepts and language should be interpreted with special care. Individuals who have lost their hearing early in life, or for a considerable time (three years or more) before the testing may have acquired language habits enough different from the nonhandicapped to depress test scores where language tasks are involved.

(*b*). The older the age of the individual when his deafness occurred, the more it can be assumed that his life experiences are common to hearing persons. Therefore, loss of hearing in later life may not be expected to affect test results involving language tasks as much as loss of hearing in childhood.

(*c*). The test results of deaf people on tests involving language or reading are more safely considered as minimal levels of abilities rather than as the upper limits of abilities.

(*d*). When deafness is an accompanying result of a more basic condition, e.g., birth injury involving the nervous system in general, the psychological results are to be considered primarily in terms of the more basic condition and secondarily in terms of the deafness and other accompanying conditions.

(*e*). The IQ as a single score is to be regarded with great caution as an index of mental ability. The subtest scores of the different mental abilities should be examined most carefully and given emphasis in the total case study.

(*f*). The total test scores and the separate items should both be studied for clues to abilities, achievements, and personality traits. A study of responses on separate items at times may give clues to a richer and more accurate interpretation of test data with other case data. For example, misses on easy items and successes with a considerable number of difficult items may give clues to such conditions as habits of carelessness or inconsistency, inattentiveness, or to neuroticism, or even to gaps in early or later education.

(*g*). The totally deaf and seriously hard of hearing should be tested individually and preferably with individualized tests such as the Wechsler-Bellevue Performance Scale.

(*h*). Special precautions should be taken to make certain that good rapport prevails between the examiner and the deaf client. The use of the manual alphabet and sign language is encouraged as a means of giving test instructions. Otherwise, a natural, somewhat restrained form of pantomime is desirable. The counselors have a special responsibility to prepare the client for the testing experience. If the psychologist does not know the manual alphabet or sign language, the client should be told beforehand by the counselor about the nature of the tests, the need for full cooperation, the need to make certain that the client fully understands the instructions before each test, and that the test results will be discussed later with the counselor. Lack of rapport definitely influences the test results. Moreover, the psychologist has more difficulty in evaluating the effects of poor rapport in the deaf because of difficulties in free and uninhibited communication.

(*i*). When the background of the deaf person shows gaps in formal education, the causes for such a fact should be ascertained and be used in interpreting test scores.

(*j*). Conditions of excessive depression, anxiety, idleness, or seclusiveness over a long period of time (about a year or more) may be expected to influence test scores. The test scores will indicate the present level of ability-functioning, but interpretations and prognoses must include an evaluation of the underlying conditions and their interaction upon the psychological test score.

(*k*). The disability of deafness may be overemphasized in the total case study. Other factors may be much more important and it is always well to be on guard lest such overemphasis obscure other major factors. For example, lack of formal school achievement may be due not to hearing loss but to physical or mental illness, or to neurotic parental concern over the deaf person, or even to poor attitudes of the deaf person himself.

(*l*). Personality traits such as the will to work, adaptability to the hearing world, persistence in solving problems, method of attacking new problems, self-confidence, etc., may be seen in actual operation before, during, and after a testing session. Qualitative observation of the behavior of the deaf client may yield information of considerable significance in the fuller and deeper interpretation of test performance.

RECORDING AND REPORTING. The psychological examination of persons with communicative handicaps can be a time-consuming operation, sometimes taking three or four times longer than the time required for the hearing. Unless the results of the examination are meaningfully reported to the specialists involved in diagnosis and treatment, it is so much time wasted. The attributes of good clinical reporting are discussed by DiMichael (DiMichael, 1948) and by Hammond and Allen (Hammond and Allen, 1953). A special point is made of avoiding the use of "psycho-jargon" semantics. However, the psychologist must be familiar with the interdisciplinary pool of terms that form the basic glossary of the field of auditory disability. Another special point is made of using a plan for reporting that will insure orderly, cohesive coverage of the important facts. (A suggested form for reporting the examination results of hearing-impaired patients may be found in Levine, 1960, pp. 283–84.)

SPECIAL CONSIDERATIONS IN REHABILITATION. Medical diagnosis and treatment (Goodhill, 1957) are the first steps taken in the treatment of persons with impaired hearing, the aim being to improve or at least arrest the condition. However, Fowler states that "medical treatment has rather little to offer to restore lost hearing" (Davis and Silverman, 1960, p. 125), while Walsh points out that surgical treatment is more or less limited to "correcting abnormalities of the conductive apparatus" (Davis and Silverman, 1960, p. 145), as in tympanoplasty (Brandow, 1960), which is the reconstruction of the tympanic membrane by skin graft; fenestration (Lempert, 1945), which aims to create a new oval window through surgery for the one closed off by otosclerotic overgrowth; and stapes mobilization (Rosen, 1954) which aims to remobilize a stapes that has become fixed through otosclerosis. While successful results in the two latter operations can be highly dramatic, the fact remains that the chances for success are at best "fifty-fifty odds for substantial improvement" (Davis and Silverman, 1960, p. 159). As for sensory-neural hearing impairment, there is no known treatment to date that will restore degenerated nerve tissue of the inner ear, the auditory nerve, or the brain. Thus despite the advances made in medical and surgical treatment, the surest approach to the problem of impaired hearing at this time is through programs of prevention, hearing conservation, and compensatory rehabilitation.

GOALS OF COMPENSATORY REHABILITATION. For the many millions with irreversible hearing loss, the primary aim of rehabilitation is to fill in the gaps left in their lives by impaired hearing. Compensatory rehabilitation begins as soon after the onset of disability as possible, and the measures taken are summarized by Menninger (Menninger, 1924, 1945) as (*a*) perceptual sharpening—of vision for speechreading, of residual hearing for the greatest possible auditory acuity and most effective use of the hearing aid, of kinesthetic controls for speech and voice monitoring, and of vision, kinesthetic controls, and tactility for speech development; (*b*) intellectual broadening to maintain mental vigor and interests; (*c*) emotional sublimation to provide healthy outlets for the strains and irritations generated by frustration, disappointments, fatigue; and (*d*) reality oriented motivation and the will to achieve "in spite of"—with the whole nicely balanced by the saving grace of a sense of humor. To this list must be added purposeful vocation, for, to quote from Hochhauser and Pattison, "Employment is nature's best physician and is essential to human happiness" (Pattison, 1957, p. 733).

At the child level, compensatory rehabilitation also begins as soon after the onset of disability (or as soon after the condition is recognized) as is feasible, and preferably under authoritative guidance if managed by parents. Infant aural rehabilitation is becoming increasingly common these days, with hearing aids fitted for babies less than a year old ((Ballantyne, 1960). However, there is sharp disagreement as to the desirability of using powerful hearing aids of the newer type with children (Kinney, 1961).

The most critical gap created by imparied hearing among children is in the area of language that is not learned because it is not heard and, hence, cannot be used to promote the normal course of mental, social, and emotional development. A major goal of rehabilitation is to get their full quota of language to these children. This involves coverage of the four basic vocabularies common to all literate beings (Laird, 1953)—the speaking, writing, reading, and recognition (heard and written) vocabularies. The educational rehabilitation provisions through which this is customarily accomplished for the various levels of hearing are summarized as follows (adapted from O'Connor and Streng, 1950):

1. *Children with slight losses.* These children are on the borderline between normal hearing and significant defective hearing. Their loss averages 20 decibels or less in the speech range of the better ear as measured by the pure-tone audiometer. This group usually needs no special considerations other than favorable seating in the classroom.

2. *Children with moderate losses.* These are the hard-of-hearing children. Their losses average from 25 to 50 decibels in the speech range of the better ear. Generally these children should be able to receive their education in classes for normally hearing children provided they are favorably seated, receive speech training if necessary, and learn speech reading. Those children whose loss is as great as or greater than 35 decibels in the better ear

should also be provided with hearing aids and should receive auditory training. Special class services may have to be provided for the more severely hard of hearing in this group if their adjustments are unsatisfactory in the regular classroom.

3. *Children with marked losses.* These children are on the borderline between the hard of hearing and the deaf. They have sustained their losses from very early childhood or babyhood and do not have enough hearing to learn language and speech with the unaided ear. Their losses range from about 55 or 60 to 65 or 75 db in the speech range in the better ear. Initially, these children receive their education in schools for the deaf or in special classes from teachers especially trained to develop language and speech. After they have achieved fluency in the use of language and speech, their educational programs may very likely be patterned after those established for hard-of-hearing children.

4. *Children with profound losses.* These are the deaf children who do not learn speech and language through their ears even with the benefit of amplified sound. Their losses range from 70 or 75 db to inability to distinguish more than one or two frequencies at the highest measureable level of intensity in the better ear. Such losses, when sustained from birth or very early childhood typify deaf children who must receive their education from teachers trained to develop the communicative process through very specialized techniques. Educational facilities are provided for these children in schools or classes for the deaf.

It is obvious from the foregoing discussion that the specialists involved in the treatment aspects of rehabilitation include the same members as on the diagnostic team.

SOME REHABILITATION PROBLEMS AND LIMITATIONS. Just as there are limitations in the medical and surgical treatment of hearing loss, so are there limitations in the compensatory aspects of rehabilitation. For example, not all hearing-impaired persons can profit from a hearing aid (i.e., the elderly and those with certain types of sensory-neural impairment), and among those who can, there are as yet frustrating limits to what the hearing aid is able to do. To continue, there are substantial numbers of hearing-impaired persons who cannot master the skill of speechreading and many who experience great difficulty in synchronizing what they see "on the lips" with what they hear through their hearing aids. As for the mastery of verbal language and oral communication in the absence of functional hearing (as in the case of the deaf), this is possibly the most complex task in the annals of human achievement, and there are more who do not approach the attainments warranted by their mental potential than who do. In addition, there are certain vocational limitations that arise over and above those imposed by increasing or severe loss of hearing, serious communicative difficulties, inadequate scholastic and/or vocational preparation, and devaluating employer attitudes. Numbers of deaf persons and many persons with tinnitus are highly sensitive to noise and vibration and cannot work in noisy environments. Others with impairment of balance cannot work in high places or near moving machinery. And there are those who cannot work where there is excessive change in temperature and pressure; chemical fumes; damp; dust; etc. Finally, one of the most serious limitations is that derived from the length of time that has elapsed between the onset of disability and the beginning of rehabilitation. The longer the time, the greater the possibility that the individual has become fixed in a pattern of inadequacy. For example, if the need is to establish effective patterns of oral communication in a deaf adult—if such patterns have not been established by the time adulthood is reached—there is little likelihood that significant gains can be made.

Hopefully, many of the foregoing limitations will in time respond to advances in knowledge, techniques, technology, and public attitudes. But such are some of the current restrictions. When psychological problems are added to the picture, compensatory benefits suffer sharp decrease.

Effective psychological treatment is therefore of particular importance in compensatory rehabilitation. However, communicative difficulties impose limitations here too. Of the thirty-six systems of psychotherapy ably summarized by Harper (Harper, 1959), each relies to a greater or lesser extent on free verbal interchange between patient and therapist. But when impaired hearing raises obstacles to verbal exchange, the therapeutic situation can become an embarrassment to both. Therapists emerge from the experience reluctant to treat any more hearing-impaired persons, and patients, unwilling to undergo any more therapy. The result is reflected in the serious current shortage of competent psychotherapeutic services for persons with auditory deficits.

In the writer's experience, therapeutic interviews with hearing-impaired persons are best begun with a frank and friendly discussion of how to resolve whatever communications problems may exist. Many cases will present no problems at all. Others will involve only the mechanics of communication (lipreading disability on the part of the patient or difficulty in understanding a patient's speech on the part of the therapist). In such instances, writing is used as required, and the therapeutic techniques are adapted to this frame. In one of the author's cases (sensory-neural auditory impairment plus dysacusic involvements) in which writing was the patient's only means of communication, therapeutic sessions were conducted entirely in this medium for a two-year period with highly successful results. As for deaf children, diagnosis involves a deep understanding of the language of child behavior, and therapy can be managed to a great extent through appropriate counseling of parents and/or teachers with the therapist in the role of chief investigator, educator, and catalyst.

The most difficult therapeutic problems arise where an adult patient is severely handicapped not only in the mechanics of communication, but in the conceptual content of everyday thinking as well. Such situations are most frequently encountered among the nonverbal deaf with their limited mental experiences and literal mental concepts. An example of such literal-mindedness in a therapeutic situation is the deaf young man who was told by a therapist (in the sign language) that he must not depend on his mother so much but must learn to be on his own. The patient carried out this innocent enough remark by running away from home the next day without plan or provision; he was found several days later, wandering vaguely about under the impresison that this was being "on his own."

Such cases of verbal and conceptual limitation require considerable experience, communicative skill, and ingeniousness on the part of a therapist. Initial planning is based on a full psychodiagnostic study of the patient with careful consideration given the patient's positive attributes and the way in which they can be used to motivate him to overcome his deficiencies. Long-range therapeutic possibilities are broken down into a succession of seemingly attainable short-term objectives. Treatment is generally begun with supportive therapy including a planned program of corrective measures (such as language tutoring, improvement in reading skills, filling in gaps in everyday information, etc.) and ego-satisfying experiences (social and recreational outlets, creative activities, vocational preparation, guidance, or placement, etc.). Plans are discussed with and explained to the patient (through an interpreter, if necessary) *in the language, concepts, and manner most suitable to the patient's comprehension.* The patient's periodic reports to the therapist serve to guide further treatment. Therapeutic techniques may change from time to time as the patient increases in understanding and capacity, and generally include reconditioning, persuasion, reassurance, environmental manipulation, and nondirective sessions. Depth analysis is contraindicated for treatment in such cases, but not for research. In most instances, individual therapy should be reinforced by family counseling and group therapy or group activities with similarly hearing-impaired persons (Hearing Loss a Community Loss, 1958). The organizations listed at the conclusion of this chapter can be of assistance in locating group-activity resources in a particular community.

Obviously, impaired hearing even in its most disturbing aspects does not alter basic psychotherapeutic principles in any fundamental way. A successful outcome is achieved if a pattern of thinking, feeling, and responding has resulted that enables a hearing-impaired individual to live with greater acceptance than resentment of his disability, to function with sufficient self-assurance and competence, and to obtain the personal, domestic, social, and vocational satisfactions he needs within the framework of reality. So far as the therapist is concerned, this disability, like others, points up the importance of therapeutic eclecticism, patient rather than technique centeredness, communicative flexibility, and, of course, therapeutic competence. In work with the hearing impaired, such competence involves a broad knowledge of the medical, communicative, psychosocial, and vocational implications of the different types of auditory defect; awareness of the limitations imposed by special disability factors and situations; knowledge of compensatory rehabilitation and communicative measures; and sufficient experience with a wide enough range of psychotherapeutic techniques to apply what is best for a given case at a given time. And finally, the therapist should possess enough interest, curiosity, and flexibility to venture into uncharted paths with a view to disclosing more effective techniques of diagnosis and treatment for hearing-handicapped persons.

PSYCHOLOGICAL RESEARCH. Psychosocial studies of the various types of auditory disability have been seriously hampered by the same factors as those responsible for the lag in clinical practice, namely: communicative problems; scarcity of valid psychological instruments; and scarcity of trained professional personnel. These factors have been most prominent in the area of the deaf. With the hard of hearing, there has until very recently been simply a general lack of psychological interest in this unspectacular group. As a result, there are as yet no wholly acceptable research data to show what constellation of attributes, capacities, and abilities constitute the norms of deaf adjustment; what, in fact, these normative patterns are; nor what influences can foster more desireable normative levels. Nor do we know much more about the hard of hearing than had already come to us through clinical observation and personal accounts.

References to psychological and related investigations will be found in the bibliography at the end of the chapter. A review of the early studies of the deaf shows great effort but indecisive results. In regard to intelligence, some of the investigators report that deaf children are mentally backward by about two years, others that they compare favorably with the normally hearing. Some hold the differences in the kinds of tests used responsible for these conflicting results; others maintain that deafness itself creates a mental backwardness. Scant insight is afforded into the actual thinking and reasoning abilities of deaf individuals. The stress is placed rather upon group comparisons of deaf and hearing pupils by means of nonlanguage and performance tests. In regard to personality and social adjustment studies, here too are found divergent reports. Some investigations indicate serious personality disturbance of the groups studied while others show little if any personality and social adjustment difficulties. Findings are based upon deaf pupil populations of widely differing ages and backgrounds, on dubious instruments, and on comparisons between deaf and hearing groups. Possibly the least contentious results are to be found in the areas of scholastic achievement, motor skills, and mechanical ability. Regarding scholastic achievement, the general conclusion is that deaf pupils show a three- or four-year retardation as compared with their hearing peers. The few studies reported on motor and mechanical ability indicate that, with the exception of the sense of balance, no significant differences exist between the deaf and the hearing in these areas.

More recent studies of the deaf are experimenting with verbal tests and projective techniques and are beginning to concentrate on older age levels in which fuller communicative relations can be established than with young deaf children (Levine, 1956, b). Some common conclusions are that although the deaf as a group are of normal mental endowment, functional lags exist in the area of conceptual thinking and abstract reasoning; and also that these lags are reflected in personality as emotional immaturity, personality constriction, and deficiency in emotional adaptability. However, we have far to go before definitive findings and valid conclusions are reported concerning the psychosocial equivalents of early profound deafness.

The present swing is away from the small, intraschool studies of the past to broad, integrated research dealing with common problems and urgent needs. Specific needed investigations of the deaf (and the hard of hearing) are listed by Levine (Levine, 1960, pp. 303–8) and are presented in the report of a workshop recently held on research needs in the vocational rehabilitation of the deaf (Rogers and Quigley, 1960). Both sources stress the critical—if heretofore generally neglected—need for the control of such variables in investigations of the deaf as: age of beginning school; age of leaving school; total length of time under instruction; type of school or schools attended; systems of instructions used; method of communication favored by the individual; nature of extracurricular learning experiences; etc. Among the host of needed investigations in the field, the following are particularly important:

1. Construction and standardization of instruments of appraisal, whether "tests" or other types of devices for the assessment of intelligence, personality, achievement, vocational

aptitudes, interests, communicative skills, social knowledge, judgment, and maturity

2. In conjunction with the foregoing, demographic studies are needed to disclose the as yet unknown normative patterns of behavior and adjustment among the deaf. One such study covering New York State is presently under way at the New York State Psychiatric Institute (Levine, 1956, a). Others are needed.

3. In view of the exceptionally close relationship between the development of the deaf and the nature of their educational experiences, investigations are needed concerning the influence of educational variables and clusters of variables on adult adjustment. The same obtains in principle for investigations of parental and family influences on adult adjustment.

4. Studies are needed of emotional disturbances among the deaf and of techniques of psychotherapy.

In addition to this highly abridged sampling of needed studies, provision is also needed for counseling centers for deaf individuals; high schools for deaf pupils who cannot derive optimum profit from the regular high schools; adult education centers for the deaf; appropriate educational facilities for multihandicapped deaf children; and sheltered workshops for those who cannot compete in a regular work situation.

In regard to the hard of hearing, there has been considerably less investigation than among the deaf. A review of the studies indicates that hard of hearing children do less well than their hearing peers on verbal intelligence tests and in scholastic achievement, with performance worsening as hearing loss increases; but when intelligence is measured by nonlanguage instruments, no significant differences are found between the hard of hearing and the hearing. In regard to emotional stability, most studies find the hard of hearing less well balanced emotionally than their normally hearing peers, but not to the extent implied by clinical observation and personal accounts. Pintner (Pintner, 1933), the pioneer in psychological investigations of the hearing impaired, found that the disturbance caused by the onset of impaired hearing was greatest in adolescence and early maturity, and much less in childhood. Common reactions were resentment, despair, and shame. Finally, both Welles (Welles, 1932) and Pintner (Pintner, 1933) found substantially higher emotional tension scores among tinnitus sufferers as compared with the hard of hearing at large.

Possibly the most significant single break-through to broader and more intensive investigations of the hard of hearing and the deaf came with the development of the discipline of audiology in answer to the needs of the aural casualties of World War II. Canfield describes audiology as including more than the medical aspects of ear disease and as embracing "every concept of art and science which can contribute to, or form a part of, the propagation of sound, its transmission to the ear, its fate within the human organism, the psychological process based upon the interpretation of perceived sound, and the consequent reaction of the person to the mental concept engendered" (Canfield, 1949, p. 3). Here in broad strokes is the area of research involved in investigations of auditory disability. As in diagnosis and treatment, it is an area that involves many disciplines working together toward the solution of problems for which we have not as yet got the answers. In regard to the hard of hearing, the whole problem of denial and rejection of compensatory rehabilitative measures and devices requires thorough interdisciplinary investigation. So too do problems of psychogenic overlays and other such involvements. Studies of the learning and conceptualization of hard of hearing children with just enough "hearing to get by" are an urgent need. We also need to know more about the mechanisms of adjustment to hearing loss, about mourning for loss, body-image concepts, the dynamics of the "suspicious" set of the hard of hearing, etc. But possibly above all else, there is need of a body of knowledge concerning the dynamics of hearing in human development and adjustment. Perhaps when more is known about hearing, we shall be able to find our way through the psychological maze created by impaired hearing with greater facility.

NATIONAL ORGANIZATIONS IN THE FIELD OF HEARING AND SPEECH (Sources of Information)

Alexander Graham Bell Association for the Deaf, Inc. Headquarters: Volta Bureau, 1537 35th Street, N.W., Washington 7, D.C.

American Federation of the Physically Handicapped, Inc., 1370 National Press Building, Washington 4, D.C.

American Hearing Society, 919 18th Street, N.W., Washington 6, D.C.

American Public Health Association, Inc., 1790 Broadway, New York 19, N.Y.

American Speech and Hearing Association, 1001 Connecticut Avenue, N.W., Washington 6, D.C.

Audiology Foundation, 175 Saint Ronan Street, New Haven 11, Conn.

Conference of Executives of American Schools for the Deaf, Inc., % Gallaudet College, Washington 2, D.C.

Convention of American Instructors of the Deaf, Inc., % Gallaudet College, Washington 2, D.C.

International Council for Exceptional Children, 1201 16th Street, N.W., Washington 6, D.C.

National Association of the Deaf, % Byron B. Burnes, 2495 Shattuck Avenue, Berkeley 4, Calif.

National Fraternal Society of the Deaf, 6701 West North Avenue, Oak Park, Ill.

National Society for Crippled Children and Adults, Inc., 11 South La Salle Street, Chicago 3, Ill.

Lists of aural rehabilitation resources may be obtained from the American Hearing Society.

Annual directories of teachers and schools for the deaf, hearing and speech centers throughout the country, and other services and resources for the hearing impaired can be found in the January issues of the *American Annals of the Deaf*, Gallaudet College, Washington 2, D.C.

Lists of professional personnel in speech and hearing can be obtained from the American Speech and Hearing Association.

For other resource information concerning the hearing impaired, contact the Office of Vocational Rehabilitation, Department of Health, Education, and Welfare, Washington 25, D.C.

REFERENCES

Allan, T., and S. Gordon. 1952. The scalpel and the sword: the story of Norman Bethune. Boston, Little, Brown.

Allport, F. H. 1955. Theories of perception and the concept of structure. New York, Wiley.

Altshuler, K. Z., and J. D. Rainer. 1958. Patterns and course of schizophrenia in the deaf. J. Nerv. Ment. Dis. 127:77–83.

American Academy of Ophthalmology and Otolaryngology. 1959. Health aspects of hearing conservation. Supplement to Trans. Amer. Acad. Ophthal. Otolaryng.

Ballantyne, J. C. 1960. Deafness. Boston, Little, Brown.

Bender, L. 1956. Psychopathology of children with organic brain disorders. Springfield, Ill., C. C. Thomas.

Berry, G. 1933. The psychology of progressive deafness. J. Amer. Med. Ass. 101:1599–1603.

Best, H. 1943. Deafness and the deaf in the United States. New York, Macmillan.

Brandow, E. C., Jr. 1960. Experiences with tympanoplasty. New York J. Med. 60:1603–13.

Brunschwig, L. 1936. A study of some personality aspects of deaf children. Contributions to Education No. 687. New York, Teachers College, Columbia University.

Canfield, N. 1949. Audiology: the science of hearing. Springfield, Ill., C. C. Thomas.

Conference of Executives of American Schools for the Deaf. 1938. Report of the Conference Committee on Nomenclature. Amer. Ann. Deaf 83:1–3.

Davis, H., and S. R. Silverman, eds. 1960. Hearing and deafness. Rev. ed. New York, Holt, Rinehart, and Winston.

DeLand, F., and H. A. Montague. 1931. The story of lipreading. Washington, D.C., Volta Bureau.

DiMichael, S. G. 1948. Characteristics of a desirable psychological report to the vocational counselor. J. Consult. Psychol. 12:432–37.

Dunlop, D. M. 1960. The dangers of antibiotic treatment. Brit. Med. Bull. 16:67–72.

Fenichel, O. 1945. The psychoanalytic theory of neurosis. New York, Norton.

Ford, F. R. 1948. Diseases of the nervous system in infancy, childhood, and adolescence. 2d ed. Springfield, Ill., C. C. Thomas.

Fournier, J. E. 1958. The detection of auditory malingering. A translation of his Le dépistage de la simulation auditive, Exposés Annuels d'Oto-Rhino-Laryngologie, 1956, pp. 107–26. Beltone Institute for Hearing Research Translations No. 8.

Fowler, E. P. 1939. Medicine of the ear. New York, Thomas Nelson.

—— 1951. Emotional factors in otosclerosis. Laryngoscope 61:254–65.

Fox, M. S. 1960. Industrial hearing conservation programs. Eye Ear Nose Throat 39:47–51.

Frampton, M. E., and E. D. Gall, eds. 1955. Special education for the exceptional. 3 vols. Boston, Porter Sargent.

Gesell, A., and C. S. Amatruda. 1947. Developmental diagnosis. 2d ed. New York, Paul B. Hoeber.

Goodhill, V. 1957. Pathology, diagnosis, and therapy of deafness, in L. E. Travis, ed. Handbook of speech pathology. New York, Appleton-Century-Crofts, Chap. 9.

Groht, M. 1958. Natural language for deaf children. Washington, D.C., Alexander Graham Bell Association for the Deaf.

Haeussermann, E. 1958. Developmental potential of preschool children. New York, Grune and Stratton.

Hammond, D. R., and M. Allen. 1953. Writing clinical reports. New York, Prentice-Hall.

Harms, E. 1953. Essentials of abnormal child psychology. New York, Julian Press.

Harper, R. A. 1959. Psychoanalysis and psychotherapy; 36 systems. Englewood Cliffs, N. J., Prentice-Hall.

Haug, C. O., and F. R. Guilford. 1960. Hearing testing on the very young child. Trans. Amer. Acad. Ophthal. Otolaryng. 64:269–71.

Hearing loss a community loss. 1958. Washington, D.C., American Hearing Society.

Hebb, D. O. 1955. The mammal and his environment. Amer. J. Psychiat. 111:826–31.

Heider, F. 1959. On perception and event structure and the psychological environment. Psychological Issues, I, No. 3. Monograph 3. New York, International Universities Press.

Heider, F., and G. M. Heider. 1941. Studies in the psychology of the deaf. II: The adjustment of the adult deaf. Psychological Monographs 53, No. 5. Evanston, Ill., American Psychological Association.

Hirsh, I. J. 1952. The measurement of hearing. New York, McGraw-Hill.

—— 1957. Classification of hearing tests. J. Speech Hearing Dis. 22:736–43.

Hoch, P., and J. Zubin, eds. 1955. Psychopathology of childhood. New York, Grune and Stratton.

Hodgson, K. W. 1954. The deaf and their problems. New York, Philosophical Library.

Hoople, G. 1957. Diagnostic audiometry. J. Speech Hearing Dis. 22:734–35.

Huizinga, E. 1954. Sense of hearing: significance in human beings. Pract. Otorhinolaryng. 16:81–90.

Hunt, W. M. 1944. Progressive deafness rehabilitation. Laryngoscope 54:229–34.

Institute for Special Workers for the Aural Disabled, 1st. 1950. Rehabilitation of the deaf and the hard of hearing. Washington, D.C., Office of Vocational Rehabilitation.

Isakower, O. 1939. On the exceptional position of the auditory sphere. Int. J. Psychoanal. 20:340–48.

—— 1954. Spoken words in dreams. Psychoanal. Quart. 23:1–6.

Johnson, K. O., W. P. Work, and G. McCoy. 1956. Functional deafness. Ann. Otol. 65:154–70.

Kastein, S., and E. P. Fowler. 1954. Differential diagnosis of communication disorders in children referred for hearing tests. Arch. Otolaryng. 60:468–77.

—— 1960. Differential diagnosis in children with communication disorders: a film demonstration. Trans. Amer. Acad. Ophthal. Otolaryng. 64:529–39.

Kietz, H. 1958. New concepts in the theory of hearing. A translation of his Neue vorstellungen in der theorie des hörens, Zeitschrift für Laryngologie, Rhinologie, Otologie, und Ihre Grenzgebiete 36 (5):241–53. Beltone Institute for Hearing Research Translations No. 9.

Kinney, C. E. 1961. High-power hearing aids believed to increase deficiency in children. Med. News, June 16.

Kleinfeld, L. 1953. The auditory mechanism and its diseases. Amer. J. Occup. Ther. 7:1–4, 53–54.

Knapp, P. H. 1948. Emotional aspects of hearing loss. Psychosom. Med. 10:203–22.

—— 1953. The ear, listening and hearing. J. Amer. Psychoanal. Ass. 1:672–89.

Knieval, W. R. 1954. A vocational aptitude test battery for the deaf. Amer. Ann. Deaf 99:314–19.

Laird, C. 1953. The miracle of language. New York, World Publishing Co.

Lawrence, M. 1957. Hearing. Ann. Rev. Psychol. 8:29–60.

Lempert, J. 1945. Fenestra nov-ovalis with mobile stopple. Arch. Otolaryng. 41:1–41.

Levine, E. S. 1956, a. The mental clinic for the deaf. Silent Worker 9:7–8.

—— 1956, b. Youth in a soundless world. New York, New York University Press.

—— 1960. The psychology of deafness: techniques of appraisal for rehabilitation. New York, Columbia University Press.

Long, J. S. 1949. The sign language: a manual of signs. Omaha, Neb., Dorothy Long Thompson.

Longerich, M. C., and J. Bordeaux. 1959. Aphasia therapeutics. New York, Macmillan.

Lowell, E. L., and G. Taaffe. 1957. A film test of lip reading. Los Angeles, Calif., John Tracy Clinic.

Lunde, A. S., and S. K. Bigman. 1959. Occupational conditions among the deaf. Washington, D.C., Gallaudet College.

Masland, R. L. 1960. Research progress in hearing disorders. J. Rehab. 26:11–13.

Mendelson, J. H., L. Siger, and P. Solomon. 1960. Psychiatric observations on congenital and acquired deafness: symbolic and perceptual processes in dreams. Amer. J. Psychiat. 116:883–88.

Menninger, K. A. 1924. Mental effects of deafness. Psychoanal. Rev. 11:144–55.

—— 1945. The human mind. New York, Knopf.

Meyerson, L. 1956. Hearing for speech in children: a verbal audiometric test. Acta Otolaryng. Supplementum 128.

Murphy, G. E. B. 1954. Your deafness is not you. New York, Harper.

Mygind, S. H. 1952. The functions and the diseases of the labyrinth. Acta Otolaryng. 41:235–321.

Myklebust, H. R. 1954. Auditory disorders in children. New York, Grune and Stratton.

New, M. C. 1949. Speech in our schools for the deaf. Volta Rev. 51:61–64.

O'Connor, C. D., and A. Streng. 1950. Teaching the acoustically handicapped, in National Society for the Study of Education. The education of exceptional children. Chicago, University of Chicago Press, pp. 152–75.

Pattison, H. A., ed. 1957. The handicapped and their rehabilitation. Springfield, Ill., C. C. Thomas.

Pierce, J. R., and E. E. David. 1958. Man's world of sound. New York, Doubleday.

Pintner, R. 1933. Emotional stability of the hard of hearing. J. Genet. Psychol. 43:293–311.

Pintner, R., and L. Brunschwig. 1937. An adjustment inventory for use in schools for the deaf. Amer. Ann. Deaf 82:152–67.

Rogers, M., and S. P. Quigley, eds. 1960. Research needs in the vocational rehabilitation of the deaf. Amer. Ann. Deaf 105:335–70.

Ronnei, E. C. 1955. The hard of hearing, in M. E. Frampton and E. D. Gall, eds., Special education for the exceptional. Boston, Porter Sargent. Vol. II, pp. 260–84.

Rosen, S. 1954. Simple method for restoring hearing in otosclerosis: mobilization of stapes. Acta Otolaryng. 44:78–88.

Ruesch, J. 1957. Disturbed communication. New York, W. W. Norton.

St. Joseph's School for the Deaf and Department of Otolaryngology Columbia–Presbyterian Medical Center. 1960. A differential study of communication disorders in a school for the deaf. Mental Health Project Grant OM-155.

Sharoff, R. L. 1959. Enforced restriction of communication, its implications for the emotional and intellectual development of the deaf child. Amer. J. Psychiat. 116:443–46.

Solomon, P., P. E. Kubzansky, P. H. Leiderman, J. H. Mendelson, R. Trumbull, and D. Wexler, eds. 1961. Sensory deprivation. Cambridge, Mass., Harvard University Press.

Stevens, S. S., and H. Davis. 1938. Hearing: its psychology and physiology. New York, Wiley.

Strauss, A. A., and N. C. Kephart. 1955. Psychopathology and education of the brain injured child. New York, Grune and Stratton.

Strauss, A. A., and L. E. Lehtinen. 1947. Psychopathology and education of the brain injured child. New York, Grune and Stratton.

Taylor, E. M. 1959. Psychological appraisal of children with cerebral defects. Cambridge, Mass., Harvard University Press.

Thorne, F. C. 1955. Principles of psychological examining. Brandon, Vt., Journal of Clinical Psychology.

Travis, L. E., ed. 1957. Handbook of speech pathology. New York, Appleton-Century-Crofts.

Warfield, F. 1957. Keep listening. New York, Viking Press.

Watson, L. A., and T. Tolan. 1949. Hearing tests and hearing instruments. Baltimore, Williams and Wilkins.

Welles, H. H. 1932. The measurement of certain aspects of personality among hard of hearing adults. Contributions to Education No. 545. New York, Teachers College, Columbia University.

Welling, D. M. 1954. Communicate! Utah Eagle 65: 1–2.

Wever, E. G., and M. Lawrence. 1954. Physiological acoustics. Princeton, N.J., Princeton University Press.

White House Conference on Child Health and Protection, Section III. 1931. The deaf and the hard of hearing. New York, Century.

Whitehurst, M. W. 1947. Train your hearing. Washington, D.C., Volta Bureau.

Wright, B. C. 1956. Orientation training for vocational rehabilitation counselors to special problems of the deaf and the hard of hearing. Washington, D.C., American Hearing Society.

Wood, N. 1959. Language disorders in children. Chicago, National Society for Crippled Children and Adults.

Zeckel, A. 1950. Psychopathological aspects of deafness. J. Nerv. Ment. Dis. 112: 322–46.

Special references to listings, bibliographies, critical reviews, etc., of psychological and related studies of the deaf and the hard of hearing:

Barker, R. G., and others. 1953. Adjustment to physical handicap and illness. New York, Social Science Research Council. Chap. V.

Berlinsky, S. 1952. Measurement of the intelligence and personality of the deaf: a review of the literature. J. Speech Hearing Dis. 17: 39–54.

Elliott, A. E. 1941. Standardized tests used with the deaf (1912–1941). Amer. Ann. Deaf 86: 242–49.

Lavos, G. 1955. Evaluating the intelligence of the deaf, in M. E. Frampton and E. D. Gall, eds. Special education for the exceptional. Boston, Porter Sargent. Vol. II, pp. 185–99.

Levine, E. S. 1960. The psychology of deafness: techniques of appraisal for rehabilitation. New York, Columbia University Press.

Louttit, C. M. 1957. Clinical psychology of exceptional children. 3d ed. New York, Harper. Chap. 12.

Lowell, E. L., and others. 1957. A bibliography of psychological characteristics of the aurally handicapped and of analytical studies in communication. Los Angeles, Calif., John Tracy Clinic.

Pintner, R., J. Eisenson, and M. Stanton. 1941. The psychology of the physically handicapped. New York, F. S. Crofts. Chaps. V and VI.

Special reference to doctors' dissertations and masters' theses:

American Annals of the Deaf, beginning in 1955, 100: 343–417, and continued in every January issue thereafter. Compiled by D. A. Padden.

Special reference to abstracts of literature in the areas of deafness, speech, and hearing:

DSH Abstracts. Editor: Stephen P. Quigley, Gallaudet College. Published by Deafness, Speech, and Hearing Publications, % American Speech and Hearing Association.

VISUAL DISABILITY

by NATHANIEL J. RASKIN

THE CONCLUSION of this chapter will be stated in the beginning: all essential psychological practices can be carried out with persons with visual defects. This includes psychological appraisal from infancy to adulthood, the evaluation of intelligence, aptitude, achievement, adjustment and personality organization, and the procedures of counseling and psychotherapy. The basic principle in evaluating and treating people with visual defects is the same one that permeates the entire volume: each person to be studied or helped should be approached as an individual, with all that this implies for the appreciation of the uniqueness of a person's perceptions, feelings, and manner of relating to other people and to the world. However, any consideration of psychological practices with visually impaired persons must take into account the extent to which there is impairment in visual acuity.

INCIDENCE AND CLASSIFICATIONS. In the health statistics gathered as part of the United States National Health Survey, a person was classified as blind if (*a*) he was six years old or older, and a negative response was given to the question: "Can you read ordinary newspaper print with glasses?" or (*b*) he was under six years of age (or was over six but had never learned

Nathaniel J. Raskin, Ph.D., is Chief Psychologist at Children's Memorial Hospital, Chicago, and Assistant Professor of Neurology and Psychiatry at Northwestern University Medical School.

to read) and was reported as blind or in terms indicating that he had no useful vision in either eye (U.S. National Health Survey, 1959). "Other visual impairment," in this same survey was defined in this manner: "Persons who were blind in one eye but had sight in the other, or who had poor vision or trouble in seeing in one or both eyes but were not blind, as defined."

Using these definitions, a rate of 5.7 per 1,000 persons was calculated for the incidence of blindness, for an estimated national total of 960,000, and a rate of 12.3 per 1,000 for "other visual impairment," for a projected total of 2,064,000.

These rates and totals are higher than those estimated on the basis of other and more commonly employed criteria. In most general use has been the concept of "economic blindness," defined by the American Medical Association and used in connection with title X (Grants to States for Aid to the Blind) of the Social Security Act. Visual acuity of "less than one-tenth," was proposed as the amount of handicap corresponding to an absence of ability to do any kind of work for which sight is essential. The criterion became, therefore, vision in the better eye when corrected of less than 20/200, or an equally disabling loss (American Medical Association, 1934). On this basis, Hurlin has calculated a national rate of very close to 2 per 1,000, which, projected to the nation's population in 1960, yields a total of 353,000.

The degree of visual defect in blind children determines their placement in braille or sight-saving classes. In terms of acuity, as measured by Snellen, children between 20/70 and 20/200 in the better eye after correction are the ones who fit into the "partially seeing" or "sight-saving" category. Thus, there is a correspondence between children who have less than 20/200 vision and must read by means of braille and the "economic blindness" class defined above.

Whereas work with children is an important part of the activity of psychologists in the area of blindness, it should be recognized that to a large extent, blindness is a disease of later years. Of the estimated 960,000 blind persons reported in the National Health Survey, 407,000 are seventy-five years of age or over, and an additional 249,000 are between the ages of sixty-five and seventy-four. Thus, 68 percent of the blind population is accounted for by those aged sixty-five years and over. The major causes of blindness in this age group is cataract, with optic nerve atrophy and glaucoma next in importance.

In addition to these older people, note should be taken of two special groups in the blind population. One consists of some 10,000 children who were blinded by retrolental fibroplasia during the 1940s and 1950s in this country, making this the most important single cause of blindness in children. Fortunately, this disease has been virtually wiped out since it was established that excessive oxygen administered to prematurely born babies in the course of helping them to survive was the responsible agent. One result, however, has been a temporary abnormal increase in the number of school-age blind children.

Another "special" group is made up of approximately 2,000 veterans blinded during World War II and Korea. The rehabilitation of these men, which has been marked by a high degree of success, has been a matter of special interest to state and federal vocational rehabilitation services and to the Veterans Administration (U.S. Veterans Administration, 1958).

For the most part, all of these groups—the older population, the veterans and other relatively younger vocational rehabilitation clients, and the school children, are "stuck" with their blindness. Restoration of vision occurs to an insignificant degree, in relation to the total blind population.

In recent years, however, there has been a growth of optical aids services for people of all ages which, through the imaginative and bold prescription of microscopic and telescopic lenses, have brought about dramatic changes for some blind persons who for the first time are enabled to distinguish print, recognize faces, travel independently, and so forth (American Foundation for the Blind, 1960).

PSYCHOLOGICAL IMPLICATIONS. The main conclusion to emerge from studies of the adjustment of blind persons is that blindness itself, while it introduces sizable problems of practical living in such areas as travel, eating, and personal care, does not produce maladjustment. The correlates of maladjustment are to be found in deficiencies of love and respect accorded the individual, rather than in a lack of visual experience. Along with his sensory handicap, the blind person falls heir to problems involving the attitudes of others, which can be staggering. Parents of any child are faced with a challenge in being good parents and providing for the emotional needs of their children. The uncertainties, doubts, and insecurities that confront the parents of blind children make the latter much more liable to experience deficiencies in the love and respect they need.

Similarly, while societal respect is something for which every individual strives, it is an uphill battle for the blind child or adult to win the genuine regard of the people around him. He is subject without notice to pity, insult, misunderstanding, and ignorance. The blind child faces the prospect of an inadequate school system or one that is in the process of learning to meet his needs. The blind adult is confronted with an abnormally difficult vocational situation.

These general conclusions about the relationship between visual handicaps and personal and social adjustment emerge to a large extent from direct personal and clinical observation but are also supported by many studies at varying age levels utilizing objective methodology.

In the most comprehensive study of preschool-age blind children (Norris, Spaulding, and Brodie, 1957), the authors conclude:

that favorable opportunities for learning as they have come to be understood by the staff are more important in determining the child's functioning level than such factors as his degree of blindness, his intelligence as measured by psychological tests, or the social, economic, or educational background of his parents.

At the adolescent level, in a study done at the University of Rochester (Cowen, Underberg, Verrillo, and Benham, 1960), the investigators sum up:

> Any prior beliefs about inevitable contingencies between visual disability and maladjustment are severely challenged by the findings of the present investigation. Our groups are strikingly similar in this regard. Comparability and overlap between visually disabled and sighted adolescents with respect to adjustment, as opposed to sharp differences and significant discrepancies, is the rule which emerges from our work.

The Rochester group found that "publicly expressed maternal attitudes are ill-suited to the prediction of adjustment in the child," but that on the other hand, "consistent and sensitive correlation[s] of adjustment are found in the cluster of indices of maternal understanding."

In an investigation covering blind clients of vocational rehabilitation agencies (Bauman, 1954), one of the conclusions reached was that

> no significant differences were found between [the well and poorly adjusted groups] in ophthalmological diagnoses, in etiology, in suddenness of visual loss, or in the age at which visual loss took place. It is not these physical facts which make the difference between an individual's being self-supporting or dependent, socially accepted or a social misfit. Nor is there much evidence that other health factors play a larger part in this adjustment pattern.

Bauman found significant differences between her two groups in respect to intelligence quotient and personality inventory scores. Also, on questions concerning feelings about family relationships the trend was "rather consistently" toward more favorable responses in the vocationally well-adjusted group. Complementing this was the finding that the poorly adjusted vocational group included a "far greater" proportion of individuals who frankly stated their feeling of maladjustment to their family standards.

The Veterans Administration follow-up survey of the postwar adjustment of blinded soldiers (U.S. Veterans Administration, 1958), while emphasizing the individual differences found among the men, makes this point in summary:

> In these figures it will be seen that wives, children, education, and emotional equipoise emerge as factors leading to employment despite blindness. Lack of family ties, lack of education, and lack of emotional equipoise emerge as factors working strongly toward unemployment.

Thus, in investigations involving blind groups which vary greatly in age and station in life, the conclusion repeatedly emerges that deprivation of vision does not, of itself, result in abnormal development or unsuccessful personal and vocational adjustment. Rather it is suggested that successful outcomes are possible and are linked to favorable psychosocial conditions.

Meyerson comes to a similar conclusion in the area of the partially seeing (Meyerson, 1953). He and others, on excellent grounds, have been critical of the methodology of the investigations on legally blind and partially seeing subjects; so the generalizations thus far stated in this chapter must be viewed as tentative and requiring confirmation by more rigorously controlled studies.

REAL LIMITATIONS. Lowenfeld, in a contemporary review of the psychological problems of children with impaired vision (Lowenfeld, 1955) states that "in general it can be said that blindness creates problems *sui generis* only in the area of cognitive functions and mobility."

Lowenfeld points out that

> blind people can observe only those things which are accessible to them. The sun, the moon, clouds, the horizon, the sky are inaccessi-

ble and can be explained to blind people only by the use of analogies from other sensory fields. This method must also be used in explaining to blind people such visual phenomena as shadows, perspective and reflection of light. Many objects are too large to be observed by touch, for instance a mountain or a large building. Other objects are too small and cannot be observed by touch with any degree of accuracy, for instance flies or ants. Of course, microscopic observations can only be made visually and are entirely impossible for the sense of touch. Fragile or delicate objects like butterflies, certain flowers or parts of flowers, snowflakes, or a spider's web also cannot be observed tactually. Objects in motion, live objects, and objects in certain conditions such as burning, boiling, or cooking cannot be observed by touch because they either change their shapes or positions or because direct contact with them would be dangerous. Liquids do not have shapes of their own and are often difficult to observe by touch when kept in containers. This is also the case with mercury in narrow glass tubes as used in thermometers and various gauges. Many of these restrictions in observation hold true not only for the blind person who has never seen but also for the person who becomes blind later in life. Although he may have a very clear idea of the visual appearance of these objects, he cannot actually observe the object itself. [Lowenfeld, 1955, p. 221.]

The writer, in his personal experience with blind persons, has been struck with the concern for cognition shown by visually handicapped children and adults. A partially sighted professional colleague seemed to go out of her way to comment on beautiful sunsets and color in other forms, as if to prove to others that she had this experience; another adult acquaintance, totally blind, characteristically made frequent remarks about places we might be passing while walking, or about the identification of vehicles going by, and so forth. Blind children in play therapy sessions with the author have shown much more than an average cognitive interest. The following comments are from summaries of two of the play contacts with an eight-year-old boy:

Brad [fictitious name] began the hour by exploring the sandtable, asking about the different objects which he picked up. Later on he got over to the sink and mouthed the stopper, for quite a while. All this time he talked, interrogatively, asking questions of this type: Is this Dr. A's office? Do you eat stoppers? Are you blind? How old are you? How old is God? What does dead mean? When do people die?

[From the next session]

Brad continued to ask questions today but seemed more settled and relaxed. The questions were more matter-of-fact, concerning the identity of objects he picked up in the sandtable, the location of different doctors' offices, etc. During the hour, Brad went once around the room, and then seemed to feel oriented. On the 16th floor, after the hour, he also went completely around the lobby, asking which doctors had which offices.

In the writer's experience, this behavior is not limited to a getting-acquainted period but is rather a continuing characteristic of the blind child's behavior.

Besides the cognitive limitation, a second "real" handicap imposed by blindness is the problem of getting about or of "travel," as this area is termed by rehabilitation workers. The white cane and the Seeing Eye dog, for many people, are the symbols of blindness, and it is significant that both highlight the blind persons's travel problems. The social and emotional implications of these problems are stressed in a recent study carried out at the Research Center of the New York School of Social Work (Firestone, Lukoff, and Whiteman, 1960). One of the findings of this investigation is that: On a combined measure of all three aspects, termed travel efficiency, three-fourths [of the subjects] fall in the category of "restricted travel." A correlative finding was that the blind population studied was dissatisfied with this state of affairs, yet for the most part resigned to it. The investigators raise the question, however, of the responsibility of the overprotective family and community for this situation, as well as of the rehabilitation field, with its "insufficiency of highly skilled resources."

Cognition and mobility problems have been discussed as "real limitations" of blindness because of their derivation from the physical aspects of the disability. No less real, however, are the handicaps imposed by social attitudes toward blind persons, as discussed in the next section.

THE ATTITUDES OF SIGHTED PEOPLE TOWARD BLINDNESS. Several objective attempts have been made to determine the attitudes of sighted people toward blindness. Meyerson (Barker, Wright, Meyerson, and Gonick, 1953) has reviewed many of the studies in this area. The populations studied in the various investigations have included 2,340 men aged twenty to sixty in the occupations of engineering, law, ministry, medicine, education, writing, YMCA work, and life insurance selling (Strong, 1943), 43 university instructors (Koehler, 1933), 130 graduate students in a social psychology class (Rusalem, 1950), 90 college students representing three levels of adjustment (Steingisser, 1954), 234 undergraduates taking a General Psychology course (Walters, 1955), 22 superintendents and 12 teachers in schools for the blind (Schaefer, 1930), and 50 mothers of adolescent blind children with seeing siblings (Sommers, 1944). It is not easy to sum up the findings of these respective studies based on varied populations and techniques, but a review suggests the following: (1) extreme negative attitudes toward blind persons, which would ascribe to them such characteristics as cynicism, laziness, impairment of sexual functions, etc., are not evident; (2) on a general positive-negative dimension, attitudes toward blind people tend to be positive, and (3) the difficulty for blind people in the attitudes expressed derives not from any lack of being liked but in deficiencies of respect. These conclusions are clarified and confirmed by studies of other types of physically disabled individuals, particularly those with orthopedic disabilities. As summarized in Barker and others (Barker, Wright, Meyerson, and Gonick, 1953), it appears that the positive attitudes of the nondisabled for the disabled include an element of disparagement. This is expressed by parents in the form of an overprotective attitude, a mode of maternal adjustment found to exist to a large extent by Sommers in her study of blind adolescents. In addition, however, it was felt both by Sommers and by those who studied parents of children with other disabilities that hostile attitudes were also prominent, expressed either as overt rejection or as rejection disguised as oversolicitousness or some other positive manifestation.

The writer, with Kittleson, has recently studied the "reputation" of thirty-four blind children attending public suburban or urban parochial schools in regular third- to sixth-grade classes. The Reputation Test employed by Tuddenham and others at the University of California was used with minor additions. The instrument as used consisted of a series of thirty-nine brief word pictures for the lower grades and forty-five for the higher grades. Except for a "best friend" item, the descriptions were paired to represent dimensions such as "popular—not many friends," "gets mad easily—doesn't get mad," and so forth, and each child was asked to write the names of children in class, including himself, who met the description. Teachers were instructed in the group use of the instrument, and the blind children answered in braille. There was nothing in the procedure to suggest that the blind children were being singled out for study.

The results show that the blind children were seen by their sighted classmates, typically, as quiet, likeable, and friendly but as needing help. The pattern was similar for the upper and lower grades. The suburban blind children received mention as many times as, or more than, their sighted classmates. Those in the larger urban parochial classes were mentioned much less frequently and with less regard. A tendency was noted, also, for two or more blind children in the same class to be rated together, especially in the larger classes where, for example, one sighted child always rated the four blind children together as "the four brailles."

Thus it appears that the three conclusions derived from the

earlier studies summarized above are confirmed by the writer's own research on school-age children. It seems, too, that attitudes of stereotypy can be encouraged or minimized by the conditions under which the blind child receives his education.

While the results of this reputation study throw some light on attitudes held toward blind children, perhaps even more edifying have been the reactions of some of the writer's colleagues with whom he has discussed the study. Many are surprised to learn that blind children are attending public schools at all. Learning that they are, many wonder, "What do they do there?" and "How could they answer the questionnaire themselves?" The lack of knowledge of the limitations and capacities of blind persons is indeed widespread, and probably about as common among professional persons as among lay people.

In the concluding section on research, some suggestions will be offered for profitable investigations in the area of social attitudes toward blindness.

DO BLIND PEOPLE HAVE SPECIAL ABILITIES? *Basic and Complex Auditory and Tactile Abilities.* Axelrod, as background for carrying out a research project on the effects of early blindness, involving the comparison of the performance of blind and sighted children on tactile and auditory tasks, made an excellent survey of the effects of blindness in the residual modalities (Axelrod, 1959). Axelrod organized his review to analyze findings on two levels of functioning: a basic sensory discrimination level, involving touch and auditory sensitivity, and a complex level, calling upon the capacities of the individual to organize data received through touch and hearing. He concludes:

> The evidence on basic haptic (touch) sensitivity in the blind is . . . conflicting. Although there are claims for compensation, much of the direct evidence seems to suggest that there is no compensatory improvement beyond the level of sighted subjects, and there are indications that blindness may elevate, rather than lower, tactile limens.

In the area of basic auditory sensitivity, "the situation is no clearer. . . . There are the usual claims and counter claims, and few studies. There is reason to believe, however, that in the probably much-practiced task of sound-localization, the blind are somewhat better than the sighted."

It appears that the over-all conclusion to be reached from Axelrod's own experiment and the investigations he reviewed is that blind persons have not demonstrated special auditory or tactile capacities and that, if anything, those who are blind from infancy may have an extraordinary cognitive problem.

Obstacle Perception. One special ability that many blind persons apparently do possess is that of "obstacle perception" or "facial vision," brought out by the ability, for example, to stop walking just before coming to a wall. This is a very good example of the way in which scientific endeavor has replaced subjective controversy and established both the existence of the ability and the basis for it. Out of the welter of theories based both on sensory perception (pressure, auditory and temperature changes, or a combination of these) and on occult extrasensory or miraculous concepts has come the conclusion, based on experiments which successively narrowed down the crucial variables, that a blind person is capable of avoiding obstacles on the basis of aural cues alone and that, specifically, it is changes in pitch (rather than the loudness or the continuity of sound) that are the necessary and sufficient condition for the perception of obstacles (Dolanski, 1930; Supa, Cotzin, and Dallenbach, 1944; Worchel and Dallenbach, 1947; Jerome and Proshansky, 1950). In one of the studies at the University of Texas following up a series at Cornell University (Worchel, Mauney, and Andrew, 1950), it was found that only seven of thirty-four totally blind students attending a school for the blind did not possess the obstacle sense and that these seven, after being given 210 training trials, "under conditions favorable for learning," developed an ability equal to experienced subjects.

The possession of obstacle perception appears, then, to be a function of the understandable use of a regular sensory modality (audition) which is learned in response to an environmental need or can be taught readily.

PSYCHOLOGICAL APPRAISAL. This section will include a discussion both of the instruments used to evaluate the intelligence and personality of blind persons and some of the generalization resulting from their use.

INFANCY AND PRESCHOOL LEVELS. The instruments most commonly used for evaluating blind infants and preschool-age children are the (1) Maxfield-Buchholz Social Maturity Scale for Blind Preschool Children (Maxfield and Buchholz, 1957), which is an outgrowth of the Vineland Social Maturity Scale developed by Edgar Doll (Doll, 1953), and (2) the Cattell Infant Intelligence Scale (Cattell, 1940).

The Maxfield-Buchholz Scale. This scale consists of 95 items, distributed as follows by age levels: 20 each at the first- and second-year levels, 15 each at the third-, fourth-, and fifth-year levels. Doll's categories of Self-Help General, Self-Help Dressing, Self-Help Eating, Communication, Socialization, Locomotion, and Occupation are employed, but not the category of Self-Direction, which, on the original scale, comes in mainly at the higher age levels. From the information given in these areas of performance by the child's mother or other informant, a Social Age and Social Quotient may be calculated. The Maxfield-Buchholz Scale thus provides a measure of development that compares a given blind child with the achievements of a standardization group of 484 blind children. A manual giving the history, description of the scale, its standardization, and directions for administering and scoring is available from the American Foundation for the Blind (Maxfield and Buchholz, 1957).

Using the original (not adapted for the blind) Vineland Social

Maturity Scale, Bradway reported on the relative social competence of blind children (Bradway, 1937; Doll, 1953). Bradway, as did Maxfield and Fjeld, obtained social maturity ratings substantially lower for blind children than for sighted children of corresponding ages.

Hayes compared Social Quotients of 145 retrolental fibroplasia babies with the quotients of 155 blind from other causes, using the Maxfield-Fjeld Tentative Adaptation of the Vineland Social Maturity Scale (the predecessor of the Maxfield-Buchholz). The two distributions were almost identical, both taking very nearly the normal bell-shaped form, although showing a piling up at the low end, resulting in a mean SQ for the combined groups of 81. Hayes felt the skewed distribution would be expected as the result of "unwise parental restriction of behavior, over-solicitude, or the emotional blocking resulting from parental rejection or lack of affectionate care" (Hayes, 1952).

The Maxfield-Fjeld scale was also used with sixty-six children studied intensively at the University of Chicago Medical Clinics (Norris, Spaulding, and Brodie, 1957). These authors concluded that "in general, the item analysis . . . supports the conclusion that the development of blind children can follow an orderly progression without the serious retardation usually expected as a result of the handicap." Noting that this conclusion differed from the results reported by others, Norris and her associates point out that Bradway studied children in an institutional setting, and they place great stress on the wide variability of functioning observed in all of the groups of blind children studied, plus their strong belief in the potency of environmental opportunities for learning as a determinant of functioning outcome.

The Cattell Infant Intelligence Scale. This scale is standardized for children aged two months to thirty months, at which point it blends into the Stanford-Binet Scale, from which the Cattell derives its essential format of several tests, each with an equal value, at each age level. At the lower levels, the test items deal largely with motor development and visual and social responses. Objects such as rattles, blocks, spoons, beads, dolls, pegs, cups, and mirrors are used. Unlike the Vineland-type instrument, it involves direct testing of children. The test was adapted for use in the Chicago study to which reference has just been made by discarding items found inappropriate for blind children. In addition, "items concerned with attending to or reaching for objects that the child could not see were altered so that he was made aware of the presence of the objects by means of touch."

This process left most of the original Cattell items as a basis for measuring the capacity of the blind child. The standard complement of items at any given month on the regular Cattell consists of five tasks plus one or two alternates. The "blind" version derived in the manner described above yielded three items at the second- and third-month levels, five items at the fourth-month, seven items at the fifth-month, five items at the sixth-month, and so on. Norris and her fellow researchers concluded:

> In general, the findings . . . show that the development of children in the intensive [*sic*] group was approximately equal to that of normal children except on items that require a background of specific experience. . . . Delayed mastery appears most significantly in certain types of motor response, with fine motor co-ordination developing easily only after the child has had wide experience in gross motor activity . . . [As an illustration] the average sighted child solves the early pegboard items at approximately fifteen months. At this age the project staff has learned, however, that the energies of the blind child who is developing will need to be directed largely toward locomotion and gross motor activity. . . . Skill in fine motor co-ordination and success in grasping spatial relationships . . . were found to develop spontaneously, though usually at a later age than for sighted children, in [the blind] children who had had adequate opportunities for gross motor activity and who had been permitted to explore their environments freely. [Norris, Spaulding, and Brodie, 1957, pp. 19–25.]

We see these investigators again stressing the importance of environmental opportunities and concluding that, when these are present, the blind child will develop in a way that is essentially normal, although it may be at a rate that is slower than for the child with vision. It should be obvious, too, that, while the Cattell Scale can provide a useful measure of the development of blind infants, in the adapted form devised by the Chicago group, the resulting mental ages and quotients are not comparable to those obtained from the examination of sighted babies.

SCHOOL-AGE AND ADULT LEVELS. *Measures of Intelligence.* Instruments commonly used for measuring intelligence among the school-age and adult blind are as follows:

The Interim Hayes-Binet Intelligence Tests for the Blind: This is a modification made in 1942 of the Terman-Merrill Revised Stanford-Binet Scale. Information concerning the publisher, the special modifications for use with blind persons and data on reliability and validity are given in *A Manual for the Psychological Examination of the Adult Blind* (Bauman and Hayes, 1951). Hayes eliminated the material requiring vision, included items from both Form L and M, and included some lower-age items from the 1930 Revision of the Hayes-Binet, in order to provide six tests at each year level beginning at the third. Braille or oral presentation are used for many of the "visual" tests and have been found to be adequate substitutes.

The Wechsler Scales: The adult forms and the Wechsler Intelligence Scale for Children are used simply by administering the verbal part of the scales. The technique recommended by Bauman and Hayes is to use all six verbal tests and to prorate the total score. They also suggest, in terms of specific technique, that

> the later arithmetic problems which are given to seeing subjects in printed form should be read aloud twice . . . before time is recorded. Give all items in the Similarities test. Continue the Vocabulary test through eight failures; in all cases where the orally presented word might be difficult to understand, spell the word after pronouncing it. [Bauman and Hayes, 1951, p. 28.]

Intelligence Test Results with Blind Persons: Most of the evidence on the intellectual status of blind persons is based on data collected on blind children. This is owing to the work of Hayes, carried on from 1918 until his death forty years later and centering around the students enrolled at Perkins Institution, although Hayes also succeeded in obtaining data on blind children at other schools throughout the country (Hayes, 1941, 1942, and 1950). The general pattern found by Hayes is a mean IQ slightly below 100, a disproportionately large percentage at the lower end of the scale (approximately 10 percent below 70 compared with 3 percent in the general population), and a somewhat smaller percentage at the upper end of the scale (approximately 10 percent above 120 compared with 12–13 percent in the general population).

More recent data on the intelligence of a smaller sample of blind school-age children is available from the group originally studied by Norris, Spaulding, and Brodie at the University of Chicago Medical Clinics and currently being followed at the Northwestern University Medical School. Of the 66 children in the original intensively studied group, 4 were found to be untestable and 5 in institutions for the mentally retarded. The median of the 57 remaining children on the Interim Hayes-Binet Scale, is 93, and there is a piling up of cases at the lower end, with 16 of the children attaining IQ's of 75 or less. Five children in the group had IQ's of 125 or more, with two above 145. The results in general appear to fit in with Hayes's earlier findings.

As part of this same study, the WISC Verbal Scale was administered and found to correlate very highly (coefficient of .95) with the Hayes-Binet. Analysis of the subtest results showed a range in mean scaled scores of a little below 10 on the Comprehension test to about 13 on Similarities, so there are no gross deficiencies for the entire group. However, when the subtest results were analyzed for the part of the group which fell below the mean IQ of 93, the Comprehension average was strikingly low, with a mean scaled score of about 3. It is hypothesized by the investigators that this may be owing "to a real lack of social experience, reduced applicability of the test problems, or a reduction in abstract capacity."

Turning to visually handicapped children who fall into the "sight-saving" classification, Pintner administered individual Stanford-Binets to over 600 such children in the ten- to twelve-year age range. He found no significant difference in intellectual potential between this and the "normal" population. Further, Pintner did systematic retesting using enlarged test materials and found no evidence that children, other than those who would fall into the "legally blind" class, were penalized by the use of the regular materials. The present author's clinical experience supports this research conclusion, that children in the "sight-saving" group, with vision worse than 20/70 in the better eye with correction, can be examined with regular intelligence test materials. It goes without saying that the verbal tests used with blind people are equally applicable to the partially seeing.

Achievement, Aptitude, and Interest Tests. Regular tests in these areas, such as the Stanford Achievement, the Metropolitan Achievement, the Minnesota Rate of Manipulation, the Pennsylvania Bi-Manual Worksample, the Small Parts Dexterity, and the Kuder Preference Record, have been used widely with blind persons. Specific information about the use of these instruments with blind subjects will be found in the manual for adult testing noted above (Bauman and Hayes, 1951) and in a more recent manual (Bauman, 1958) that is concerned more exclusively with measures of manual dexterity and, in addition, Bauman's Emotional Factors Inventory, a personality inventory of the questionnaire type. Both of these booklets contain valuable information on general considerations in testing blind persons, and Bauman's 1958 manual presents norms based on a large population of blind persons.

Personality Measures. Although the personality inventory of the questionnaire type has been used most commonly in research with blind subjects, the counselor or clinician who wishes to gain an understanding of the personality organization and dynamics of a blind client will probably wish to employ projective tests. The two most widely used projective tests with sighted people, the Rorschach Test and the Thematic Apperception Test, are so visually based that they obviously cannot be employed with blind persons. Attempts to produce three-dimensional tactual analogues of the Rorschach have not "caught on," perhaps because of the very great differences between the characteristics of the visual and tactual modalities (Morris, 1950; Twitchell-Allen, 1947). Auditory projective techniques, while they have not been generally adopted either, may still prove to be successful procedures. Some of the earlier methods tried have been reviewed by Morris and include the "Tautaphone," which called upon the subject to reproduce meaningfully an unclear auditory stimulus (Shakow and Rosenzweig, 1940), and Kunze's Musical Reverie Test (Murray, 1938), which requires the subject to tell what images are evoked by passages from such works as Tschaikovsky's Symphony No. 4, Richard Strauss's *Don Juan*, Mozart's Quintet in G Minor, and Debussy's *Afternoon of a Faun* (Morris, 1950). Raskin and Weller surveyed more recent auditory projective techniques (Raskin and Weller, 1953); two of these will be described.

Palacios and Wilmer developed a Sound Association Technique consisting of a series of twenty-one sound situations that included interpersonal relationship situations, nonverbal sounds suggesting various kinds of human interaction, and impersonal sounds such as liquid running (Wilmer and Husni, 1953). The subject was asked to respond to each stimulus with whatever came to his mind. A newer version of this procedure is known as The Sound Test and has been put out by Palacios through the Purdue Research Foundation of Purdue University. It has been shortened to fifteen stimuli, recorded on two sides of one 33⅓ RPM twelve-inch disc.

Braverman and Chevigny devised the Auditory Projective Technique, which is more complex in its make-up. It consists of (*a*) 20 "sound riddles" (readings by one male voice that are descriptions of feelings and/or objects but are ambiguous as to meaning), (*b*) 7 conversations depicting various interpersonal relationships, such as young girl and older woman, young woman and older man, etc., these being recorded in a nonsense language that allows for the retention of emotional content but leaves word meaning ambiguous, (*c*) 3 of the above 7 conversations recorded in English in addition to the nonsense language, and (*d*) 8 sound effects designed to portray a scene and a brief activity. Subjects are asked to make up a story in response to each stimulus. This test is distributed by the American Foundation for the Blind in the form of two 33⅓ RPM twelve-inch discs.

Two projective techniques that require no special equipment and that have the advantage of having been used with sighted populations a good deal are the sentence completion method, of which there are numerous versions, and the Insight Test developed by the late Helen Sargent, who reported on the clinical use of the instrument with blind persons and on its prognostic ability in rehabilitation with blind persons (Sargent, 1953, and 1956).

Dean used Bauman's Emotional Factors Inventory, the Minnesota Multiphasic Personality Inventory, the Rotter Incomplete Sentences Blank, and the Sargent Insight Test, in a study of fifty-four vocational rehabilitation clients. The adjustment of the subjects was rated independently as good, fair, or poor, and, although Dean found that none of the tests was able to differentiate these adjustment groups by the use of any single score, "the tests used are as applicable to blind persons as to the sighted" (Dean, 1957).

In the study of blind children in the Chicago area which was mentioned under "Intelligence Test Results," it was decided to employ, for measures of personal adjustment, the children's form of the Insight Test (Engel, 1958) and the Sentence Completion Test compiled by Dorfman for use in her study evaluating the outcome of client-centered play therapy (Dorfman, 1958). In addition, the Reputation Test described above in the section on attitudes toward blindness was employed (Tuddenham, 1952).

When it comes to the personality assessment of the partially sighted, there is no particular problem, as any of the standard projective or nonprojective techniques may be employed.

Findings regarding the personal adjustment of blind and partially seeing persons have already been summarized in the section on Psychological Implications.

REHABILITATION AND THERAPY. An understanding of the rehabilitation or therapy process with blind people must start with the original shock of being blinded in the adventitiously blinded person, with the parallel shock suffered by the parent of the child who is born blind or becomes blind in infancy or childhood, and with the awareness of his condition as it comes to the blind child himself.

A particularly vivid description of a first reaction to being blinded is given in an autobiographical account by Chevigny:

> It's not just an experiment in being without sight, that first walk. That you have been for three months; dressings have been kept over your eyes, you have seen nothing since the day you entered the hospital.
>
> Bathrobe and slippers on, you rise from your bed and test the strength of your knees, gingerly. You feel pleased with yourself to note they don't immediately buckle. You walk toward the place where you know there is a window—you know there's a window there because you've felt the draught, and the sound of fighting you hear every night from the Russian café across the street comes from that direction. You find the window; your first emotion is surprise that it is so quickly reached. The room is smaller than you

had imagined it. Well, let's follow the wall. Suddenly your hand touches a steampipe. The response is one of anger—rage at the inanimate thing that hurt you. There is a sudden, almost overwhelming temptation to return to the safety of that bed; everything you need in the world is there within reach—your water, food, even such intellectual nourishment as comes by a turn of the radio dial. But you remember that the food and water have to be put there by somebody—somebody you pay to do it—and you aren't going to find the wherewithal to pay unless you continue as you are going.

Making too quick a turn to cross to the other side of the room, you become suddenly disorientated. The other wall isn't where you thought it would be; the bed, the table, the chairs are somewhere other than you think they are. You haven't yet learned to listen; if you knew how to rely on your hearing, a split second of listening would indicate the position of the windows by the traffic sounds outdoors. But that knowledge isn't going to come for a long while yet—and you don't know that it's ever going to come. You are suddenly too engulfed in the realization that a whole dimension has dropped out of living. The physical world which used to have length, breadth, thickness, now has only breadth and thickness. The only faculty on which you used to rely for estimating length is gone, and you are startled to discover how important it was.

You have to ask for help at last from the nurse who has been standing by watching you in sympathetic silence. You've got to find that bed because your knees are beginning to buckle. But it's hard to ask her for that help, to admit that you're lost—even though you know damned well that she knows you're lost. It seems a surrender, a lowering of your pride. And you wonder why it is so difficult to admit that you need her help.

Maybe Miss Calkins knew what my next reaction would be, because after getting me back in bed she shut the door and left me alone. I wept, for perhaps the first time in thirty years. They were tears of frustration, rage, emotional exhaustion, and considerable self-pity. "It can't do this to me," I said in effect to the pillow—meaning fate or nature or whatever it was that had done precisely this to me. And there was no escaping the realization that this was only the beginning, only the first fifteen minutes of a new lifetime. [Chevigny, 1946, pp. 19–21.]

This vivid account is very consistent with Cholden's formulation of the adjustment process for an adult who loses his sight (Cholden, 1958). Cholden describes the initial shock stage and then the depression that constitute the initial steps of reintegration. Cholden emphasizes that the depression is not something to be avoided, but that it needs to be experienced in order for the person to progress.

> In essence, the newly handicapped individual must realize with his whole being that he has lost something of himself and is now a new person with different capacities and potentialities from the person he was. Besides experiencing the loss of an organ, he experiences the loss of his accustomed inner picture of his physical self and his psychological self. This loss of inner concept of self and the change to a different internal structure of self is what constitutes the essential fact of reorganization or rehabilitation to the disability. The awareness of this need for intrapsychic change is basic to an *acceptance* of himself as a handicapped person. [Cholden, 1958, p. 76.]

Cholden believes that the opportunity for working through this "mourning" period is made more difficult by efforts on the part of the physician and society in general to prevent the depression. "One often gets the feeling that the physician or relative is attempting to forestall his own despair and depression by helping the patient believe he is not actually blind. . . . Of course, those who persistently offer hope . . . are unaware that they are thereby impeding the rehabilitation process" (Cholden, 1958).

What can the physician do that is positive? Cholden advocates complete frankness combined with sensitivity and understanding of the patient's shock, and with the provision of information and experience demonstrating that blind people can make a good adjustment.

In his autobiographical account, Chevigny devotes a whole chapter to the issue of frankness in informing the patient of blindness. The chapter is entitled "Truth and Consequences," and its conclusion is a line borrowed by Chevigny from an old song, "It's the truth that makes you free." Chevigny explains:

> To some of my friends who were keeping in close touch with me during those dark days, it seemed an excessively cruel thing

that my doctor told me the final truth as bluntly as he did and with so little promise for any hope. They felt he could have mitigated the blow, could have told it to me gradually. There would have been less shock; it would have been better for me to come to an awareness of my new state in easy stages.

With this point of view I emphatically disagree. I didn't even agree with it at the time. Doctor Berens did exactly right, I feel. The time had come for surgery other than a bodily kind, and he had grasped the scalpel with courage. That this particular operation on me was successful is shown by the fact that after the shock I had a healthy reaction. I can't say truthfully that I awaited with any eagerness the opportunity to widen the experience of my new life, but one thing I did want—and very greatly—was to leave behind me, and as quickly as possible, everything that had to do with doctors, hospitals, and surgeries. I had had enough of them. They had tried to do their job and I was grateful; now there was another job to be done and to delay its beginning, I felt obscurely, might endanger the outcome. [Chevigny, 1946, p. 25.]

REHABILITATION FACILITIES. Once over the shock and, having been given an opportunity to experience the consequent depressive reaction described by Cholden and Chevigny, the person typically passes from the role of a medical patient to a rehabilitation client. It has been estimated that of the approximately 355,000 blind persons in the United States, some 90,000 can profit from vocational rehabilitation services. With approximately 30,000 additional persons losing their sight each year, at least 2,000 more may be added to the national vocational rehabilitation case load (American Foundation for the Blind, 1960). The role of rehabilitation client may be carried out in different ways. The blind person may be living at home and pay periodical visits to a government-supported vocational rehabilitation agency (one in each state) or to a voluntary agency (over 400 in the nation) set up to help the visually handicapped. These visits may be for the general purpose of receiving assistance in finding employment or to develop special skills, such as braille reading and writing, mobility, and so forth. Or, the blind person may be the client of a rehabilitation center, residing there for a period of weeks or months, and participating in a comprehensive training program aimed at facilitating the full realization of his potentialities not only vocationally but personally and socially. There are approximately twenty such centers in the nation.

One of the outstanding centers of this type has been the Blind Rehabilitation Section at the Veterans Administration Hospital in Hines, Illinois, which provides a rigorous program of training in orientation and mobility, braille, writing skills, and shop, and also includes counseling, physical reconditioning, and group recreation (Williams and Flank, 1955). This center is known particularly for the contribution it has made toward increasing the independence of blinded veterans through a bold new program of training in the use of the "long cane." The directors of this rehabilitation center, rating the outcomes for clients who had completed the program, felt that the great majority had received significant benefit.

A general description of rehabilitation center programs oriented toward a set of ideal principles and standards is given in a publication on *Rehabilitation Centers for Blind Persons* (U.S. Office of Vocational Rehabilitation, 1956).

A significant aspect of rehabilitation counseling deals with emotional problems, the resolution of which may make the difference between fully functioning, independent living, and a life marked by routine, safety, segregation, isolation, and dependence.

Cholden, in doing group therapy with clients of a rehabilitation center for the blind, was struck first of all by an exceptional difficulty in the expression of emotion and by the superficiality of the client's interpersonal relationships in the center (Cholden, 1958). Cholden hypothesized that expression of feeling is related to an awareness of the manner in which the expression will be received; the blind person finds it more difficult to assess the reactions of his listeners.

After working with a number of groups, quite heterogeneous in character, with ages varying from 16 to 65, intelligence quotients from 65 to 145, visual handicaps from total congenital to partial adventitious blindness, and with wide differences in ethnic, social, educational, and cultural backgrounds, Cholden found he could make some generalizations about the problems that seemed to emerge in the discussions of all the groups.

One general development was the feeling of hostility toward sighted people, which often was expressed in relating jokes about the "stupid" behavior of the sighted in relation to the blind. This resentment was often expressed, too, in relation to group members with some vision. Cholden reports that some of the other topics discussed generally were "the reactions to the limitations of blindness, feelings of isolation and fear when lost, reactions to the necessary dependencies resulting from blindness, feelings during periods of silence, the effect of childhood experiences on present reactions and methods of dissipating anger" (Cholden, 1958).

The light thrown on the feelings experienced by blind people is really a by-product of these group therapy sessions. Their primary purpose was therapeutic, and Cholden felt that they were successful in helping the participants to express their feelings more freely, to realize the commonness of existing problems, to see how others handle their problems and perceive their own reactions in this perspective, and to learn that they could say how they felt without getting hurt. Cholden felt that he could see significant personality change and social maturation in many of the clients but did not claim credit for the group therapy in achieving this result, because it existed within the framework of a general rehabilitation center program.

It is no surprise that a psychiatrist should feel that attitudes and feelings are an important aspect of the rehabilitation process. Support for this point of view also comes from MacFarland, an administrator of a state agency for blind persons, with a background principally in vocational rehabilitation counseling. MacFarland has been impressed with both the negative and positive influence of family attitudes in affecting the success of vocational rehabilitation. He concludes that the problem is of large enough magnitude to warrant the employment of a specialist on the vocational rehabilitation staff to concentrate exclusively on this phase of the work (MacFarland, 1956). Similarly, it was the recommendation of the New Orleans conference on rehabilitation centers that the staff of a residential rehabilitation center for a clientele of twenty persons include a full-time psychologist, a full-time social worker, and a part-time psychiatrist (U.S. Office of Vocational Rehabilitation, 1956).

The field of rehabilitation counseling has been greatly strengthened by the support given by the federal government through the Office of Vocational Rehabilitation to help establish and maintain courses of study leading to advanced degrees in rehabilitation counseling. Characteristically, these curricula are for the purpose of training counselors not just for blind people or for those with any other individual disability but for the handicapped in general. However, it is certain that the standard of services for blind persons will be raised as a result of this general program, which is supported to the extent of hundreds of thousands of dollars a year and includes the facilities of many of the nation's leading colleges and universities.

Whereas the discussion of rehabilitation and therapy in this section has dealt with adults, there is a parallel and equally important area that includes giving help to the parents of blind children and education to and therapy for the blind child himself. Perhaps the outstanding study of the attitudes of parents of blind children was done by Sommers, who classified five types of reaction: acceptance, denial, overprotectiveness, disguised rejection, and overt rejection (Sommers, 1944). Of the 50 parents who were interviewed in her investigation, Sommers rated 9 as accepting, 4 as denying, 13 as overprotective, 16 as rejecting in a disguised way, and 8 as being overtly rejecting. Sommers found that the adjustive behavior of the blind adolescents she studied was closely related to these parental reactions.

Comparatively little has been written about how to help parents of blind children. One of the valuable publications in this area came out of the University of Chicago study cited earlier in this chapter, which emphasizes the importance of opportunities for learning, broadly conceived, in the development of blind children (Norris, Spaulding, and Brodie, 1957).

Tremendously relevant, also, to the development of a blind child is the kind of education he receives. A recent publication of the American Foundation for the Blind, by compiling ten articles in the field, gives a valuable overview of the education of blind children. The three major types of education—public school, residential school, and itinerant teaching—are described in separate articles (American Foundation for the Blind, 1959). There is an unquestionable trend toward integration, with greater percentages of blind children attending public schools, and also, within the public schools, for the children to have their activities integrated earlier and more fully with the regular programs of the sighted children. It is now not uncommon, for example, for children even in the lowest elementary school grades, to spend only a small part of the school day with their resource teacher, learning braille and going over other specialized problems, while spending the major part of the day with the regular grade. Greenberg, in a study of blind children in secondary schools that also included Negroes and women as members of other "disadvantaged" groups, concluded that for the blind and Negro populations, integrated education had a more beneficial effect on the personality than segregated education. The results were based on data on the Bernreuter Personality Inventory, the F-Scale, and a Personal Data Form (Greenberg, 1955).

Axline and Raskin have discussed play therapy with blind

children (Axline, 1954; Raskin, 1954). Both stress the individuality of the children, which is more impressive than their common handicap, and the therapist's efforts, by providing understanding, acceptance, and respect, to help the blind child to develop positive self-regarding attitudes, in response to what are frequently disparaging parental and societal attitudes.

RESEARCH. The attempt has been made up to this point in this chapter to describe the state of existing knowledge in the areas of statistics on blindness, the implications of blindness for general psychological development and adjustment, the real limitations of this disability in cognition and mobility, the attitudes of sighted people toward blindness, the auditory and tactile abilities of blind persons, obstacle perception, intelligence testing at various age levels, achievement, aptitude and interest testing, personality evaluation, and rehabilitation and therapy. Not a one of these areas could not do with further research, as has been pointed out in a survey (Graham, 1960) that summarizes recent investigations and makes suggestions for future efforts. Earlier, Raskin and Weller had published a report on *Current Research in Work with the Blind* (Raskin and Weller, 1953). These authors had found a particular interest in the personal adjustment of blind persons and summarized the investigations in this area as follows:

> There is first of all a difference in emphasis regarding the purpose of the research. In the past, two major questions have been primary: (1) How well adjusted are the blind? and (2) How does the adjustment of the blind compare with that of sighted people? The current studies reveal a distinct shift toward a more functional emphasis, so that many of the investigations are concerned with the factors that underlie adjustment and with the effectiveness of procedures designed to improve the adjustment of blind persons. . . . Secondly, the current studies are characterized by the employment of more advanced instruments for measuring personal adjustment . . . there is not a single one which relies solely on the inventory-type of test in this field, but instead there is a noticeable development in the wide-

spread use of projective tests of personality which aim at a deeper understanding of adjustment patterns. Indeed, several of the research projects center around the creation of such instruments. . . . Together with these advances in methods of investigation, the concepts being studied show more interest in the total adjustment of the person and in central variables of personality organization such as the concept of self and a lessening of attention to such concepts as neuroticism and introversion—extroversion, which are more traditional and tend to describe rather than explain. [Raskin and Weller, 1953, pp. 18–19.]

Raskin and Weller also called attention to the growing interest, within the adjustment area, of evaluations of treatment programs, and of longitudinal studies. They felt that there was "a strong trend in current and past studies of the blind which leads to the important conclusion that, in regard to basic personality variables such as self-respect, feelings of security and realism of outlook, the process of adjustment in blind persons is not significantly different from that of people with sight."

It was found in this survey that one area not being currently investigated was that of attitudes toward blind persons. After reviewing the literature in this and the related fields of other disability and minority groups, the author suggests the following lines of research:

1. A more accurate determination of the extent and nature of stereotypic attitudes toward blind people.
2. The development of attitudes toward blindness in sighted children.
3. The specificity or generality of stereotypic attitudes toward blind people.
4. The role played by weaknesses in thinking in stereotypic attitudes toward blind people.
5. The relationship of personality variables to attitudes toward blindness.
6. The relationship of a particular family pattern to stereotypic thinking about blind people.

7. The relationship of situational factors to stereotyped notions about blindness.
8. The effect of intergroup contact on attitudes toward blindness.
9. The relationship to attitudes toward blindness of social class variables.
10. The effectiveness of programs designed to increase understanding and respect for blind people as individuals.

Similar formulations could be made of the other areas covered in this chapter that should be bolstered by research and advances in knowledge. In his experience in research administration in the "blind field," the author has found that the greatest obstacle in furthering knowledge was the attitude on the part of otherwise well-qualified investigators that blindness represented a narrow field and one of insufficient general significance. Evidence to the contrary is shown by the interest and contributions of people outstanding in their general professional work, such as Axline, Cholden, Cowen, Critchley, Cruickshank, Dallenbach, Drever, Meyerson, Mittelman, Myklebust, Sargent, and Worchel. Equally encouraging is the work of newer investigators such as Axelrod, Engel, and Jervis, who have already made contributions of significance to our understanding of blindness.

REFERENCES

American Foundation for the Blind. 1959. Concerning the education of blind children. Compiled by G. L. Abel. New York, American Foundation for the Blind.

—— 1960. Services for blind persons in the United States. New York, American Foundation for the Blind.

American Medical Association. 1934. Resolution on the definition of blindness. J. Amer. Med. Ass. 102:2205.

Axelrod, S. 1959. Effects of early blindness: performance of blind and sighted children in tactile and auditory tasks. New York, American Foundation for the Blind.

Axline, V. M. 1954. Understanding and accepting the child who is blind. Childhood Educ. 30:427–30.

Barker, R. G., Beatrice A. Wright, L. Meyerson, and Mollie R. Gonick. 1953. Adjustment to physical handicap and illness: a survey of the social psychology of physique and disability. Social Science Research Council Bulletin 55 (Revised). New York, Social Science Research Council, pp. 228–64.

Bauman, M. K. 1954. Adjustment to blindness. Harrisburg, Pa., Pennsylvania State Council for the Blind.

—— 1958. A manual of norms for tests used in counseling blind persons. New York, American Foundation for the Blind.

Bauman, M. K., and S. P. Hayes. 1951. A manual for the psychological examination of the adult blind. New York, Psychological Corporation.

Bradway, K. P. 1937. Social competence of exceptional children. III: The deaf, the blind, and the crippled. Exceptional Children 4:64–69.

Cattell, P. 1940. The measurement of intelligence of infants and young children. New York, Psychological Corporation.

Chevigny, H. 1946. My eyes have a cold nose. New Haven, Yale University Press.

Cholden, L. S. 1958. A psychiatrist works with blindness. New York, American Foundation for the Blind.

Cowen, E. L., Rita P. Underberg, R. T. Verrillo, and F. G. Benham. 1960. Adjustment to visual disability in adolescence. Unpublished MS, University of Rochester.

Dean, S. I. 1957. Adjustment testing and personality factors of the blind. J. Consult. Psychol. 21:171–77.

Dolanski, W. 1930. Les aveugles, possedent-ils "le sense des obstacles"? L'Année Psychologique 31:1–50.

Doll, E. A. 1953. The measurement of social competence; a manual for the Vineland Social Maturity Scale. Minneapolis, Educational Test Bureau.

Dorfman, E. 1958. Personality outcomes of client-centered child therapy. Psychological Monographs 72, No. 3. Washington, D.C., American Psychological Association.

Engel, M. 1958. The development and application of the Children's Insight Test. J. Project. Techn. 22:13–25.

Firestone, S., I. F. Lukoff, and M. Whiteman. 1960. Aspects of the travel adjustment of blind persons. New York, American Foundation for the Blind.

Graham, M. 1960. Social research on blindness. New York, American Foundation for the Blind.

Greenberg, H. M. 1955. Some effects of segregated education on various aspects of the personality of those members of disadvantaged groups experiencing this form of education. Dissertation Abstracts. Publication No. 13,609.

Hayes, S. P. 1941. Contributions to a psychology of blindness. New York, American Foundation for the Blind.

—— 1942. Alternative scales for the mental measurement of the visually handicapped. Outlook for the Blind 36:225–30.

—— 1950. Measuring the intelligence of the blind, in P. A. Zahl, ed. Blindness. Princeton, N.J., Princeton University Press, pp. 141–73.

—— 1952. First regional conference on mental measurements of the blind. Watertown, Mass., Perkins Institution.

Jerome, E. A., and H. Proshansky. 1950. Factors in the assay and use of guidance devices, in P. A. Zahl, ed. Blindness. Princeton, N.J., Princeton University Press, pp. 462–94.

Koehler, M. E. 1933. The personnel problems of the blind students in a university. Unpublished Master's thesis, University of Minnesota.

Lowenfeld, B. 1955. Psychological problems of children with impaired vision, in W. M. Cruickshank, ed. Psychology of exceptional children and youth. Englewood Cliffs, N.J., Prentice-Hall, pp. 214–83.

MacFarland, D. C. 1956. A study of work efficiency of blind and sighted workers in industry. New York, American Foundation for the Blind.

Maxfield, K. E., and Sandra Buchholz. 1957. A social maturity scale for blind preschool children; a guide to its use. New York, American Foundation for the Blind.

Meyerson, L. 1953. The visually handicapped. Rev. Educ. Res. 23: 476–96.

Morris, W. W. 1950. A survey of projective techniques for use with the blind adult, in W. Donahue and D. H. Dabelstein, eds. Psychological diagnosis and counseling of the adult blind. New York, American Foundation for the Blind, pp. 114–29.

Murray, H. A. 1938. Explorations in personality. New York, Oxford University Press.

Norris, M., P. J. Spaulding, and F. H. Brodie. 1957. Blindness in children. Chicago, University of Chicago Press.

Raskin, N. J. 1954. Play therapy with blind children. National Association for Remedial Teaching News 4:1–6.

Raskin, N. J., and M. Weller. 1953. Current research in work for the blind. New York, American Foundation for the Blind.

Rusalem, H. 1950. The environmental supports of public attitudes toward the blind. New Outlook for the Blind 44:277–88.

Sargent, H. 1953. The insight test. New York, Grune and Stratton.

Sargent, H. 1956. Insight test prognosis in successful and unsuccessful rehabilitation of the blind. J. Project. Techn. 20:429–41.

Schaefer, F. M. 1930. The social traits of the blind. Unpublished Master's thesis, Loyola University, Chicago.

Shakow, D., and S. Rosenzweig. 1940. The use of the Tautophone (Verbal Summator) as an auditory apperception test for the study of personality. Character and Personality 8:216–26.

Sommers, V. S. 1944. The influence of parental attitudes and social environment on the personality of the adolescent blind. New York, American Foundation for the Blind.

Steingisser, E. R. 1954. The influence of set upon attitudes toward the blind as related to self-concept. Unpublished Master's thesis, University of New Hampshire.

Strong, E. K. 1943. Vocational interests of men and women. Stanford, Calif., Stanford University Press.

Supa, M., M. Cotzin, and K. M. Dallenbach. 1944. Facial vision: the perception of obstacles by the blind. Amer. J. Psychol. 57:133–83.

Tuddenham, R. D. 1952. Studies in reputation. Psychological Monographs 66, No. 1. Washington, D.C., American Psychological Association.

Twitchell-Allen, D. 1947. A Three-Dimensional Apperception Test; a new projective technique. [Abstract.] Amer. Psychologist 2:271–72.

U.S. National Health Survey. 1959. Impairments by type, sex, and age, United States, July, 1957–June, 1958. Washington, U.S. Dept. of Health, Education, and Welfare, Public Health Service, Division of Public Health Methods.

U.S. Office of Vocational Rehabilitation. 1956. Rehabilitation centers for blind persons. Rehabilitation Service Series No. 380. Washington, D.C., U.S. Dept. of Health, Education, and Welfare.

U.S. Veterans Administration. 1958. War blinded veterans in a postwar setting; a social work followup of rehabilitation measures for blinded veterans with service-connected disabilities between December 7, 1951 and March 31, 1953. Washington, D.C., Government Printing Office.

Walters, G. T. 1955. Certain background factors of college students associated with their attitudes toward the employment of the blind. Unpublished Master's thesis, Pennsylvania State University.

Williams, R. G., and M. D. Flank. 1955. Therapy for the newly blinded as practiced with veterans. J. Amer. Med. Ass. 158:811–18.

Wilmer, H. A., and M. Husni. 1953. The use of sounds in a projective test. J. Consult. Psychol. 17:377–83.

Worchel, P., and K. M. Dallenbach. 1947. Facial vision: perception of obstacles by the deaf-blind. Amer. J. Psychol. 60:502–53.

Worchel, P., J. Mauney, and J. G. Andrew. 1950. The perception of obstacles by the blind. J. Exp. Psychol. 40:746–51.

AGENCIES AND ORGANIZATIONS

A *Directory of Agencies Serving Blind Persons in the United States and Canada* is published and periodically revised by the American Foundation for the Blind, Inc., at 15 West 16th Street, New York 11, New York. The twelfth edition, the most recent, was published in 1961.

The National Society for the Prevention of Blindness, at 1790 Broadway, New York 19, New York, is a source of general information in the field of vision impairment which may not be as severe as legal blindness.

DEAF-BLINDNESS

by JACOB ROTHSCHILD

THE DISABILITY and related psychological practices dealt with in this chapter are confined to "deaf-blindness" exclusively. Hard-of-hearing–blindness is not included in this category; it is considered a separate entity. Also, specific aspects of deafness and of blindness will not be dealt with here since these two disabilities are discussed in the preceding chapters and many of the characteristics of deafness and of blindness may be applied to deaf-blindness as well. This chapter aims to present those aspects that go beyond deafness and blindness and are characteristic of deaf-blindness per se.

Although the term "deaf-blindness" refers to a multiple handicap involving two sensory areas, the simultaneous impairment of both vision and hearing represents a special handicap-Gestalt that cannot be adequately formulated by the combined presence of blindness plus deafness in the same person. Obviously any rehabilitative, diagnostic, or educational approach to a blind person will make comprehensive use of his hearing. Conversely, with impairment of hearing, visual stimuli are largely used as substitutes for auditory ones. However, neither of these approaches is applicable when the visual as well as the auditory senses are impaired or fully nonfunctional. A deaf-blind person can be successfully approached only if other, nonimpaired senses can be utilized, particularly the tactile sense. In short, the com-

Jacob Rothschild, Ph.D., is Chief Psychologist at the Industrial Home for the Blind, Brooklyn, New York.

bined effects of the double sensory deficits of deafness plus blindness results in a distinctive disability that is a separate entity from either deafness or blindness alone.

Concerning which of the sensory deficits of deaf-blindness entails the greater handicap, in the total process of perception in the human being the visual sense is by far the predominantly preferred one. Estimates as to the share of vision in the total process of perception in the sensorially intact vary, but are generally placed within a range of 84–90 percent. The auditory sense is generally considered the second most extensively employed sense in the perceptual process. This would seem to imply that a person whose vision is totally absent is handicapped in the major area of perceptual functioning and would suggest that blindness rather than deafness serves as the greater rehabilitation determinant in serving deaf-blind persons. However, it would be entirely erroneous to view deaf-blindness in such quantitative terms. As will be emphasized throughout this chapter, a satisfactory approach to a deaf-blind patient is determined by the global handicap rather than by concepts that are exclusively applicable to either deafness or blindness.

DEFINITIONS AND INCIDENCE. The incidence of deaf-blindness in the United States has been estimated by Handel (Handel, 1958) to be 3,000 persons. Estimates by Parnicky and Onken (Parnicky and Onken, 1958) put the figure closer to 4,000, with 180 deaf-blind persons living in New York State. It is interesting to compare these figures with estimates made thirty years ago by Rocheleau and Mack (Rocheleau and Mack, 1930), who, "after three years of painstaking and thorough research work . . . succeeded in unearthing 618 'living cases' in the United States as a whole," of whom 123 were New York State residents.

As to what is meant by deaf-blind, the disability has been defined in terms of the following combined descriptions (Handel,

1958): *deaf*—the inability to understand connected discourse through the ear; plus the generally accepted legal definition of *blindness*—central visual acuity of 20/200 [1] or less in the better eye, with correcting glasses; or central visual acuity of more than 20/200 if there is a field defect in which the peripheral field has been contracted to such an extent that the widest diameter of the visual field subtends an angular distance no greater than 20 degrees. The definition of blindness is legally accepted in most states, but the definition of deafness is a pragmatic one as here used, and to date no legal description has been established.

Whereas deafness as defined in connection with deaf-blindness represents a profound or total amount of hearing loss, the definition of blindness involves a less drastic amount of sensory deficit. Visual acuity below 20/200 can include a considerable range of residual vision, which means that individual deaf-blind persons can have varying degrees of visual acuity. Even though all fall within the legal category of blindness, the difference between an acuity of 20/200 and total blindness is a wide one, and the continuum between these extremes of "legal" blindness encompasses many variations ranging, for example, from ability to read print to inability to make any distinctions on a visual basis. A critical line of demarcation (which is also among the critical determinants in psychological test administration) is the visual acuity level of about 5/200, at which the use of residual vision tends to become quite minimal. And even here there is still a substantial difference between the deaf-blind person who has "light perception" and the one who is completely deprived of all visual perception.

Finally, concerning the order of onset of disability, deafness precedes blindness in a majority of cases (Parnicky and Onken, 1958). In only rare instances are deafness and blindness both

[1] Visual acuity of 20/200 represents the ability to see at 20 feet what should normally be perceived at 200 feet.

present in early childhood, and but 1.7 percent of the deaf-blind have been so since birth (Parnicky and Onken, 1958).

MEDICAL ASPECTS. GENERAL HEALTH. In a pilot study of 39 deaf-blind subjects (Kolbrenner, 1958) comprehensive physical examinations were administered. They included: urinalysis, chest X-ray, electrocardiagram, and, in some instances, a blood-sugar and cholesterol analysis, and a gastrointestinal series. Full conformity with the expectations for a nonhandicapped population was found in these deaf-blind persons. Also, the response to these examinations on the part of the subjects was normal. In contrast to the findings with blind subjects with which this group was compared, a complete absence of psychosomatic complaints was observed.

OTOLOGICAL INVESTIGATIONS. Among a study group of 28 deaf-blind subjects Fowler (Fowler, 1958) found 10 with impacted cerumen. In only 3 were there indications of past inflammatory episodes in the middle ear. In all the subjects, the drum membrane was present. Gentle inflation of the middle ear did not cause vertigo in any of the cases. Although the Eustachian tubes were patent, there were very few subjects who had no sensation whatsoever. Twenty-four of the subjects were congenitally deaf, and 2 had partial hearing loss since birth.

Fowler points out that "in all cases of inherited deafness there is a recessive hereditary trait not infrequently correlated with other hereditary defects" (Fowler, 1958). In the case of this group of 28 subjects, a high incidence (23 cases) of retinitis pigmentosa (primary degeneration of the retina of the eye) was found. In none of the cases was there a history of maternal infection or disease during pregnancy. Further examination revealed negative findings in all routine neurological tests; an abnormally acute tactile sense; and no recruitment of loudness.

Even a 5 db. change of loudness was not sensed as a change. All subjects were diagnosed as cases of neural deafness. Fowler was of the opinion that neither medical nor surgical treatment for deafness would be advisable in these deaf-blind subjects.

OPHTHALMOLOGICAL STUDY. Gilroy (Gilroy, 1958) examined a group of 38 deaf-blind subjects of whom 31 were diagnosed as "retinitis pigmentosa." In 23 cases, there was a family history of deaf-blindness. The subjects outside the retinitis pigmentosa group maintained better vision over an eleven-year period, whereas all the retinitis pigmentosa cases showed a gradual loss of vision. Progress of the disease was more rapid in subjects with central deafness.

Gilroy was of the opinion that there was no formula for predicting exactly when loss of light perception would occur in patients who had previously had residual vision. She recommended surgical correction for all cases where this would prolong the visual life of the patient, and vision was improved in a number of cases of this group after surgery (cataract extraction, draining operation for glaucoma, corneal transplant for scarring due to burns or disease).

PSYCHOLOGICAL IMPLICATIONS. Since the sensory deficits of deaf-blindness involve the loss of such a comprehensive part of the perceptual system, the difficulties involved are more complex and extensive than those found among any other group of handicapped people. As Waterhouse (Waterhouse, 1957) points out, when "both sight and hearing are impaired so that substitutions of one for the other are impossible, both handicaps are rendered more profound."

To add to the complexity, the many variables present among the deaf-blind seem almost more numerous than the common denominators. In addition to the variations within the legal definition of blindness, the age of onset of the visual deficit is an important determinant of psychological implications. Whether blindness was congenital, whether a deaf-blind person was very young when he started to have difficulty with his vision, or whether he had grown to adulthood before the onset of blindness—all of these produce considerable variation in the effect of blindness on personal functioning and on the amount of resultant handicap. In this connection, a critical line of distinction seems to be the age of about five or six years. If blindness has set in after this age, it appears that many of the visual images that have been obtained prior to the onset can be successfully retained and meaningfully complemented with impressions acquired thereafter. But if blindness was present before the age of about five or six years, the visual impressions gained while there was unimpaired vision do not seem to be of substantial help in the orientation process afterwards. The same applies to the age of onset of deafness.

Further, when deafness, blindness, or deaf-blindness are present since childhood, the person will have been exposed to one or another kind of special education and special school either for the blind or for the deaf. Variables involved in the kind of special education required, and in the type and effectiveness of the techniques of training also make for differences in the functioning of deaf-blind persons. Another variable in psychological impact as well as in approach to the deaf-blind concerns the presence or absence of verbal communication. This is generally related to the age of onset of the disability. Lipreading, for example, which plays such an important communicative role in deafness may have been learned at one time and then subsequently excluded by the onset of blindness; or an individual may or may not have had speech training before or after the onset of deaf-blindness. Whether or not speech is present is of the greatest importance in determining the open avenues of communication for and with deaf-blind persons.

Such being the variations in visual acuity, in precedence of onset of blindness or deafness, in schooling and training experiences, and in communicative skills, there would appear to be only one common characteristic among the deaf-blind—the total absence of hearing. It appears, however, that individual differences among deaf-blind persons are not quite as outstanding in the areas of personal functioning, goals, and rehabilitation approaches as the variables would imply. All share the tremendous isolation to which they are subjected. Nevertheless, individual differences become quite manifest when the various modes of adjustment to and coping with this isolation are investigated.

The isolating impact may well be considered *the* handicap of deaf-blindness. This disability represents possibly the most comprehensive and most incapacitating example of isolation, especially of social isolation. This being so, it follows that a primary goal of rehabilitation is to reduce the effects of this isolation and open whatever avenues are feasible for increasing the contact of a deaf-blind person with his surroundings. In this respect, any communicative techniques that will enable a deaf-blind person to establish effective contacts with his surroundings are encouraged.

From the viewpoint of psychological functioning, the nature and extent of this isolation—the comprehensiveness of the visual and auditory disabilities, the age of onset, the length of time since onset, the order of handicap, the abrupt or gradual onset, the rehabilitative measures, therapies, and services rendered—all of these will exert modifying influences and are important considerations in individual appraisal. Putting these variables aside for the moment and considering the essential factor of isolation, a number of effects, both direct and indirect, primary and secondary, of greater or lesser incapacitating influence, can be observed. The following section summarizes the characteristic impressions found in a number of areas of personality function in a study of a group initially composed of 25 deaf-blind persons and subsequently expanded to include an additional 20 persons (Rothschild, 1958).

INTELLECTUAL FUNCTIONING. *General Information.* In comparing the various areas of intellectual endeavor with each other, it appears that the majority of the deaf-blind subjects possess a satisfactory range of general information. Even with a very limited educational background, most of them are able to acquire a fair amount of basic knowledge. A large number are aware of the value of this information. This can be considered a significant achievement considering the difficulties that are posed in the attainment of such knowledge. Most of them show a keen interest in obtaining information about their surroundings as well as about topics that are less directly related to their daily activities. It appears that the acquisition of a certain scope of general information at the time of schooling is something that has impressed the deaf-blind person, and the desire to expand the scope is frequently found. The level at which a particular individual is informed seems related to the initiative he displays in maintaining good general contact with his surroundings. A deaf-blind person who actively seeks to establish comprehensive social contacts may be more aware of the need for an adequate background of information than is the one who is more passive in this respect.

Although interest in accumulating personally relevant as well as more general information may be rather keen in many deaf-blind persons, it is quite difficult for them to apply criteria of accuracy concerning the information acquired. Because of the limitations imposed by the handicaps, considerably fewer standards are available to them by which such information can be viewed critically. Further, the need for critical evaluation may not be experienced very intensively. Often, information is accepted at face value without critical reasoning concerning its reliability.

There seems to be a fairly close relation among the time of the onset of deaf-blindness, the level of accumulated information, and the desire to acquire further information. While the alertness for acquiring knowledge may be present, the means by which this can be achieved are obviously limited by the reduction of channels through which impressions from the outside can be relayed. A certain shift in the character and nature of information that has been acquired after the onset of deaf-blindness can be noticed—for example, the individual may be better informed on topics that pertain closely to his sector of daily living. Also, the individual will have to rely more on his memory for retaining the general information he had acquired before the onset of deaf-blindness since he is now largely without the benefit of stimuli which aid in the retention of knowledge.

General Comprehension. As to the ability to comprehend, facility in this particular area may provide the key to the general intellectual functioning of deaf-blind persons. Comprehension in terms of basic understanding of a situation on which an intellectual effort is to be applied depends very much on the communicative efficiency through which a description of the situation is conveyed. Deaf-blindness obviously handicaps the communicative process considerably. For one, the frequency of being exposed to situations that have to be comprehended is reduced. For example, in the course of a day, a deaf-blind person is more isolated from situations in which the need to comprehend is stimulated. Second, the variety of situations that have to be comprehended by him is of narrower scope than is the case with non-handicapped persons. Third, the "inventory" of accumulated impressions from the past is smaller, and this makes it more difficult to use past impressions for appraising new situations. Consequently, new situations have more of a "novelty" character and are therefore more difficult to comprehend. Fourth, to achieve successful comprehension, the deaf-blind person has to lean heavily on interpretation by another person by means of the slow techniques of special communication that are available, and this "detour" and delay in the process of comprehension is likely to render it more difficult, if not entirely impossible, to perceive the total *Gestalt* of a situation.

Because of the various difficulties mentioned, the deaf-blind person's ability to comprehend may not be as keen or as "natural" in its employment as that of persons whose channels of perception are fully available. In terms of actual intellectual performance, these inadequacies appear to resemble lack of intellectual competence. If, however, the direct effects of deaf-blindness on intellectual activity could be artificially isolated and studied, the difficulties in comprehension would appear in a different light. All other factors being equal, the potential ability to comprehend would be seen as adequate and efficient. Obviously, the methods currently used for measuring a person's ability to comprehend, such as psychological tests, do not take the disabling effects of deaf-blindness into consideration. Nevertheless, the comprehension facility of a deaf-blind person may well reflect his over-all intellectual potential more aptly than any other attribute of intelligence since the ability to understand is the basis for a good part of intellectual attainment; and difficulties in this ability are likely to be reflected in other intellectual endeavors.

In applying his ability to comprehend, a deaf-blind person may experience difficulties in finding the proper perspectives for assigning the various components of a given situation their proper value-relationship to one another. The disability complications that interfere with basic comprehension may lead to a certain ineptitude in grasping cause-effect sequence and hence to poor efficiency in the total performance. In this respect, there appears to be a strong relationship between comprehension-ability and the extent of schooling. Training the ability to comprehend often depends on specially adapted techniques to induce optimal "comprehension-acuity," and consequently skill in this area will reflect the success of such training. Similarly, the age of onset of the disabilities also appears to have some bearing on the level of comprehension-ability attained, since the attainment of a favorable level of comprehension aptitude prior to onset may be of subsequent help even under the limiting conditions of deaf-blindness. The implementation of what is commonly called "common sense" as part of the comprehension process generally depends on how much it had been developed under more favorable conditions. A goodly amount of previously developed common sense will give a deaf-blind person adequate support for carrying on with the comprehension process. His ability to express himself will, in turn, determine how much evidence he can give of what and how well he has understood.

Reasoning. As to the reasoning power of deaf-blind persons, this ability demonstrates effects that may be considered secondary to the influences of deaf-blindness on comprehension; for, when the ability to comprehend is adversely affected, this will show up in the ability to apply reasoning. Further, with reasoning as with comprehension, deaf-blindness is likely to curtail opportunities for applying a reasoning process and for developing reasoning aptitudes. Because the deaf-blind person's contact with his surroundings frequently requires intermediary interpretation, the occasions in which he can perform independent reasoning are less frequent, as is the need for relying on his own reasoning powers. Situations that a sensorially-intact person would have to think out for himself are often "pre-thought-out" for deaf-blind persons and are presented to him as facts in their final form. For example, directions, pieces of information, descriptions, events, and so forth, that are presented to deaf-blind persons are frequently confined to their essential characteristics. They may omit historical background, factors that have lead to the present situation, effects that it may have on contiguous situations, possible consequences to future events and arrangements, and so forth. This discourages opportunities and practice in reasoning from the known to the unknown, from the concrete to the abstract, and from fact to assumption and developing interests in abstract matters or performing theoretical abstractions. It encourages a tendency to rely exclusively upon what is conveyed by the interpreter without giving much thought to factors that are not directly contained in the interpreted message.

In going through a reasoning process, the deaf-blind person is apt to be handicapped by a limitation in experiences. He may have only inadequate knowledge of the difference between the essential and the secondary qualities of a subject. To perform abstractions may make relatively little sense to him, because the limited contacts and relationships available to him are largely of a practical nature without much room for theoretical abstraction. Here again, the educational and social background of the individual become important variables. The deaf-blind person with substantial academic training and a broad background of experiences is in a better position to reason effectively than is the one without this background.

Memory. Memory for retaining absorbed impressions does not seem to be substantially affected by deaf-blindness. The deaf-blind person is in fact forced to rely heavily on memory because he is not exposed to the repetitive perception of impressions to the same extent as the sensorially intact. For such a person to grasp and comprehend the range of even essential messages that are conveyed daily and on many occasions each day requires the extensive use of memory if a complete message is to be absorbed, particularly since communicative presentation moves slowly and its fractions have to be integrated and retained over a span of time.

Since the deaf-blind person is subjected to the need for a good deal of memorizing in his daily living, this performance is closely related to the practical purposes toward which it is geared, as for example in moving from one location to another in which memorization of all and every previous impression of the locations involved is essential. Any clues that are offered in the course of this activity are useful only if they can be associated with recollections of preceding impressions. It can be assumed therefore that a deaf-blind individual is generally better equipped to apply memory to purposeful material than to meaningless matter. Hence, he may not perform as well on rote memory tasks as on practical and personally relevant items. In view of the heavy burdens to which a deaf-blind person's retentive powers are subjected, it may be an economical use of memory to reserve it for tasks of practical value.

Word Power. It seems quite difficult for deaf-blind persons to define and in some cases comprehend single words. Words out of context seem too incomplete and fragmentary to represent meaningful entities in themselves. For example, the word "assemble" from the Wechsler Vocabulary test may make little sense when presented by itself, whereas any combination of this word with others, as in assembly-work, assemble parts of a machine, and so forth, is easily comprehended by most deaf-blind persons. Thus, although a deaf-blind individual may be unable to handle the isolated word, he can employ the same term successfully in the context of a complete sentence or idea. In other words, the individual finds it difficult to handle what might be called "dictionary vocabulary." This is possibly related to the ways of communication which are available to the deaf-blind. These are employed to describe whole situations, and the individual's grasp of verbal material is geared to such global description. He is accustomed to have a given word preceded and followed by other words. Out of context, the single word loses significance.

As for the verbal abilities of deaf-blind persons in terms of connected language, considerable variation is found depending upon the extent written matter is used. If the use of verbal expression is confined to conversation, then verbal abilities are likely to be poorer than if the deaf-blind person has reading skills, either in braille or print. Verbal abilities are apt to be more comprehensive in the latter situation. A direct relation between verbal abilities and available means of contact with the surroundings seems quite certain.

The difficulties of communication for deaf-blind persons tend to encourage relatively simple and confined verbalizations. In view of the slowness of the communicative process and of the effort required, communication proceeds most economically if the vocabulary used is simple and the sentences short. Deaf-blind persons who are able to write fairly well frequently show a greater readiness to express themselves in writing than in conversation. Occasionally one can observe good verbal abilities in a deaf-blind person's writings whereas in direct communication they may have seemed on a lower level.

General Use of Intelligence. Deaf-blindness per se does not appear to impair native intellectual capacity. However, the level of intellectual functioning of deaf-blind persons is influenced by a number of restrictions and variables associated with the condition of deaf-blindness. Predominant among them are difficulties in communication, differences in schooling and background of experiences, and limitation of available channels of contact with the environment. These among other factors make for considerable variation in the intellectual performance of deaf-blind persons and must be taken into consideration when the evaluation of intellectual capacity is made. Also to be considered are possible influences of the following factors. Limits in perception may interfere with the acquisition of basic information. Communicative and perceptual difficulties may affect the rate and quality of comprehension. Aptitude in using verbal material may be inhibited because of limited accessibility to such material. Theoretical-abstract material may be largely outside the scope of everyday living experiences since the major efforts have to be devoted to practical considerations. The range of experiences and the criteria to be used as standards of comparison and of integration of new impressions may be confined to a smaller range of reality. Because of the need for reliance on other people's assistance, a degree of dependency may be encouraged that is apt to be reflected in intellectual endeavors. Finally, an unrealistic personal view of the handicaps of deaf-blindness may reduce the individual's self-confident use of his intellectual abilities.

GENERAL PERSONALITY FUNCTIONING. Because of the severity of his disability, the deaf-blind person is obliged to rely on assistance from other people to a far greater extent than most other physically disabled individuals. Even for performing a number of functions that are essential to daily living, he requires help from the outside and is in fact fully dependent on such help. This dependency may leave certain areas of his personal potential unused and undeveloped. Being dependent on the assistance of other people also fosters anxiety about not getting it. Sometimes this concern is pushed into an unrealistic focus with the reassurance of the availability of help becoming as important as the help itself.

Whereas similar anxieties and outcomes exist among other physically disabled persons as well, they appear to be of particular significance in the deaf-blind person. Because of the nature of his disabilities, perception of his surroundings is profoundly impaired, and the individual is in a poorer position to ascertain the indications of available help by himself. He can obtain only limited clues as to the forthcoming of the assistance that he needs and expects. He has little possibility of surveying the provisions that have been made for his welfare and only inadequate means of assuring himself as to the reliability of his helpers. This applies to immediate as well as future needs. Furthermore, because of the relatively wide range of needs for which he requires assistance, he is frequently reminded of his dependency and is thereby more compelled to recognize and to feel it.

In addition, because of the deaf-blind individual's very limited ability to perceive his surroundings, his position in them can be very difficult for him to comprehend. Because of this, any adjustment to the environment becomes more complicated. While the individual may try to obtain a picture of himself for his own purposes, it may be well nigh impossible for him to see himself in a fully realistic light. This applies to himself as an individual as well as to the role and significance of his handicap. His image of the effects of his limitations may make him feel less capable than he actually is. Even after some of these limitations are removed, this feeling of incapacity may still remain. This results in considerable restriction of ego function and of drive to make use of as many opportunities, stimulations, and gratifications as possible. The deaf-blind person has a very diffuse image (if any) of his personality strengths and weaknesses.

In terms of the range of reality experiences, that of a deaf-blind person is very restricted. The number and scope of situations with which he comes into significant and frequent contact are much fewer and more restricted than those of sensorially-intact persons. It can therefore be assumed that reality for a deaf-blind person is much different from that of the nonhandicapped person. Hence, personality processes take on a substantially different aspect since the reduction in meaningful contacts with reality will in all likelihood be accompanied by a difference in the quality of relationship to it.

Also affected by the deaf-blind person's limited contacts with reality is the application of reality principles and experiences to future planning. This is manifested as a difficulty in abstracting the essentials of a known situation for the purpose of applying them to a projected situation. The totality of conditions to which the deaf-blind are exposed at a given time seems inextricably bound to a given situation. To select certain parts of the totality for application to another situation presents a problem that is difficult for the deaf-blind to meet. The separation of parts represents to them the abolishment of the whole. This rigidity and perseveration in adjustment to prevailing conditions does not leave sufficient flexibility for adaptation to changed conditions.

Though the social functioning of a deaf-blind person may be very limited, the wish for interpretation of the environment may nonetheless be quite strong. Here again, frustrating restrictions are met. The deaf-blind person's range of experiences that can be used as points of reference for interpretation is necessarily small. The comprehension of many of the social processes in the environment may be beyond his understanding. Attempts to relate them to his personal experiences may easily lead to confusion. All of these make it particularly difficult for a deaf-blind person to achieve even superficial identification with others. "Face-to-face relationship," in the usual sense of the term, is more or less denied him and without this, identification with others is difficult to make and intuitive insight into their attitudes and motivations is difficult to achieve.

So few are the clues afforded a deaf-blind person from his environment that those he does obtain acquire a special degree of significance. The latter are generally transmitted to him through "mechanical" verbal communication, unmodified by gestures, facial expression, or vocal intonation. The possibility of interpreting the speaker's intention beyond the actual text of the verbalization is therefore limited. Further, difficulties of communication may force the speaker to restrict his verbalizations to a basic minimum. Extensive descriptions and explanations are generally omitted. However, since the stark verbal message represents word from the "outside," it acquires unusual value for the deaf-blind recipient. Such messages are often considered more important and directive than they are intended to be. The deaf-blind person tries to comply with his interpretation of the message as best he can. This kind of adjustment, without full knowledge of what has to be adjusted to but with the strong desire to do so just the same, is a situation that confronts deaf-blind people quite frequently throughout the course of a day. The desire to comply with and to integrate themselves into situations, regardless of the paucity of leads that are available to do so successfully is apt to become an overly important endeavor to which the deaf-blind may devote excessive effort.

Along similar lines, a great share of direction is sought by the deaf-blind and is obtained by them from the regulations and conventions of social living. Often, this kind of direction takes strong precedence over guidance that the individual could have obtained from his own inner resources. Self-fulfillment and self-confidence are partially relinquished in favor of behavior rules and socially accepted standards. This can be understood in view of the deaf-blind person's dependence on the judgment of others. In fact, much of what contributes to the development of "personality" and the display of "individuality" has to be adopted by the deaf-blind from the direct guidance, judgments, values, and services of other people.

In reviewing the total scope of a deaf-blind person's needs and dependencies, there may be numbers of needs that cannot be met either at the time they arise or even at a later date. Naturally, this situation obtains for most people. But with the deaf-blind, there is a larger number of very basic needs that defy successful gratification. The help that is available may not be comprehensive enough to cover even basic personal requirements. Then again in some cases, it is not the deaf-blind person but others who decide how essential a need is and the feasibility of meeting it. Thus, the gratification of needs that are quite basic so far as the individual is concerned may be completely abrogated by an authority figure.

Helping a deaf-blind person make adjustments to his surroundings generally goes along with selecting the surroundings for him. Being compelled to rely on outside services for both these objectives obviously deprives the person of a good deal of self-determination. As the scope for self-determination is narrowed, so is the area of self-expression. This restricts even further the range of free personal functioning, which is already very limited because of deaf-blindness, and may inhibit the chances for the development of certain potentials even more than is the case with other handicapped persons who also have to depend on service. In fact, deaf-blind persons appear to have restrictions imposed on them to which no other group of physically disabled persons is subjected.

SPECIAL CONSIDERATIONS IN PSYCHOLOGICAL APPRAISAL. Psychological examinations and the use of tests generally utilize just those perceptive processes of which the deaf-blind person is deprived. Visual and auditory stimuli are predominantly the ones which are the tools of the psychologist. Hence, in appraising deaf-blind persons, various communicative substitutions and other adaptations must be made. Following is a brief list of feasible means of communication used in testing the deaf-blind:

Manual Alphabet: The use of the manual alphabet requires the psychologist's familiarity with it, both to transmit messages as well as to receive them. For clients who are totally deaf and who do not have any useful vision, who do not know braille, who cannot type or write, and who do not have speech, this may be the only available means of communication. Obviously this results in a very slow progress of examination. It may also limit the length of the individual question or direction that can be conveyed at one time.

Interpreter: Since familiarity with the manual alphabet cannot be assumed for all psychologists who have to deal with deaf-blind persons, an interpreter who is thoroughly familiar with the client can be employed as an intermediary. It is advisable to brief the interpreter in advance about the nature, purpose, and emphasis of various tests. This means of conducting a psychological examination will deprive the psychologist of the advantage of direct contact with the client, of some impressions thereof, and of their likely interpretation.

Tellatouch: This device (developed by the American Foundation for the Blind) resembles an ordinary typewriter. It has the same keyboard and, with it, letters are transmitted into braille characters which the client then reads manually. The instrument assumes the client's knowledge of braille. If the examiner also knows braille the client can respond to him by using the additional keys for answering in braille. The use of the Tellatouch is particularly practical where the client has speech but no hearing and no vision. It is a much faster mode of communication than manual alphabet, and hence is considerably less taxing on the client.

Printing in the Palm: This method can be employed with most clients, since familiarity with the standard alphabet is generally the rule. It is a fairly simple and quite satisfactory means of communication. However, since it imposes a good deal of physical strain on both examiner and client, frequent pauses in the course of the examination are advisable.

Large Type: This means of communication may be preferred in cases where the client has sufficient residual vision to read larger than standard size type. Each question and direction are transcribed in this type on individual cards that have been prepared in advance. (The need for clear typing or printing and for white paper is obvious.) In some cases the use of large type may be supplemented by having a magnifying glass available.

Braille: As with large-print individual cards, questions and directions can be transcribed in braille and then presented to the client. If this method is indicated, the individual cards should contain the text in regular print as well, to make sure that the examiner will choose the card with the proper text.

Any one or combination of the preceding methods of communication generally assures a fairly satisfactory test administration. It is important to ascertain in advance what the client's communicative skills are in order to prepare for the appropriate mode of contact. In composing the psychological report, the modes of communication that were used should be mentioned as well as a description of the client's visual, auditory, and speech abilities.

THE PSYCHOLOGICAL EXAMINATION. (For a general guide in testing blind persons see *A Manual for the Psychological Examination of the Adult Blind* (Bauman and Hayes, 1951) and *Psychological Tests for Use with Blind Adults in Vocational Rehabilitation* (DiMichael, 1947) where a more detailed description of necessary adaptation of tests can be found.)

Psychological Testing. In a study to develop a battery of feasible tests for deaf-blind persons (Rothschild, 1958), the following psychological tests proved practical:

1. *Intelligence*

a. *Wechsler Intelligence Scales:* The Verbal Scales of these tests can be administered with satisfactory results. If others than the WAIS verbal items are employed, the Vocabulary tests should be included. On the Comprehension subtest, the questions re fire, forest, deaf (5, 9, 10 of the WAIS) should be replaced by the "alternate questions" of WB I and by 10 of WB II ("Why should a promise be kept?"). The time limits of the Arithmetic subtests may have to be ignored in many cases because of the expectedly slower comprehension by the subject. In some cases, administrations of Digit Span may not be practical. When presenting Digits Backward in printed form for example, the subject could easily read the digits in the reverse order, which would then make this subtest merely a repetition of Digits Forward. The administration of the Similarities subtests may pose some problems since, as previously mentioned, it is very difficult for many deaf-blind testees to grasp abstractions. If this is the case, thorough preparation for this intellectual operation is necessary before the actual test is administered. Testees whose deaf-blindness set in early in life generally do poorly on the Vocabularly subtest because of their difficulty in handling isolated words.

b. *Hayes-Binet Intelligence Tests for the Blind* (Hayes, 1942): This adaptation for the blind of the Stanford-Binet Test is an additional tool for measuring intelligence of the deaf-blind. However, in contrast with the Wechsler tests, many of its questions are too lengthy, and this often proves a considerable handicap in administering it to deaf-blind subjects. The test does not seem practical for subjects who lack speech or sufficient vision to read the questions if they are presented in print.

c. *Performance Scale for Adult Blind* (Shurrager and Watson, 1958): This new adaptation of the Wechsler Performance Scale for the blind shows exceptional promise for the deaf-blind, and its administration follows the same directions as with the blind plus supplementary directions given by manual guidance. The test is currently still in the process of standardization for the blind, and it may yet take some time until its results can be incorporated to yield a Full Scale score.

d. *Copple Sentence Completion Test* (Copple, 1956): This test, which uses the sentence completion technique for measuring intelligence, can be used with the deaf-blind as a supplementary test to the Wechsler or the Hayes-Binet tests. Its administration is simple, and the practices employed with the Projective Sentence Completions (discussed below) can be applied.

2. *Manual Dexterity*

For this category of tests, the Pennsylvania Bi-manual Work-sample (Roberts, 1943), the Purdue Pegboard (Tiffin, 1948), the Minnesota Rate of Manipulation Test (Ziegler, and others, 1946), and the Crawford Small Parts Dexterity Test (Crawford and Crawford, 1946) are suggested. Directions and modifications for blind subjects (Roberts and Bauman, 1944) are applicable to the deaf-blind. Occasionally, the transition from a performance that is scored by length of time to one that has to be done within a pre-set time limit may be somewhat confusing to deaf-blind subjects. This calls for a more explicit introduction to allow for the necessary adjustment.

The Non-Language Learning Test by Bauman (Bauman, 1951) proved to be of little success with deaf-blind clients. Because of the necessarily extensive introductory directions, the instructions were too lengthy and complex for full comprehension, and it was found inadvisable to include this test in a battery for deaf-blind subjects.

3. *Projective Techniques*

There is a particular paucity of tests for the deaf-blind in this area as well as of tests that could be modified for the deaf-blind. The physical disabilities involved exclude the administration of a number of the popular techniques. In some cases however Projective Sentence Completions are feasible if the subjects can respond orally or through written communication. Some minor modifications are necessary. A number of sample "sentence stems" may have to be administered to give the deaf-blind client the opportunity to adapt himself to the procedure before the actual test is begun. Some of the wording may have to be simplified. Deaf-blind subjects often assume that the first person pronouns in the sentence-stems refer to the examiner, and he may have to be assisted in applying them to himself in order to complete the sentences. Where this test can be given, it is a valuable clinical tool and will often elicit significant clinical information about the intrapersonal dynamics of the subject.

The Twitchell-Allen (Twitchell-Allen, 1948) Three-Dimensional Apperception Test proved impractical with the deaf-blind and, in instances where its administration was attempted with blind persons, was found to elicit generally poor cooperation.

4. *Achievement Tests*

A number of tests measuring school achievement have been adapted for use with the blind. These are published by the American Printing House for the Blind, Louisville, Kentucky, and references can be found in the Bauman and Hayes manual (Bauman and Hayes, 1951). In view of the highly specialized nature of the education of the deaf-blind, the use of these tests and their validity in a particular case would have to be determined by an educator in the field.

General Examination Cautions. As to the psychological examination in general, it is often very difficult with deaf-blind persons to assure a feeling of comfort and ease in the examination situation because of the communicative difficulties. The better informed the psychologist is beforehand about the communicative abilities and the case history of the client, the more likely he is to employ the proper approach and to make the examination situation a comfortable one. The deaf-blind person should be prepared for the examination by people who usually deal with him. This will go far to alleviate some of his initial apprehensions. The thought of a psychological examination is often associated with questions about mental health, and the client may approach the session with a good deal of suspicion that could be alleviated by advance preparation. Sometimes the psychologist is considered a person who is expected to provide additional services, and hostile feelings may be aroused if the expected services are not forthcoming. On the other hand, the extensive and exclusive attention that the client receives during the course of the psychological examination may represent a rarely afforded social situation. He is likely to appreciate the attention and reward it with conscientious cooperation. Because of the social aspect the session has for him, the deaf-blind client may employ it for expressing thoughts that do not strictly pertain to the examination. He should be given ample time and opportunity to do so.

In view of the difficulties in communication, the time required by a deaf-blind individual for a complete psychological examination is extensive. Testing proceeds at a very slow pace. Frequent repetitions and clarification of questions are necessary.

Both subject and examiner may reach the point of fatigue well before the conclusion of the examination. It is best, therefore, to plan for several examination sessions. The slower the means of communication used, the more sessions will be required.

A deaf-blind person is likely to have fewer standards available by which he can evaluate his test performance. It is good practice to keep him informed throughout the session of how well he is doing, to point out his successes to him, and to encourage him frequently. On the other hand, he may appreciate being told why he failed on a particular item and to what extent his physical disabilities contributed to his failure. Because of the likelihood that he may apply unrealistic criteria to his own abilities, such comments provide helpful reality-orientation. Finally, the psychological examination may be an entirely new experience for the client, and having his performance evaluated and recognizing its degree of adequacy task by task often proves to be particularly challenging and significant to him.

Interpretation. The interpretation of the test results of deaf-blind persons has to be done with closer reference to case history data than is generally the case with the nonhandicapped. History data concerning the onset of the disabilities, educational experiences, and background of development all play a vital role in the determination of a client's potentials. An extensive case history, as suggested by Parnicky (Parnicky and Onken, 1958, Appendix E) on the basis of his research with deaf-blind persons, is indispensable. Because of the necessary limitations in psychological testing of the deaf-blind, the gap in test findings has to be filled in with information about the subject's performance in other situations, past and present, and by correlating background particulars with specific observations made during the test sessions. This mode of interpretation, although deviating somewhat from conventional procedure, would seem to assure a measure of validity in assessing the secondary effects of the disability upon a deaf-blind subject's abilities and potentials.

SPECIAL CONSIDERATIONS IN REHABILITATION.

THE REHABILITATION TEAM. Because of the complicated nature of the disability of deaf-blindness as well as of its secondary effects, the team concerned with the rehabilitation of deaf-blind persons embraces a number of disciplines. A program for rehabilitation has to begin with diagnosis in the widest sense of the word to determine the extent of the disability and the area and scope of a projected rehabilitative program. As practiced by an agency known for its comprehensive services for deaf-blind people, the Industrial Home for the Blind in Brooklyn, New York, the following specialties participate in the rehabilitation program:

General Medicine: for evaluation of the general health status (preferably by a physician who is experienced in medical services to blind people)

Otology: history, diagnosis, and prognosis of deafness

Audiology: exploration of possible residual hearing and fitting of hearing aids

Ophthalmology, Optometry and Vision Rehabilitation: diagnosis, prognosis, exploration of low-vision rehabilitation and the prescription of optical aids

Neurology: diagnosis, with particular emphasis on tactile facilities

Psychology: clinical evaluation and counseling

Speech Therapy: speech rehabilitation

Social Casework: supplying of history and for casework

Recreation and Group Work: planning recreational programs

Vocational Counseling: evaluation, training, and planning vocational rehabilitation

This extensive list of participants in a rehabilitation program points up the comprehensive scope of operations that has to be encompassed. Rehabilitation of deaf-blind persons is often tantamount to planning a full scheme of living whereby they may be enabled to find the means for gratifying the full gamut of personal needs. To divide rehabilitation into special areas is often very inadequate for the deaf-blind, since function in one area is very likely to affect all the others, and progress in each conditions as well as depends on progress in all.

RELATIONSHIPS WITH SURROUNDING REALITIES. The area from which the deaf-blind person is most significantly excluded is that of functioning as a well-integrated member of a group. To refer again to the theme of isolation, the perceptive and communicative disabilities make participation in a group particularly difficult. The demands which are made upon the environment in order to relate to the deaf-blind person are very great and often discourage people from pursuing sustained contact with such individuals. The same applies to the deaf-blind person's contacts with those about him. As a result, deaf-blind persons are commonly deprived of social outlets for self-expression, for conveying of need, and for close mutual exchange of feeling. Their efforts for intensive personal relationships are often met with such frustrations as to discourage attempts to socialize in favor of deeper withdrawal into isolation.

These limitations in relating to the surroundings, particularly in the social aspects, produce an almost continuous state of tension. Depending on the degree of personal security and stability, the tensions impose a greater or lesser toll on the adequacy of the personal functioning of the deaf-blind person. However, a setting in which these tensions may be substantially reduced is in a group of deaf-blind persons. Here, because of the similarity of personal needs, availability of easier communication by association with a group composed of persons who all communicate in the same manner, and through a sharing of comparable reality, individual integration is made substantially easier. It is often the preferred setting in which the deaf-blind person can feel most comfortable and least tense. Association with a group of other deaf-blind individuals, and possibly living with them, is in many cases the most realistic goal in planning for long-range placement. While this represents a certain extension of isolation, it is not individually isolating since it at least facilitates an isolated group-living, as it were. In the care of deaf-blind persons this arrangement is frequently followed by the agencies that are responsible for them.

Although such group-living is the most practical arrangement for a number of deaf-blind persons, it should not be considered the ideal solution. Reality cannot be confined to such a small scope, and many contacts with a variety of other settings is necessary. Depending upon the degree and extent of handicap, there are many deaf-blind persons who are capable of functioning fairly adequately within a family setting. Where this is the case and where such an arrangement has lasted a long time, it should be continued if at all feasible. It offers a great many satisfactions that are excluded by living in a group of deaf-blind persons.

The isolation resulting from the handicap of deaf-blindness, especially if its onset occured in the earlier years of life, will make a good many of the ordinary goals of life impossible to attain. Objectives, such as marriage or parenthood may often have to be excluded. Recognition of such severe deprivation of life-goals makes the deaf-blind person even more aware of his isolation and encourages a greater focus of interest upon himself, his needs, and well-being. The success with which the individual adapts to this limitation of life-goals depends, of course, on the inner resources that are available to him.

EDUCATION. If deaf-blindness occurs during the preschool years, the problems with which educational training has to cope are all but insurmountable. Conventional educational approaches are almost entirely impossible. The efforts and the time that are necessary for the education of deaf-blind children require unusual dedication and devotion on the part of the educator. Biographies of deaf-blind persons (Keller, 1954; Smithdas, 1958; Howe and Hall, 1904) describe what is entailed far more convincingly than any review of educational methods could. However, beyond the demands made upon the educator as described by Myklebust (Myklebust, 1956), the deaf-blind child must himself offer very particular assets in order to assure the success of his education. Above all, a basic wish to reach out toward and integrate himself with his surroundings must be present to a substantial measure as well as the capacity for so doing. The child who tends to withdraw, who functions in autistic directions, and who demonstrates a less consistent and less intensive drive to be part of what is going on around him is a relatively poor prospect for successful education. Even moderate retardation is likely to be much more difficult to overcome in the deaf-blind child than in other physically handicapped and nonhandicapped children. In general, the better integrated the many aspects of total functioning and performance, the more favorable the educational potential is apt to be. The picture is, of course, very different if either or both disabilities set in later in life. Then schools for the blind or for the deaf offer the educational facilities required, and with them invaluable preparation if deaf-blindness appears later in life.

VOCATIONAL REHABILITATION. Vocational rehabilitation for the deaf-blind is a relatively new field since deaf-blind persons had traditionally been considered incapable of attaining significant vocational objectives, and it warrants particular attention. Rusalem (Rusalem, 1958) in an extensive study has suggested ways of vocational diagnosis and has emphasized the employability of deaf-blind people if the proper training approaches are observed. He found the critical point in the vocational endeavors of deaf-blind persons to be the time when blindness begins to set in. Since the majority had previously functioned as deaf people and had thus established themselves vocationally, the onset of blindness presented drastic interference with their vocational status and imposed completely new demands in vocational adjustment and rehabilitation. The vocational success of deaf-blind workers is closely correlated with their ability to communicate with their co-workers and with the capacity to make effective social-personal adjustment to the work situation. A highly important determinant in employment planning is the factor of mobility and general skill in coping with surroundings. Training must of course be coordinated with and complemented by counseling conducted by specially trained personnel who are deeply familiar with the problems of deaf-blindness. The determination of vocational potentials requires the participation of the full rehabilitation team.

Rehabilitation programs for the deaf-blind are most practically organized within facilities that serve blind persons, since the relatively small number of deaf-blind individuals does not warrant exclusive facilities. Although vocational opportunities for the deaf-blind are drastically limited, with specialized training and counseling the goal of job placement is nonetheless a realizable one.

RESEARCH. The most authoritative text on the rehabilitation of deaf-blind persons to date is a seven-volume report of a comprehensive research project conducted by the Industrial Home for the Blind in Brooklyn, New York, and sponsored by the Office of Vocational Rehabilitation of the United States Department of Health, Education, and Welfare (Industrial Home for the Blind, 1958). Whereas this investigation concerned itself with deaf-blind adults, the Perkins School for the Blind in Watertown, Massachusetts, has long been a pioneer in the education and investigation of deaf-blind children and young adults and has contributed a substantial amount of literature on the subject, including many case histories (Industrial Home for the Blind, 1958, I, Appendix A). International activities in regard to deaf-blindness are united in the Committee on Services for the Deaf-Blind of the World Council for the Welfare of the Blind, which issued a report at the conclusion of its World Assembly held in July, 1959 (World Council for the Welfare of the Blind, 1959).

Methods of communication and the expansion of communicative facilities are currently receiving much attention, particularly the use of electronic devices such as the Hadley Tactaphone and the Electro-Braille Communicator (World Council for the Welfare of the Blind, 1959). Success in improving communicative facilities will stimulate progress in many other areas of investigation with the deaf-blind. In this connection, Bergman (Bergman, 1958, a) states that in certain isolated cases the hearing aid may play an important part in the conservation of residual hearing even though deafness is "near-total," and stresses the need for early attention in the interest of such conservation. He also describes the role of speech therapy with the deaf-blind as well as indicated approaches and modifications (Bergman, 1958, a). De Angelis reports (De Angelis, 1958) encouraging results in vision rehabilitation attempts with deaf-blind persons and stresses the great need for such service especially in view of the multiple handicap present and the role that even a small amount of usable vision can play. An interesting study by Bettica and associates (Bettica, and others, 1958) describes the audiological, anthropological, and neurological aspects of the methods of communication used with deaf-blind persons.

In the area of psychological studies, research has been handicapped by the widely scattered distribution of the relatively small group of deaf-blind persons and by the scarcity of appropriate psychological instruments. Since the designation "deaf-blind" encompasses a variety of disabilities, psychological tests should optimally be designed for the various subgroups included. Total deafness being common to all deaf-blind persons, these subgroups include persons with (*a*) useful vision and intelligible speech, (*b*) useful vision but no speech, (*c*) no vision but usable speech, and (*d*) no vision and no speech. Further, since the scope of vocational opportunities will undoubtedly expand as a result of continued research in vocational rehabilitation, additional psychological tests will be required to investigate vocational potentials more precisely and specifically. Probably the least explored area in the field of deaf-blindness is that of the personality dynamics of deaf-blind persons. Here, too, is an urgent need for special instruments and techniques. Among other approaches, a critical analysis of available case studies and biographies of deaf-blind persons seems a highly promising source of pertinent information about personality dynamics. The volume of such literature is considerable, some of it dating back to the early nineteenth century.

It is true that the actual number of persons who will be helped by continued research of deaf-blindness is relatively small. However, this should in no way detract from the needed efforts. Considering the tremendous isolation to which deaf-blind individuals are subjected, every bit of help they can be given in bringing them closer to their surroundings represents a substantial reduction of handicap. Progress in rehabilitation depends upon increased knowledge of the individual, and research as well as service must be geared to persons rather than to numbers.

REFERENCES

Bauman, M. K., 1951. The Non-Language Learning Test. Philadelphia, Personnel Research Center.

Bauman, M. K., and S. P. Hayes. 1951. A manual for the psychological examination of the adult blind. New York, Psychological Corporation.

Bergman, M. 1958, a. The audiological approach, in Industrial Home for the Blind and U.S. Office of Vocational Rehabilitation. Rehabilitation of deaf-blind persons. II: Communication a key to services for deaf-blind men and women. Brooklyn, N.Y., pp. 42–46.

—— 1958, b. Speech and hearing services for deaf-blind persons, in Industrial Home for the Blind and U.S. Office of Vocational Rehabilitation. Rehabilitation of deaf-blind persons. III: Report of medical studies on deaf-blind persons. Brooklyn, N.Y., pp. 34–49.

Bettica, L. J., and others. 1958. Communication a key to service for deaf-blind men and women, in Industrial Home for the Blind and U.S. Office of Vocational Rehabilitation. Rehabilitation of deaf-blind persons, II. Brooklyn, N.Y.

Copple, G. E. 1956. Effective intelligence as measured by an unstructured sentence completion technique. J. Consult. Psychol. 20:357–60.

Crawford, J. E., and D. M. Crawford. 1946. Small Parts Dexterity Test. New York, Psychological Corporation.

DeAngelis, G. J. 1958. Vision rehabilitation for deaf-blind persons, in Industrial Home for the Blind and U.S. Office of Vocational Rehabilitation. Rehabilitation of deaf-blind persons. III: Report of medical studies on deaf-blind persons. Brooklyn, N.Y., pp. 51–61.

DiMichael, S. G. 1947. Psychological tests for use with blind adults in vocational rehabilitation. Rehabilitation Service Series No. 29. Washington, D.C., Office of Vocational Rehabilitation, Rehabilitation Standards Division.

Fowler, E. P. 1958. Otological investigations, in Industrial Home for the Blind and U.S. Office of Vocational Rehabilitation. Rehabilitation of deaf-blind persons. III: Report of medical studies on deaf-blind persons. Brooklyn, N.Y., pp. 21–25.

Gilroy, R. V. 1958. Ophthalmological study of deaf-blind persons at the Industrial Home for the Blind, in Industrial Home for the Blind and U.S. Office of Vocational Rehabilitation. Rehabilitation of deaf-blind persons. III: Report of medical studies on deaf-blind persons. Brooklyn, N.Y.

Handel, A. F. 1958. Introduction, in Industrial Home for the Blind and U.S., Office of Vocational Rehabilitation. Rehabilitation of deaf-blind persons. I: A manual for professional workers. Brooklyn, N.Y., pp. 21–31.

Hayes, S. P. 1942. Interim Hayes-Binet Intelligence Tests for the Blind. Watertown, Mass., Perkins School for the Blind.

Howe, M., and F. H. Hall. 1904. Laura Bridgman. Boston, Little, Brown.

Industrial Home for the Blind and U.S. Office for Vocational Rehabilitation. 1958. Rehabilitation of deaf-blind persons. I: A manual for professional workers; II: Communication—a key to service for deaf-blind men and women; III: Report of medical studies on deaf-blind persons; IV: A report of psychological studies with deaf-blind persons; V: Studies in the vocational adjustment of deaf-blind adults; VI: Recreation services for deaf-blind persons; VII:

Survey of selected characteristics of deaf-blind adults in New York State, fall, 1957. Brooklyn, N.Y.

Keller, H. A. 1954. The story of my life. New York, Doubleday.

Kolbrenner, L. 1958. Health in general, in Industrial Home for the Blind and U.S. Office of Vocational Rehabilitation. Rehabilitation of deaf-blind persons. III: Report of medical studies on deaf-blind persons. Brooklyn, N.Y., pp. 17–18.

Myklebust, H. R. 1956. The deaf-blind child. Watertown, Mass., Perkins School for the Blind.

Parnicky, J. J., and R. E. Onken. 1958. Survey of selected characteristics of deaf-blind adults in New York State, fall, 1957, in Industrial Home for the Blind and U.S. Office of Vocational Rehabilitation. Rehabilitation of deaf-blind persons, VII. Brooklyn, N.Y.

Roberts, J. R. 1943. Pennsylvania Bi-manual Worksample. Minneapolis, Education Test Bureau.

Roberts, J. R., and M. K. Bauman. 1944. Motor skills tests adapted to the blind. Minneapolis, Education Test Bureau.

Rocheleau, C., and R. Mack. 1930. Those in dark silence. Washington, D.C., Volta Bureau.

Rothschild, J. 1958. A report of psychological studies with deaf-blind persons, Industrial Home for the Blind and U.S. Office of Vocational Rehabilitation. Rehabilitation of deaf-blind persons, IV. Brooklyn, N.Y.

Rusalem, H. 1958. Studies in the vocational adjustment of deaf-blind persons, in Industrial Home for the Blind and U.S. Office of Vocational Rehabilitation of deaf-blind persons, V. Brooklyn, N.Y.

Shurrager, H., and S. Watson. 1958. Performance scale for adult blind. Chicago, Psychology Research.

Smithdas, R. J. 1958. Life at my finger-tips. New York, Doubleday.

Tiffin, J. 1948. Purdue pegboard. Chicago, Science Research Associates.

Twitchell-Allen, D. 1948. Three-Dimensional-Apperception Test. New York, Psychological Corporation.

Waterhouse, E. J. 1957. Helping the deaf-blind to face the future. J. Rehab. 23:6–7.

World Council for the Welfare of the Blind, World Assembly, Rome, Italy. 1959. Report of Committee on Services for the Deaf-Blind. Brooklyn, N.Y.

Ziegler, W. A., and others. 1946. Minnesota Rate of Manipulation Test. Minneapolis, Education Test Bureau.

SEVERE CHRONIC ILLNESS

by FRANKLIN C. SHONTZ

IT IS DIFFICULT to assess or to predict the significance and impact upon society of severe chronic illness without first considering the meaning of the term itself and its implications. As a classificatory device, the expression commonly denotes such a broad range of physical and psychological phenomena as to include within its scope all that are commonly meant by the phrase "physical disability" and considerably more besides.

The term "chronic illness" seems to have a history like Topsy—it wasn't born; it just grew. Its meaning has scarcely ever been logically analyzed, and it has only rarely been carefully applied. Furthermore, its nature in common usage is such that any attempt to define it systematically soon becomes hopelessly entangled in a web of semantic confusion.

Because of the difficulties inherent in arriving at a satisfactory definition of the broad concept of chronic illness, it will be necessary to devote the first sections of this chapter to the task of exposing and untangling some of the worst of the semantic snarls that must be contended with in this field. When these have been exposed, it will become possible to specify a meaning for the more limited and more immediately relevant concept of "severe" chronic illness and thus to delimit the scope of subsequent chapter sections. In the course of this effort it will be shown that the necessary delimitation can be accomplished most meaningfully

Franklin C. Shontz, Ph.D., is Assistant Professor and Director of Training and Research in Somatopsychology at the University of Kansas.

through the medium of rehabilitation concepts, and it will be further demonstrated that the process of definition and delimitation itself implies the nature of the essential problems that must be dealt with in the course of psychological practice with the severely chronically ill. Examples will then be presented to show how these essential problems manifest themselves in the lives of patients. Some preliminary suggestions will be made regarding the general methods for helping such patients work through their difficulties, with particular regard to the psychologist's role in the appraisal and treatment processes. Finally, a brief review of research needs will be attempted, and conclusions will be drawn.

MEDICAL, SOCIAL, AND REHABILITATION ASPECTS. Interestingly enough, virtually all of the medical conditions considered in the preceding chapters may reasonably be said to be "chronic," in that they are all "long continued" or "of long duration" (Hoerr and Osol, 1956, p. 251); and practically all the persons afflicted with these disabilities may just as reasonably be said to be "ill," either in the sense of their being "not healthy" or "sick," or in the broader sense of their being in one way or another "indisposed" (Hoerr and Osol, 1956, p. 587). In fact, a good case could be made to support the proposition that this entire volume deals with the subject of chronic illness, especially if the case is based upon a definitive concept as broad as the one proposed by the Commission on Chronic Illness. According to the Commission, chronic illnesses are:

> all impairments or deviations from normal which have one or more of the following characteristics: are permanent; leave residual disability; are caused by non-reversible pathological alteration; require special training of the patient for rehabilitation; or may be expected to require a long period of supervision, observation, or care. (Roberts, 1955, p. 149.)

On the basis of this definition, the incidence of chronic illness in the United States in 1955 was estimated at 28,000,000, a figure including, conservatively, about one out of seven persons in the total population. Admittedly, this estimate was qualified by the observation that most of those afflicted with chronic illnesses are not, in fact, handicapped severely enough to require specialized facilities or services for their care (Roberts, 1955); but the figure is large enough to illustrate how broad the application of the concept of chronic illness may be construed to be.

The working definition of chronic illness adopted by the *Journal of Chronic Diseases* for editorial purposes has apparently been at least as broad as the one proposed by the Commission. Since its founding in 1955, this journal has published comprehensive symposia on such problems as coronary heart disease; neurological disease; cancer; the management of hematologic disorders; congestive heart failure; rheumatoid arthritis; congenital malformations; psychiatric disorders; and, screening for asymptomatic disease, as well as a number of single articles on specific physical disorders outside the limits of the symposia themselves.

A prominent Midwestern hospital for chronic physical disease recently gave the following examples of the disease characteristics of its population:

> Major fractures; major burns; spinal cord injuries; amputations; major head injuries; strokes, chronic degenerative neurological diseases such as multiple sclerosis; chronic degenerative muscular diseases such as muscular dystrophy; arthritis; malignancy; and chronic degenerative diseases such as nephrosis; cirrhosis of the liver. (Highland View Hospital, 1959.)

An obvious characteristic of the expressed and implied definitions of chronic illness that are taken from primarily medical sources, such as those cited above, is that they deal exclusively with the nature of the physical impairment and not with the nature of the physically impaired person. This characteristic has been noted by many authors. For example, Cohen, while allowing for some exceptions, noted that "the sick person, with his unique constellation of circumstances, still remains less the focus of attention than his disease" (Cohen, 1955, p. 465).

Unfortunately, it is often forgotten that the logic of disease classification is not at all a logic of person classification. Consequently, it is not surprising to find that while the results of disease classification serve an admirably useful purpose when appropriately applied (i.e., for the study and treatment of illnesses that afflict people), they engender considerable confusion when they are applied to inappropriate ends (i.e., for the classification and treatment of people). It is regrettable that we are all more or less guilty of referring to the patient as "that hemiplegic on ward 3A" or "the quad in bed 4"; for this form of verbal usage frequently implies a serious misuse of the logical concepts of modern medicine.

The difficulties that stem from misuse of medical terminology have been recognized by several authorities. Tobis, Lowenthal, and Belmont have stated (Tobis, Lowenthal, and Belmont, 1958), that there is no such thing as a purely chronically ill person. It is even impossible to distinguish clearly between acute and chronic disease in so-called chronically ill patients, for both types of disease are part of the same basic process, and neither term alone can be considered to be adequately descriptive of the person at all times. Cherasky (Cherasky, 1959) raised the question as to whether "chronic disease" hospitals are in any essential way different from general hospitals. He noted the terminological confusion in the area and implied that the effort to separate out the "chronically ill" from all other sick people serves only to increase the degree of semantic disorder already existing in the field.

Indeed, it is not possible to identify any special medically defined group of individuals as *the* chronically ill, to be distinguished in any meaningful way from the acutely ill or from, simply, those with disabilities. Within almost all relevant diagnostic categories are to be found people who are more disabled than ill, more acutely ill than chronically ill, and so on. Besides, the diagnostic category that lies within the scope of a purely physically based conception of chronic illness today may well lie outside of it tomorrow. Witness, as ready examples, the changes in concept and treatment with respect to persons with epilepsy in the past few years (Hammill, 1958; U.S. Dept. of Veterans Benefits, 1960) and the rapid progress in the development of prosthetic and orthetic devices for extending the usefulness of lost, paralyzed, or weakened musculature (Bennett, 1960), as well as the countless other medical advances that have so significantly reduced the incidence of fatal complications in conditions like quadriplegia, paraplegia, and multiple sclerosis. A major effect of these striking achievements has been to remove many people from the rolls of the medically defined chronically ill and to change considerably our concept of who is sick and who is not.

It certainly is not germane at this point to attempt to arrive at logically consistent and practically usable definitions of all the medical terms that must be contended with in the field of chronic illness. Nor is it within the realm of the author's competence to do so. What has already been presented on the subject is sufficient to establish, first, that terminological confusion exists; second, that the major characteristic of the medical approach to the necessary definitions has been, and still is, to focus upon the disease or illness processes; and, third, that the application of purely medical criteria for the classification of individual cases is highly unsatisfactory, both from a logical and from a practical point of view, in so far as current rehabilitation interest lies with the total person rather than with his physical condition alone.

An alternative approach to the definition of chronic illness might be to classify individuals by existing social criteria. It would be simplicity itself to identify as the chronically ill those patients who are found in hospitals for chronic diseases; and as a practical convenience such a definition may be adequate or even necessary. But a purely "operational definition" of this sort ignores important medical realities. It would have to follow from the definition that "chronic illness" is whatever people in institutions for chronic diseases have. That important medical knowledge would be by-passed is obvious when one considers that people with illnesses that are definitely chronic in character are to be found not only in chronic disease hospitals but also in general hospitals, in nursing and boarding homes, and even in some private homes. People with acute illness are frequently found in hospitals for the chronically ill; and every chronic disease hospital contains its share of "custodial" patients who are not at all diseased and who often are not disabled in any sense of the medical meaning of these terms. What is gained for practical convenience through the use of an "operational" social definition of this type is lost in terms of medical reality; for one is left with no better idea of what people with chronic illness are like than one would possess without any definition at all.

There is an additional related point to be considered when discussing the social criteria of chronic illness. The fact should be especially noted that the medical and social characteristics (indeed, even the personality characteristics) of the patient population of a hospital for people with chronic diseases are largely determined by the pressures brought to bear on that institution by the community. When public acceptance is low, one finds these institutions to be overcrowded with "custodial" or "domiciliary" patients who, as the staff will usually say, "really don't belong here."

The discussion may be summarized by the following statements: on the one hand, a medical definition of "chronic illness" is useful for the analysis and description of disease characteristics but is not usable as a device for the classification of persons. On the other hand, a social definition is useful as a device for isolating a particular group of individuals for study but is not satisfactory from a medical point of view. The two approaches are not easily reconciled, yet full justice can not be done to the various accepted meanings of the concept of chronic illness unless both the medical and social realities of the situation are granted full and equal definitive consideration. The discussion also suggests that common usage dictates a virtually identical referent for the terms "chronic illness" and "disability" (Wright, 1960, p. 9, and Hamilton, 1950, p. 17); and the subject of much of the present volume may just as well be said to be that of psychological practice with the chronically ill as that of psychological practice with the physically disabled.

The concern of this chapter is with the more restricted problems associated with especially severely limiting physical conditions. The problem at hand, therefore, is not to bring precision to the over-all idea of chronic illness, but to frame for the more limited concept of severe chronic illness a definition which will do justice to both medical and social reality and yet serve to delineate a region of unique immediate concern. A definition which meets these requirements is best formulated in rehabilitation terms, because rehabilitation practices and goals are as much a function of a patient's medical status as they are a function of the level of community acceptance of persons with disabilities.

Stated most simply then, the present chapter deals with *individuals* who are afflicted with *especially severe disabilities*. That is, the chapter deals primarily with people, rather than with disease entities, and it deals with the special group of people whose physical and social limitations are such as to restrict drastically the long-range goals of their economic rehabilitation. A severe physical limitation may exist either as a function of a person's extreme or pervasive physical involvement (which may or may not require active medical care) or as a function of his susceptibility to recurrences of periodically disabling, and often progressively worsening, conditions. A severe social limitation may be described as one which does not permit the patient maximal use of his functional physical capacities for independent economic activity. Taken in combination, these limitations define what is meant here by the term "severe chronic illness"; and the people whose physical and social conditions are such as to preclude the likelihood of long-range vocational rehabilitation are those individuals who are here referred to as the "severely chronically ill" or the "especially severely disabled."

The most critical term in this rehabilitation oriented definition is the word "economic," for the statement says, in effect, that the severely chronically ill person is one for whom financially remunerative employment is not feasible, on the basis of existing knowledge of the person's present and probable future medical condition vis à vis the opportunities afforded by society. This focus upon the economic aspects of rehabilitation is wholly justified in terms of the history of the rehabilitation movement in this country, which has traditionally been so closely identified with economic factors that it has not been uncommon to hear the fitting of the patient into the economic framework of society extolled as "one of the highest goals in the rehabilitation of the physically handicapped" (Lesser and Darling, 1953).

Recent developments have greatly broadened the concepts of work and gainful employment. A most important change has been to eliminate the narrow presumption that vocational rehabilitation necessarily implies employment in already established industrial plants and business organizations. As rehabilitation has grown in scope and concept, it has become increasingly legitimate to define successful rehabilitation in terms of patient placement in sheltered workshops, homebound employment, or even in homemaking itself. However, the change initially occurred through expanding the meaning of "vocation," rather than through any change in the concept of "rehabilitation," per se. The following quotation from a welcoming address to a 1959 conference of rehabilitation workers in Cleveland, Ohio, expresses the characteristic way of thinking prompted by the liberalization of vocational goals:

> You aren't finished with your person (patient) until you restore him to a job. And this should be the goal for every patient that is admitted to a chronic disease hospital. Now this job can be defined in a great many different ways: it may be the job of the housewife . . . or it may be partial rehabilitation of the seriously crippled . . . and it may be rehabilitation to the point where the individual gets a payroll card and works in competitive industry. But the payoff is really restoring this individual to useful occupation. . . . I hope that more and more people in the field of rehabilitation and care of the chronically ill will develop the attitude that you haven't finished the job until you've put this person back into some useful occupation. [Weir, 1959.]

An even more recent development, not yet fully realized, but clearly in its early stages, is the tendency to avoid the logical and semantic problems inherent in the concept of *purely* vocational rehabilitation and to talk in terms of "independent living," either outside the institutional setting or even within its walls, as a legitimate rehabilitation goal for the severely chronically ill (Wright, 1959, a, p. 16; Rehabilitation Record, 1960, p. 11). This new development expands even further the range of interest of modern rehabilitation effort; and it does so, again, on the basis of a sound economic argument. When a patient is removed from his hospital bed to his home, or when he is moved from an active treatment ward to a domiciliary installation, his bed is freed for use by another needy person. When a patient is brought to the point where he no longer requires the services of a paid attendant, the attendant is freed to attend to someone else who requires his services. When a patient learns to administer his own prophylactic skin care, decubiti are prevented, and valuable medical time is freed for the assistance of others. In the long run it must follow that the pursuit of the goals of independent living will lead to a drastic reduction in the numbers of "custodial" patients in our hospitals as well as to vast economies for society, if not in terms of absolute dollars saved then in terms of greatly increased efficiency of use of the welfare funds spent on physically disabled persons (Rosenfeld, Goldmann, and Kaprio, 1957).

It is a matter of record, therefore, that the "economic argument" has consistently provided a firm basis for the growth and expansion of the concept and practice of rehabilitation. The point has been belabored for two reasons: first, as a justification for the importance accorded economic considerations in defining severe chronic illness; and, second, as a backdrop for the forthcoming discussion of the unique problems of patient motivation which must be faced when dealing with this special group of severely disabled individuals.

PSYCHOLOGICAL IMPLICATIONS. Each advance in rehabilitation brings the rehabilitation worker into contact with more severely disabled clients. Individuals who were once dealt with by simply writing them off an agency's books as "unemployable" are now becoming an increasing concern of rehabilitation; and the newest concepts require that these clients be actively treated, motivated, and brought to the peak of their total capabilities.

It has been shown that, from society's point of view, the newly formulated goal of "independent living" for the severely chronically ill is readily justifiable on economic grounds. What has not yet been mentioned is that, from the patient's point of view, the same goals often cannot be as easily justified in a psychologically meaningful way. Earlier in the history of rehabilitation, the problems of patient motivation were largely solved by holding before the patient the same psychological carrot that was dangled before the community: the goal of economic independence, financial self-sufficiency, a return to society in a position of dignity that would afford the patient a sound basis for self-respect among his fellow men. These motivating prospects were generally, though not always, effective because what society wanted from the patient was congruent with what the patient wanted for himself. The rehabilitation worker did not often have to concern himself with any conflict between the wants of one and the needs of the other.

If one accepts the proposition that, for many people, work is necessary for psychological independence and self-respect, then it follows that the newer concepts of rehabilitation lack, in their basic formulation, adequate motivating forces for the severely disabled patient. From the point of view of the patient with severe chronic illness, the motivating forces he perceives are frequently only the negative ones associated with becoming *less burdensome* to a community. Society grants no special acknowledgment of gratitude to the person who manages to live without an attendant or who learns to care for his skin so as to free his physician's and nurses' time. No special privileges are gained, no special self-respect restored to the patient who leaves a congenial, secure hospital for a lonely, frequently empty apartment. The patient himself does not get money because he saves it for society; and, as a rule, he is unwilling to give up his bed if he feels he still needs it. The author's experience suggests that these facts circumscribe the key issue around which the whole subject of psychological practice with the severely chronically ill revolves. What the severely chronically ill person needs, in order to succeed in rehabilitation, is a *positive* reason for living that is not premised upon his financial value either to himself or to society. This is what all persons with disability seek, even when they select employment as the means to the end; and this is essentially what rehabilitation must help them find. The critical question is "where?"

To seek the answer to this question, it is worthwhile to examine further the concepts of *positive* and *negative* motivation as these apply to the rehabilitation of the especially severely disabled person. Socially recognized work, a paycheck, self-respect, contact with those who understand, a feeling of involvement in progress toward something personally valuable and important, a sense of growing mastery—all represent *positive* gains from a patient's point of view. However, becoming less helpless is *negative* and is not equivalent to becoming more capable. Not being as bad off as the next man is different from being better off than he. Most crucial of all, not being a burden is different from being a help; and not getting worse seldom offers the same kind of satisfaction as getting better. The problem is not merely one of "positive thinking"; it is one of conflict of interest. If the rehabilitation worker is not careful he all too easily falls into the trap of believing that the goals of rehabilitation as a social phenomenon are the same as those of the individual patient.

The only seemingly positive motivating force that the present author has seen mentioned in the literature on rehabilitating the severely chronically ill is the prospect of returning home to more familiar surroundings, and this has usually been mentioned *en passant*, while the heaviest weight has been given to economic considerations. (Cherasky, 1955; Dacso and Rusk, 1955; Rosenfeld, Goldmann, and Kaprio, 1957). In this connection, the author's own informal observations have disclosed that many severely disabled patients prefer to remain in the hospital for precisely the reason that they feel themselves to be less burdensome there than they would be at home, especially if they can pay for their own institutional care. In this way they solve the *negative* motivational problem by being the least possible burden on those they love at home, and they solve the *positive* problem by maintaining self-respect through paying their own way. For this reason and for many others too complex to be considered in detail, it is not at all safe to assume that "anybody would rather be home than in the hospital."

Essentially what is being said here is that, when dealing with the severely chronically ill person, rehabilitation workers in all specialties must become more sensitive to motivational problems than they may have found necessary to be in the past. It is crucial to understand as thoroughly as possible the patient's point of view; to communicate with him psychologically as well as medically; and to understand as fully as possible how the world looks to the patient (Shontz, Fink, and Hallenbeck, 1960; Shontz, Fink, Nadler, and Hallenbeck, 1959; Shontz and Fink, 1957).

It is not hard to justify the argument that the patient himself, particularly the patient with severe chronic illness, is not primarily concerned with physical health, home, and job, *except* as these hold for him the prospect of furthering his deeper human wants. From his difficult position, the patient seeks for what might best be called a "meaning in life."

It may now be helpful to examine briefly some specific psychological reactions to especially severe disability.

Among the reactions that represent the *negative*, threatening side of the picture may be listed:

- Gross confusion and uncertainty
- Panic or non-specific anxiety, nightmares
- Fear of loss of sanity
- Fear of death and dying
- Fear of becoming a physical, emotional, and financial burden
- Feelings of being essentially different from others: shame on physical exposure to the non-disabled
- Feelings of increased vulnerability to rejection or to emotional or physical attack by others as well as to one's own emotional impulses
- Interpretation of disability as a punishment for past misdeeds or for a poorly lived life
- Suicidal thoughts and ego-alien death wishes
- Uncontrollable hostility, inwardly or outwardly directed
- Feelings of rejection by family, friends, society
- Identification of disability as an unjust visitation by a cruel and merciless fate
- Feelings that adult status has been permanently and completely lost

- Worry and concern over the availability of needed physical assistance

Another group of reactions may be thought of as being *neutralizing* responses, in that they serve the function of managing the threats aroused by disability and provide for the patient a degree of relief from the pressure of anxiety and depression. These reactions are not "satisfying" in the positive sense of the term, for they do not provide gratification. Their only function is to counteract threat. Among the neutralizing responses may be listed:

- Intellectual denial of illness, either in terms of its current status or of its future implications
- Withdrawal from emotional reactivity, with resulting apathy, blandness, passivity
- Euphoric conversion of unpleasant affect
- Perception of the situation as a relief from the responsibility and competitive tension of normal life
- Isolation of loss through reorganization of values so as to "decentralize" the place of physical condition in the total personality
- Identification of the disability as a paid-up debt for past sins
- Exploitation of others as a compensation for experienced loss

Once threat has been neutralized by one or more such mechanisms, it then becomes possible for the patient to seek out the more *positive* aspects of his situation. Since each person is assumed to be a self-consistent, dynamic whole, the choice of positive responses in the individual case will, to a considerable extent, be a function of the nature of the earlier threat experience and the type of neutralization brought to bear against it. Among the *positive* reactions may be listed:

- Development of fantasies of glorious future accomplishment and success
- Perception of the disability as a "new chance" to correct the errors of pre-disability life
- Identification of the self as one who fully appreciates and

understands life because of having experienced proximity to death

Development of faith and hope for a miracle cure

Gratifications associated with the renewed awareness of interpersonal worth derived from the care and concern afforded by others

Gratifications associated with assisting others who have disabilities, through inspiration and personal example

Identification of the self as one especially selected for spiritual trial through personal suffering

Development of a set of positive personal values based upon the still available, nonphysical aspects of existence

Vocational gratifications have not been listed, since these are excluded by the definition of the group that is being discussed. The lists are not complete, of course; nor is it maintained that the reactions suggested are confined to patients with severe chronic illness. Furthermore, no effort was made to classify responses in terms of their desirability or reality-basis. The list conveys rather the qualitative character of responses to especially severe disability, and it points up the fact that the problems of adjustment to severe chronic illness are, first, to neutralize threat effectively and, second, to find, if possible, a new or modified (yet personally consistent) meaning in life which makes of it something more than mere defensive existence. With the assistance of rehabilitation guidance, this meaning may be such as to encourage maximum physical and economic independence and self-sufficiency. It is, in brief, the problem of rehabilitation as an applied art to see that this becomes the case.

It is instructive to examine the written works of those who have suffered severely disabling conditions. A book by the famous baseball player, Roy Campanella, who is now quadriplegic, provides several meaningful illustrations of the problems raised here. Campanella described his experience in physical therapy when he first realized he had lost his vocational potential:

It didn't hit me at first. I didn't get the full meaning of it all at once. But then it came through to me . . . she [the therapist] was gonna teach me—Roy Campanella—how to catch a ball. . . . There I was, a guy whose claim to fame—such as it's been—had been built on my ability to catch a ball. Cripes, Roy Campanella. Campy—Number 39 with the Brooklyn Dodgers . . . a $50,000 a year man . . . because of his ability to do one thing better than most: catch a ball. . . . She lobbed the ball to me—gentle-like from only seven or eight feet away. . . . Gee, the way I used to catch standing up and now I can't even catch sitting down. Not only that, but when I would try to catch it I would topple over. Not once, but several times. . . . "That wasn't fair, Nurse!" I managed to stammer. "You're cheating. You caught me off guard!" We both knew it wasn't so. She wasn't cheating, and I was ready all right, but my body was not. [Campanella, 1959, pp. 207–9.]

It is well known that Campanella was able to return to work closely related to his old profession, though not, of course, as an active player; so his case is not entirely typical of the group discussed here. In spite of his comparatively good fortune, however, he wrote of his acute difficulty adjusting to the feeling of physical helplessness brought on by his condition. At the same time, he hinted at the reason why the meaning in life he sought was not necesarily to be found only in the outside world:

You see, the biggest trouble with quadriplegics is that they're ashamed to have people see them. . . . In the hospital, you feel at home because you have a lot of company . . . you don't feel like a freak. . . . But in public you're afraid to face normal people. . . . You feel ashamed; you want to hide. You become even more aware that you're a helpless cripple. [Campanella, 1959, p. 235.]

The hospital has a positive attractive force, and it gains this partly because the "outside" is a danger and a threat and everything that reminds one of his helplessness.

Campanella also gives insight into the kinds of mechanisms brought into play for coming to terms with such a negative reality.

So far, there's no way medical science knows to make a severed or badly damaged spinal cord heal and function. But I've got to keep that hope! And I intend to hold onto it . . . one day—maybe tomorrow, maybe next week, maybe next year—another human, or a team of humans will come through with a cure. . . .

And let me say that this refusal of total or full acceptance all hooks up with one thing—Faith. . . .

Without faith you don't have much chance. I pray every day now, as I have every day of my life. . . . I don't think the good Lord has turned his back on me. . . .

Come to think of it, I don't think I ever asked the doctors, all the time I was in the hospital, how long it would be before I could walk again or if I'd *ever* walk again. I just prayed to the good Lord for help and guidance and I read the Bible every chance I had. . . .

[On the day of discharge from the Institute] "I've got to think I'm fortunate," I thought to myself as I looked through the picture window out onto the waters of Long Island Sound. "Thank God I had a house to come back to and a family to come back to and the jobs I've been able to do all this time. . . ." [Campanella, 1959, pp. 287, 195, 205, 229.]

Campanella was aware of the positive value in having meaningful work available for him to do, in having the acclaim and attention of his fans and of the other patients. He apparently spent much of his free time proselytizing these patients into acceptance of their conditions, using himself as an example for them; and it is clear that some of the greatest satisfaction he has received from life as a person with quadriplegia has been derived from the inspirational benefit he could bestow on others in similar physical condition. It is especially interesting that this should be so, for it is obvious that Roy Campanella, like many other severely disabled individuals, has derived some of the most significant meaning in life from behavior that would have been impossible without his disability which necessitated prolonged experience in the hospital environment.

The negative aspects of Campanella's adjustment were his awareness of the loss of skills and adjustments that had served him so well for years as the basis for his self-esteem and feelings of personal worth; his feelings of fear and shame at exposure to a gaping world; his feeling of helplessness and uselessness. The positive, counteracting forces brought to bear against these were religious faith; the gaining of attachments to others like himself and the assisting in the improvement of their condition; his search for signs of his own personal good fortune in comparison to the fortune of others; and his desperate (though in his case successful) attempts to revive as much as possible of the old life either through direct action or, failing that, through fantasy and remembrances; in short, his concentrated search for good fortune in the midst of personal catastrophe. That he felt he had succeeded is indicated by the content of the following passage:

> Until January 28, 1958, I was a ballplayer whose aim, then, at least, was to catch one more full season with the Dodgers. . . . Baseball was my only world. . . . Today I'm still an ex-ballplayer whose life centers around the game, but I know that I'm something else, too. Because, where before I might have been a fellow with a fair understanding of life, today I understand a great deal more about many more things . . . especially this wonderful thing called the human spirit. And so, while this accident made me a cripple, it also made me a better human. . . . [Campanella, 1959, p. 283.]

One wonders what Campanella's fate would have been while in rehabilitation had it not been for the attentions of his family, his professional associates, his fans, and the other patients. No one can be sure what it would have meant to his total adjustment at the time had the prospect of financial security and meaningful employment not been realistically held out to him. The question remains open. Certainly the process would not have been a simple subtractive one. He would probably not have lost these isolated things and retained everything else. Campanella's faith, for example, was premised upon his sense of good fortune; and his sense of good fortune was premised to some degree upon the acclaim shown him by the "significant-others" in his life as well as upon the realization that he could yet work and support himself. What his adjustment would have been had these things not been available, as they most frequently are *not* with especially severely disabled people, is a matter for speculation.

A final point can be made from the study of Campanella's life.

It is conceivable that one would classify this man's adjustment, at least in part, as *denial* (Diller, 1959; Weinstein and Kahn, 1955; Hamburg, 1953). Campanella was aware of the nature of his injury; yet he did not wish to accept his condition fully; he wanted and required that element of hope, that counting on the one-in-a-million chance. He called it "faith" because he knew it to be unrealistic in the face of medical reality. Such is the condition of many especially severely disabled individuals; and it is precisely this wish to hope that places the rehabilitation worker in a difficult psychological position. Dembo (Dembo, 1955) first stressed the problem of "hope versus stark reality" and concluded that in many cases it is best to support hope. Wright, however, says that "hope built upon evasion is hardly reassuring," although "Coating reality with hope does not mean living in a world of unreality. Accepting a disability does not mean abandoning hope" (Wright, 1960, p. 303). Obviously, it is difficult to decide. On the one hand, the rehabilitation worker cannot allow himself, or be allowed, to hold out false hopes that may support a denial process of dangerous proportions. On the other hand, the positive values of life are certainly not necessarily tied entirely to the physical aspects of existence. If it were so, rehabilitation with this group of patients would be a lost cause before it ever began.

SPECIAL CONSIDERATIONS IN PSYCHOLOGICAL APPRAISAL. The following two sections, this one on appraisal and the next one on treatment, will not deal in any more extensive a manner with the issues already raised. The implications of what has been said are clear: the content of the psychological life of the patient with severe chronic illness is in many ways different from that of the vocationally rehabilitable person. The severely disabled individual is faced with an essentially negative reality to which he must be reoriented in a positive way. The reorientation can occur only when individually meaningful positive aspects of life can be found, whether these be realized in a semivocational, permanent sheltered workshop setting (Stubbins, 1960; Institute for the Crippled and Disabled, 1959), in the setting of the patient's own home, in the setting of a domiciliary placement; or whether they stem from vocational, religious, social, or strictly personal self-actualization interests that may be pursued in the silence of isolated meditation. Considerably more needs to be known about this group of people before any broad generalizations may be safely made as to which of several motivating possibilities will be most useful in the long run. In the meantime, it is necessary to content ourselves with a brief consideration of problems of technique and adjustment processes.

The most serious technical problems in the psychological appraisal of the severely chronically ill stem from the lack of basic tested knowledge of the mechanisms of adjustment to especially severe disability. Though convinced that the psychologist is constantly obliged to apply the best and most valid psychological knowledge at his command when appraising any patient with a disability, the author accepts with considerable reserve the practice of wholesale uncritical application of existing theories and techniques for the explanation and prediction of behavior and feelings of this group of individuals. It is probably safe to assume that basic psychological processes are much the same for all people; and certainly the conservatively cautious warnings and principles of psychological appraisal do not change when one is dealing with a physically ill individual. The concern here is not with the basic principles of examination or the identification of psychological processes themselves. It is, rather, with the possibility that psychologists will fail to realize the very special circumstances under which these principles are applied and these processes are evoked when the subjects of their concern are persons with especially severe disabilities. In fact, no time at all will be spent here in detailing either basic personality theory or basic appraisal practice. A knowledge of these will be assumed. Attention will be given almost exclusively to the unique problems encountered in appraising the severely chronically ill, since it is these problems which are of greatest immediate concern.

When one ignores the slapdash kind of speculation that hurriedly dispenses with all the psychological problems of the chronically ill by labeling them as merely "castration anxiety," "motivational problems," or some such thing, there is not much in the rehabilitation literature to be discussed. The author is familiar with two well-formulated, semitheoretical articles that attempt to explain the mechanisms of psychological adjustment of the especially severely disabled person, and these will be reviewed briefly.

Nemiah (Nemiah, 1957) considered injury or severe disability to be a frustrating agent that threatens the injured person's self-esteem by impeding the progress of his development toward the achievement of his own ideals. The emotional sequelae of the frustration incurred are a complex of unpleasant affects, including self-hatred and feelings of helplessness and inadequacy. These unpleasant affects become manifested as anxiety and/or depression; and a process of denial of significance of the disabling condition may follow as a means for avoiding these painful emotions. Other possible defensive efforts may involve prolonging of symptoms, with associated dependency and aggression.

Litin (Litin, 1957) noted the lack of "untoward" emotional reactions during the acute phases of physical illness and identified the critical psychological stage of adjustment as occurring during the "early chronic phase" of disability. The patient's first concern, during the early chronic phase, is his need for a massive evaluation and psychological reorganization of his life situation. During this period, the patient is likely to feel intense anxiety and depression; and it is at this point that defenses against these painful affects begin to appear. Aggression, either directly expressed or projected, and bitter, hostile feelings may provide one outlet for tension; or the patient may even develop a gay, euphoric manner. Following this phase, there is a period of calming and more stable adjustment; during this time the danger of the development of emotional dependency on the hospital may appear.

Both authors agree that the critical emotional period is the early one, when the patient first realizes the full extent of his disability. It is during the "early chronic stage," apparently, that prototypical responses, which may anticipate future adjustive difficulties, may be observed. There then follows a calming trend and, one may suppose, a settling upon more or less permanent adaptive devices. Both authors also seem to agree that depression and anxiety are the common emotional reactions of the early phase, with defensive responses of greater variety occurring later in reaction to these. It also seems agreed that the common course of adjustment must be gone through before adjustment may be considered complete, that is, that a "working through" of painful affect is required, rather than a prolonged and unmodified defense against it, such as might be afforded by the mechanisms of denial, manic reactions, projection of aggression, and so on. Finally it appears that both authors recognize the role of "dependency on the institution" as a functional attempt on the part of the patient to solve the problems raised by the impact of the disability.

Thus a fairly clear common course of psychological reaction to chronic illness may be inferred, irrespective of how one wishes to explain it. The first job of psychological appraisal is, then, to assess the point within this emotional sequence at which the individual patient lies. Related to this assessment is the evaluation of what psychologists like to call the patient's personality and intellectual "resources," or capacities for dealing effectively with difficult or unusual situations. The purpose of an evaluation of "resource potential" is to permit the formulation of some sort of prediction of probable future adjustment. It would seem reasonable to suppose that the evalution of resources is most subject to error during the patient's most excited moments; yet it is possible to anticipate future adjustment to a surprising degree even in the early stages of the process. It is a ticklish thing to do, one which requires a high degree of "clinical sensitivity"; and no objective devices that will accomplish the same end by themselves are currently available. Although one must certainly rely upon the tests that are currently in vogue for much essential psychometric information, these data can at best provide the formal basis for what must be as yet an "intuitive" though not uneducated process of judgment.

The most valuable psychological resource is intelligence. Intelligence is probably the thing psychologists measure best; and, as one rehabilitation worker put it: "IQ is the only measure that seems to correlate consistently with good performance on everything we want the patient to do." Naturally, one has to use considerable ingenuity in testing many of the severely chronically ill for intellectual capacities. Aphasic individuals present special problems, as do quadriplegics, severely athetoid persons, and most others with disorders affecting organs of communication and object manipulation. There is no need to consider in detail at this point the manifold possibilities for examining the intelligence of severely chronically ill persons. Stated simply, the basic principles are: (1) The examiner should be familiar with and have at hand during the examination as wide a range of tests as possible. Each subject presents unique problems and requires individually selected "tailor made" examination procedures. Standard, universally administered test batteries will not work in a medically heterogenous population of severely disabled persons. (2) In his own mind and in his written reports the examiner must differentiate clearly between *intellectual capacity*, as this is revealed by the patient's maximum performance on tests that do not penalize him for any specific physical incapacities, and *practical, functioning intelligence* of a more general kind. A patient with aphasia may do poorly on the verbal tests of the WAIS, thereby demonstrating his obvious lack of expressive verbal facility. The same patient may do well on a test like the Columbia Mental Maturity Scale, which does not penalize him for his verbal communicative deficiency, thereby indicating that, despite his inability to perform on some kinds of tasks, he nonetheless possesses a considerable intellectual capacity that may well serve as a valuable adjustive resource. The more limited the economic goals of rehabilitation, the less significant are measures of practical functional intelligence and the more important are the measures of intellectual capacities (Shontz, 1957). (3) Extreme caution should be used in the interpretation and communication of questionable intelligence test results. A psychologist administered the verbal scales of the WISC to a severely disabled girl who was diagnosed "cerebral palsy, athetoid." The psychologist used a multiple choice form of administration in which the subject responded "yes" or "no" to series of suggested answers to each question. The psychologist then evaluated the raw scores obtained in this way against standard IQ tables. The result was an IQ value 15 points higher than that arrived and agreed upon by three other psychologists who had tested the patient previously and later with more suitable instruments. The effect of the communication of the erroneous results to the already overly optimistic parents was nearly disastrous to the whole future course of the girl's rehabilitation. If standardized norms are to be used, it is always better to use tests that may be less sophisticated in design but that permit the subject a maximum degree of effective communication than it is to modify the administrative procedures of more complex instruments.

Personality resources are more difficult to assess than are intellectual resources. Here again, the rule is to select materials that permit the subject maximum expression. Often, the only materials at hand are those inherent in the person-to-person relationship of the interview situation. While some empirical efforts have been made to identify the personality correlates of successful vocational rehabilitation, there is good reason to believe, on the basis of what has already been said, that these indices will not suffice for evaluating the personality resources of the severely chronically ill person. In fact, the whole question of personality appraisal of the person with especially severe disability must, in all honesty, be left entirely open at the present time, and the clinician must be left to his own judgment and experience. A recent study on the evaluation of the psychosocial adjustment of the chronically ill (Shontz and Fink, 1960) suggested that experience is, indeed, an important determinant of this type of judgment; for student raters were found to be consistently less reliable in making judgments about a patient's adjustment than raters who had worked in the field for at least two years. It is clear that, in lieu of organized knowledge, direct patient contact with the severely disabled is, by all odds, the best teacher, so far as personality appraisal is concerned.

Several other important principles for the appraisal and management of the severely disabled have been proposed by Tobis, Lowenthal, and Belmont (Tobis, Lowenthal, and Belmont, 1958). While these principles were proposed for the use of specialists in physical medicine, their value is general, and they serve an excellent purpose for psychologists. With respect to appraisal, the following two ideas are especially cogent and may be paraphrased as follows:

1. Chronic disease is not a static condition. The patient's situation is constantly changing (especially, as was shown above, during the early stages of his illness) and must, therefore, be frequently reevaluated.

2. Small increments or decrements of function in the severely disabled may alter the whole picture and evaluation of the patient's degree of disability and rehabilitation potential.

The first principle hardly needs elaboration. The processes described by Nemiah and by Litin are clearly dynamic ones; and the implied need for constant reevaluation of each patient's situation is obvious. It should only be added that each successive psychological appraisal increases the amount of information available for integration and therefore simultaneously increases the number of opportunities for predictive checks and interpretive refinement.

The second principle implies an important, even crucial, psychological process and spells out a further reason why reevaluation is essential. The psychologist, and through him the entire rehabilitation team, must be aware of all changes in the patient, no matter how small the changes may be. The psychologist must be prepared to anticipate the significance of these changes, for they are often the signs of highly important changes soon to come, and they may, in and of themselves, alter completely the patient's potential for self-care. Even such apparently minor occurrences as the development in the patient of a positive attitude toward a special occupational therapist may make the difference between that patient's success or failure in the performance of the whole range of activities of daily living. An additional idea suggested by the second principle is one which might be didactically called the concept of psychological "amplification." To the especially severely disabled person, in a state of pervasive ambiguity, the slightest alteration in status often becomes a *signal* to be amplified. A change of bed or ward takes on the meaning of complete hope or despair: certain rooms may be identified as the ones where the "best" or "worst" patients are put. Spasms in the legs become signs of miraculous return of function. A word, dropped casually by a therapist, is taken to be a full-scale prognosis. Referral to the psychologist is equated with a diagnosis of insanity.

Patients' intense emotional reactions to minor changes are often naively interpreted by the staff to be manifestations of "rigidity." Actually, they are best seen as manifestations of the patient's acutely felt need for any kind of structure during a period that requires and demands an agonizing reappraisal of all that is important in one's life. Because of the tendency to amplify change, it is of critical significance for the psychologist to be aware of these changes too, and to be sensitive to their meanings, actual and potential. Some psychologists find contact with the patient "grapevine" to be a useful source of information about generally held superstitions and currently circulating rumors. And for this purpose, the great American coffee break is probably the most obviously exploitable social institution.

The psychologist needs all the information he can get when appraising the situation of the severely chronically ill person. He should get all he can from formal test instruments, but he must also doggedly pursue every other avenue that is open to him. He should remember, finally, that the independent, though more casual, psychological observations made by the physicians, ward nurses, therapists, and other staff members are equally valid grist for the psychological mill. No form of psychological practice demands of the psychologist more acumen, breadth of knowledge, and sensitivity than the appraisal of the capacities and potentials of patients with severe chronic illness.

SPECIAL CONSIDERATIONS IN PSYCHOLOGICAL TREATMENT AND REHABILITATION. Rather little can be said regarding psychological treatment practices with the severely chronically ill. First, little is known about what can (or, for that matter, should) be done. Second, the psychologist rarely has time available in which to do it, even when he knows what must be accomplished. The service pressure on some hospitals for the chronically ill is so great that patients are frequently not kept within their walls for any longer a period of time than that which is necessary for the stabilization of disease processes and the accomplishment of maximal physical restoration. Furthermore, in most settings staff shortages alone would prevent the institution of prolonged individual psychotherapy with any appreciable proportion of patients.

Fortunately, the hospital society is itself a kind of therapeutic community, if for no other reason than that it attends to the patient's primary needs for physical survival and provides him with important contacts with others in his own physical condition as well as with a variety of professionally trained staff members who are there to help him over the hump of his adjustive problem. It is probably true that many patients progress through the emotional sequence of reaction to severe disablement with little need for professional psychological help. But there will always be those who require special care and attention in this regard. It is therefore appropriate to consider briefly the little that can be said in the space available about what distinguishes the psychological treatment of the severely chronically ill from the psychological treatment of others.

As always, basic principle number one is that prevention is better than cure and that treatment, when necessary, is most efficiently rendered when it comes early in the process of the development of a difficult or "untoward" condition. A process of denial, for example, if spotted early, may often be prevented, or at least controlled, by the relatively simple device of presenting factual information to the patient in an acceptable manner as soon as the initial signs of denial appear. Once established as a quasi-permanent mode of adjustment, however, the mechanism is well nigh irreversible. (It is a moot question as to whether denial is in all cases and to all degrees unfavorable as an adjustment to especially severe disability. The author is inclined to feel that denial is not always undesirable; but the point will not be developed further in this discussion.)

Preventive care of the sort that is called for here is seldom the direct responsibility of the psychologist alone. Usually the responsibility for its administration falls to the physician or to the therapists who deal with the patient daily. The psychologist's responsibility is to assist in detecting the early signs of disturbance and, more importantly, to educate, by any means available, the rest of the staff to an awareness of the necessity for the application of remedial measures.

Suppose, however, that a "maladaptive" process gets under way and someone on the staff begins to sense the existence in the patient of emotional difficulties that require special attention. It is still not always necessary for a psychotherapist to step in with intensive, individual, and regular patient contact. Once a maladjustive process has set in, it is usually best to continue to utilize existing patient-staff relationships wherever possible for the correction of the condition. Frequently the individual staff member who first detects and reports the existence of a patient's psychological problem is the very one who can be best utilized for assisting the patient to a better form of adaptation. Use of existing interpersonal staff-patient relations has the major advantage of efficiency without loss of efficacy. All too frequently a psychologist undertakes to build a counseling relationship with a disturbed patient (a matter of weeks or months) only to have the patient discharged before the relationship can be therapeutically exploited. It is much more desirable to use the already meaningful staff-patient interactions that exist; and here again, the psychologist's job is educative rather than directly therapeutic in nature.

At first blush it may appear that the methods recommended are too superficial and do not penetrate to the core of the *real* psychological problem. In some cases the criticism may be a just one. Usually it is only so, however, when the psychological disturbance considerably antedated the disability. Generally speaking, the psychological condition of the recently severely disabled person is not one which requires the "analyzing of defenses" or any particular "penetration" to the personality core. One reason why the principle of psychological amplification operates so strongly in the severely chronically ill person is that he is without defenses to begin with; the shock of illness has already taken these away. What patients in the "early chronic phase" of disability need is not analysis at all, but synthesis. Synthesis is a process which often takes place by itself. The requirements for successful rehabilitation are that the process be intelligently and realistically guided and that the guidance begin early. There are many people on the rehabilitation team (and among the patient population) who can do this as efficiently as any psychologist, providing only that a trained person is available to assist and to supervise the interaction.

It is now appropriate to present the last two principles proposed by Tobis, Lowenthal, and Belmont:

3. *Functional* treatment is the purpose of rehabilitation, irrespective of the particular disease entity involved.

4. Treatment of the severely chronically ill person is essentially symptomatic.

The third principle, in its psychological application, is based upon a generally accepted, empirically justified proposition in somatopsychology that personality variation is not correlated in any significant way with medical diagnosis (Wright, 1960, p. 374). It means, first, that treatment focuses upon the functional, immediately significant aspects of personality and, second, that the types of problems the psychologist encounters and the techniques he will apply to the solution of these problems do not differ in any systematic way as a function of the patient's particular medical diagnosis. The latter aspect of meaning is often expressed by the statement that "personality variation is greater within medical categories than among medical categories." It does not mean that the same counseling technique is applicable to all patients. Flexibility of approach is as much required in dealing with the psychological problems of the severely chronically ill as it is in dealing with any other psychologically heterogeneous group of individuals. It only means that the counselor gets very little information as to how he should proceed from the medical diagnosis alone.

Taken together, the third and fourth principles imply that the counselor should deal almost exclusively with problems that are of immediate concern to the patient or the staff. His function is not to alter basic personality but to help the patient to use his personality and intellectual resources for arriving at a solution and adjustment to currently existing situational problems. Symptomatic treatment in these cases is not only an adequate challenge, even to the best trained counselor, but it is also the best means for accomplishing the necessary personality reorganization of the chronically ill individual.

Little mention has been made of the chronically ill patient who also suffers from psychiatric disorder, either on a pre-physical-illness basis or as something premorbidly latent but precipitated by the stress of disability. Problems presented by these patients are obviously most complex and do not represent the kind of problems with which the psychologist should regularly have to deal. The lack of space devoted to these patients in this presentation is not intended to minimize the importance of the problems they present. The current state of knowledge, however, is such that the psychologist must take first things first. If he can evolve techniques for dealing efficiently and effectively with the "routine" problems of adjustment to severe chronic illness, he may then move to the even more difficult problems presented by the special cases.

RESEARCH. No other subject is quite so open to imaginative psychological research as severe chronical illness. Little that has been said in this entire chapter was founded on conclusions drawn from the findings of experimental investigation. In fact, very few real findings exist upon which conclusions may be based.

There is good reason to believe that the psychological problems of the especially severely disabled are in some ways different from those of patients with less limiting afflictions. At the moment, however, one makes such a statement only as a kind of educated guess, and it remains to be seen whether it will be borne out in the course of controlled research. The statement must also be interpreted in the light of and with due consideration for those broader aspects of common humanity that are shared by all people, disabled or not: there is no reason to expect that a new psychology will be required for the explanation of adjustive problems of the severely disabled. At the same time, there is a good basis for the belief that an intensive study of the psychological content and structure of the dynamic processes that characterize this group will shed new light upon the whole general question of how and why people behave as they do.

Several specific needs for research have already been implied in this report. They will not be reviewed at this time. Instead, attention will be turned to the recommendations for research made in a summary article by H. R. Leavell (Leavell, 1955). Leavell's recommendations were made for all the behavioral sciences, but only those suggestions that are of special concern to psychologists are recounted and commented upon here.

Reactions to stress is a subject of both general and specific concern—general because it is presumed that all such reactions have a common organismic denominator and that stress itself is an inescapable fact of life for us all; specific, because the severely chronically ill patient is under especially intense and prolonged threat and thus presents unusually difficult problems in the management of stress responses.

The effects of child-rearing practices, as these influence attitudes toward disease and healing, is a second area of needed research. If it is true that the basic attitude of the patient toward his disability and toward its treatment are determined largely in the early formative years, it becomes a matter of immediate concern to learn how this comes about and how the children of today and tomorrow may be best imbued with attitudes that will enhance, rather than impede, the effectiveness of future treatment of severe chronic disease. Related to the developmental problem is the need to discover *personality correlates of the ability to endure discomfort and pain*, such as that which must frequently be tolerated by the severely chronically ill.

The importance of the general and specific study of *motivation* need hardly be elaborated. Most of this chapter has been devoted exclusively to the problem. Similarly, the need for research on the subject of *learning*, as this applies in particular to the practical and emotional training and reeducation of the especially severely disabled, has equally obvious and important implications.

Under the broad heading of *needed social research* may be included the following of Leavell's suggestions: study of the hospital as a social system; self-perception of roles by patient and staff; social class and health; decision-making processes (particularly as these are manifested in rehabilitation team behavior); cultural change through education; problems of interprofessional communication.

Few of these suggestions are new. The need for research appears to exist in areas that have, for the most part, already been exposed to at least the first tentative explorations of research investigation. What seems to be called for is not any startlingly new theoretical approach or investigative methodology, but, rather, a program of study that follows essentially the course and direction already mapped out by the existing interests of general psychology. The list presented here is not exhaustive. Any attempt to make it so would ultimately involve the discussion of virtually every aspect of human behavior. Implicit in all that could be said about research needs in the area of severe chronic illness is the basic proposition that people with severe chronic illnesses are first of all people, and, secondarily, that they are people in such special circumstances as to justify further investigation of their unique psychological traits. Psychological practice with the especially severely disabled person does not raise any globally new issues. Rather, it presents the psychologist with the challenge of applying and improving, in the most efficient way he can, his basic knowledge of theory, method, and technique to the end of aiding a particular group of individuals who currently need all the scientifically sound assistance they can get.

REFERENCES

Bennett, R. L. 1960. Use of orthetic devices in rehabilitation. Rehab. Rec. 1(4):29–33.

Campanella, R. 1959. It's good to be alive. New York, Dell Books.

Cherasky, M. 1955. Home care of chronic illness. J. Chron. Dis. 1:346–49.

—— 1959. Some comments on "The rehabilitation potential of patients in chronic disease institutions." J. Chron. Dis. 10:160.

Cohen, E. 1955. Comments on the patient with prolonged illness. J. Chron. Dis. 1:465–67.

Dacso, M. M., and H. A. Rusk. 1955. The problem of chronically ill and custodial patients in public institutions. J. Chron. Dis. 2:600–3.

Dembo, T. 1955. Suffering and its alleviation: a theoretical analysis. Report submitted to the Association for the Aid of Crippled Children. New York.

Dembo, T., G. L. Leviton, and B. A. Wright. 1956. Adjustment to misfortune: a problem of social-psychological rehabilitation. Artif. Limbs 3:4–62.

Diller, L. 1959. The phenomenon of denial in rehabilitation, in D. R. Martin and L. S. Downey, eds. Whither diagnosis? Boulder, Colo., Pulver Press, pp. 89–101.

Hamburg, D. A. 1953. Psychological adaptive processes in life-threatening injuries, in Symposium on stress. Washington, D.C., Army Medical Graduate School, Walter Reed Army Medical Center, pp. 222–35.

Hamilton, K. W. 1950. Counseling the handicapped in the rehabilitation process. New York, Ronald Press.

Hammill, J. F. 1958. Epilepsy. J. Chron. Dis. 8:448–63.

Highland View Hospital. 1959. Report: 1952–1958. Cleveland, Highland View Hospital.

Hoberman, M., and C. Springer. 1958. Rehabilitation of the "permanently and totally disabled" patient. Arch. Phys. Med. 39:235–40.

Hoerr, N. L., and A. Osol, eds. 1956. Blakiston's new Gould medical dictionary. 2d ed. New York, McGraw-Hill.

Institute for the Crippled and Disabled. 1959. Report of Third Rehabilitation Counselor Training Workshop: a broadening concept of the role of the rehabilitation counselor in the total community rehabilitation effort. New York, Feb. 19–21.

Klumpp, T. H. 1953. Work and happiness. Arch. Phys. Med. 34:669–75.

Leavell, H. R. 1955. Chronic disease and the behavioral sciences. J. Chron. Dis. 2:113–18.

Lesser, M. S., and R. C. Darling. 1953. Factors prognostic for vocational rehabilitation among the physically handicapped. Arch. Phys. Med. 34:73–81.

Litin, E. M. 1957. Emotional aspects of chronic physical disability. Arch. Phys. Med. 38:139–42.

Meyerson, L., N. Cohn, S. Toombs, and E. Portnoy. 1959. Some sources of delay in the medical referral of rehabilitation clients. Monograph in Somato-Psychology No. 3. Houston, Texas, University of Houston, Baylor University College of Medicine.

Moriyama, I. M. 1960. The classification of disease: a fundamental problem. J. Chron. Dis. 11:462–70.

Nemiah, J. C. 1957. The psychiatrist and rehabilitation. Arch. Phys. Med. 38:143–47.

Rehabilitation Record. 1960. A tide in the affairs of men; highlights of vocational rehabilitation legislation. Rehab. Record 1(3):3–12.

Roberts, D. W. 1955. The overall picture of long-term illness. J. Chron. Dis. 1:149–59.

Rosenfeld, L. S., F. Goldmann, and L. A. Kaprio. 1957. Reasons for prolonged hospital stay. J. Chron. Dis. 6:141–52.

Shontz, F. C., and S. L. Fink. 1957. The significance of patient-staff rapport in the rehabilitation of individuals with chronic physical illness. J. Consult. Psychol. 21:327–34.

—— 1960. A method for evaluating psychosocial adjustment of the chronically ill. Amer. J. Phys. Med. 40:63–69.

Shontz, F. C., S. L. Fink, and C. E. Hallenbeck. 1960. Chronic physical illness as threat. Arch. Phys. Med. 41:143–48.

Shontz, F. C., S. L. Fink, E. B. Nadler, and C. E. Hallenbeck. 1959.

Establishing follow-up criteria in rehabilitation. Paper read at American Psychological Association Convention, Cincinnati, Ohio, Sept. 4.

Stubbins, J. 1960. New horizons for workshops for the handicapped. Los Angeles, Calif., Los Angeles State College.

Tobis, J. S., M. Lowenthal, and I. Belmont. 1958. Physical medicine and rehabilitation in a chronic disease hospital. Arch. Phys. Med. 39:82–86.

U.S. Dept. of Veterans Benefits. 1960. Occupations of epileptic veterans of World War II and Korean Conflict. Washington, D.C., Veterans Administration.

Weinstein, E. A., and R. L. Kahn. 1955. Denial of illness. Springfield, Ill., C. C. Thomas.

Weir, D. 1959. Welcoming address. The Cleveland Symposium. Cleveland, Ohio, Highland View Hospital. Nov. 4–6.

Wright, B. A. 1959, a. The problems of educating the public and monetary return. Paper delivered at the Cleveland Symposium. Cleveland, Ohio, Highland View Hospital, Nov. 4–6.

—— 1959, b. Psychology and rehabilitation. Washington, D.C., American Psychological Association.

—— 1960. Physical disability: a psychological approach. New York, Harper.

ABBREVIATIONS USED IN REFERENCES

Acta Otolaryng.	Acta Oto-Laryngologica
Amer. Ann. Deaf.	American Annals of the Deaf
Amer. Heart J.	American Heart Journal
Amer. J. Card.	American Journal of Cardiology
Amer. J. Dis. Child.	American Journal of the Diseases of Children
Amer. J. Med. Sci.	American Journal of Medical Sciences
Amer. J. Ment. Defic.	American Journal of Mental Deficiency
Amer. J. Occup. Ther.	American Journal of Occupational Therapy
Amer. J. Orthopsychiat.	American Journal of Orthopsychiatry
Amer. J. Phys. Med.	American Journal of Physical Medicine
Amer. J. Psychiat.	American Journal of Psychiatry
Amer. J. Psychol.	American Journal of Psychology
Amer. J. Psychother.	American Journal of Psychotherapy
Amer. J. Public Health	American Journal of Public Health
Amer. Practit.	American Practitioner and Digest of Treatment
Amer. Psychologist	American Psychologist
Ann. Intern. Med.	Annals of Internal Medicine
Ann. N.Y. Acad. Sci.	Annals of the New York Academy of Sciences
Ann. Otol.	Annals of Otology, Rhinology, and Laryngology
Ann. Phys. Med.	Annals of Physical Medicine
Ann. Rev. Physiol.	Annual Review of Physiology
Ann. Rev. Psychol.	Annual Review of Psychology
Ann. Rheum. Dis.	Annals of the Rheumatic Diseases
Arch. Intern. Med.	Archives of Internal Medicine
Arch. Neurol.	Archives of Neurology
Arch. Neurol. Psychiat.	Archives of Neurology and Psychiatry
Arch. Otolaryng.	Archives of Otolaryngology
Arch. Phys. Med.	Archives of Physical Medicine and Rehabilitation
Artif. Limbs	Artificial Limbs

Ass. Res. Nerv. Ment. Dis. Proc.	Association for Research in Nervous and Mental Diseases Proceedings
Brit. J. Med. Psychol.	British Journal of Medical Psychology
Brit. J. Plast. Surg.	British Journal of Plastic Surgery
Brit. Med. Bull.	British Medical Bulletin
Brit. Med. J.	British Medical Journal
Bull. Menninger Clin.	Bulletin of the Menninger Clinic
Can. Med. J.	Canadian Medical Journal
Cancer Res.	Cancer Research
Cereb. Palsy Rev.	Cerebral Palsy Review
Chicago Med. Soc. Bull.	Chicago Medical Society Bulletin
Childhood Educ.	Childhood Education
Circ.	Circulation
Conn. Med. J.	Connecticut Medical Journal
Eye Ear Nose Throat	Eye, Ear, Nose and Throat Monthly
Heart Bull.	Heart Bulletin
Industrial Med.	Industrial Medicine
Int. J. Psychoanal.	International Journal of Psychoanalysis
J. Abnorm. Soc. Psychol.	Journal of Abnormal and Social Psychology
J. Amer. Geriat. Soc.	Journal of the American Geriatrics Society
J. Amer. Med. Ass.	Journal of the American Medical Association
J. Amer. Psychoanal. Ass.	Journal of the American Psychoanalytic Association
J. Chron. Dis.	Journal of Chronic Diseases
J. Clin. Exp. Psychopath.	Journal of Clinical and Experimental Psychopathology
J. Clin. Psychol.	Journal of Clinical Psychology
J. Comp. Physiol. Psychol.	Journal of Comparative and Physiological Psychology
J. Consult. Psychol.	Journal of Consulting Psychology
J. Exp. Psychol.	Journal of Experimental Psychology
J. Genet. Psychol.	Journal of Genetic Psychology
J. Hillside Hosp.	Journal of the Hillside Hospital
J. La. Med. Soc.	Journal of the Louisiana Medical Society
J. Mich. Med. Soc.	Journal of the Michigan Medical Society
J. Nerv. Ment. Dis.	Journal of Nervous and Mental Disease
J. Project. Techn.	Journal of Projective Techniques
J. Psychol.	Journal of Psychology
J. Rehab.	Journal of Rehabilitation
J. Social Issues	Journal of Social Issues
J. Speech Hearing Dis.	Journal of Speech and Hearing Disorders
Med. Econ.	Medical Economics

Med. News	Medical News
Med. Sci.	Medical Science
Med. Social Work	Medical Social Work
New Engl. J. Med.	New England Journal of Medicine
New York J. Med.	New York State Journal of Medicine
Northw. Med.	Northwest Medicine
Ohio Med. J.	Ohio Medical Journal
Plast. Reconstr. Surg.	Plastic and Reconstructive Surgery
Postgrad. Med.	Postgraduate Medicine
Pract. Otorhinolaryng.	Practica Oto-Rhino-Laryngologica
Proc. Roy. Soc. Med.	Proceedings of the Royal Society of Medicine
Psychoanal. Rev.	Psychoanalytic Review
Psychoanal. Quart.	Psychoanalytic Quarterly
Psychol. Bull.	Psychological Bulletin
Psychol. Rev.	Psychological Review
Psychosom. Med.	Psychosomatic Medicine
Public Health Rep.	Public Health Reports
Rehab. Lit.	Rehabilitation Literature
Rehab. Record	Rehabilitation Record
Rev. Educ. Res.	Review of Educational Research
Southern Med. J.	Southern Medical Journal
Texas Rep. Biol. Med.	Texas Reports on Biology and Medicine
Trans. Amer. Acad. Ophthal. Otolaryng.	Transactions of the American Academy of Ophthalmology and Otolaryngology
Volta Rev.	Volta Review
Yale J. Biol. Med.	Yale Journal of Biology and Medicine

INDEX

Abbott, M., 160
Abel, T. M., 270, 271
Acetyl-salicylic acid, 62
Achievement and aptitude testing, *see* Psychological appraisal
ACTH, 69
Agnosias, transmissive, 201; auditory and visual, 203-4
Agraphias, 204
Allan, F. N., 102
Allan, T., 295
Allen, R. M., 171-72, 175
Allport, F. H., 294
Alphabet, manual, *see* Finger spelling
Altshuler, K. Z., 302
Amatruda, C. S., 314
American Academy for Cerebral Palsy, statement of Nomenclature Committee, 160
American Academy of Ophthalmology and Otolaryngology, 284
American Foundation for the Blind, 344, 353, 364, 368, 395
American Heart Association, 85, 88, 94, 98, 102, 110, 126, 127, 149
American Medical Association, 342
American Printing House for the Blind, Louisville, Ky., 398-99
American Rheumatism Association, 52, 56
Ammons Full-Range Picture Vocabulary Test, 175, 176-78
Amputation: 1-46; definition of, 1; problems of, depending on individual's chronological age, 1-2, 2 (*fig.*); major types of: (*congenital, traumatic, selective*), 2-4; etiology and incidence of major, 1-4, 3 (*table*); "site of," 4-6, 3 (*fig.*); upper extremity: (*below-elbow*) 4-6, 5 (*fig.*), (*above-elbow*) 4-6, 5 (*fig.*); lower extremity: (*below-knee*, between Syme's and knee disarticulation) 4-6, 5 (*fig.*), (*above-knee*, between knee disarticulation and hip disarticulation (4-6, 5 (*fig.*); chronic medical difficulties resulting from continuous prosthetic wearing and, 7-8; medical-physical aspects of, 8-9; preposthetic conditioning of body tissues after, 8-9; "clinic team" concept and rehabilitation after, 8-9; gangrenous conditions prompting, 8; psychological implications of, 9-28; functional limitations after, 10-11; functional failures after, 11-12
Amputee(s): congenital, 1; upper extremity, 4-6, 5 (*fig.*); wrist disarticulation, 4-6, 5 (*fig.*); below-elbow, 4-6, 5 (*fig.*); elbow disarticulation, 4-6, 5 (*fig.*); above-elbow, 4-6, 5 (*fig.*); shoulder disarticulation, 4-6, 5 (*fig.*); forequarter, 4-6, 5 (*fig.*); lower extremity, 4-6, 5 (*fig.*); partial foot, 4-6, 5 (*fig.*); Syme's, 4-6, 5 (*fig.*); below-knee, 4-6, 5 (*fig.*); knee disarticulation, 4-6, 5 (*fig.*); above-knee, 4-6, 5 (*fig.*); hip disarticulation, 4-6, 5 (*fig.*); hemipelvectomy, 4-6, 5 (*fig.*); unilateral, 6; bilateral, 6; multiple, 6; prosthetic replacement for, 6; psychological difficulties of, 6; medical care of, 6-7, 8; postoperative and preprosthetic care of, 7; ability to wear prosthesis by, 7, 36-37, 39; physical and psychological adjustment of, 7;

Amputee(s) (*Continued*)
physiological and psychological changes taking place in, 7; prescription, fabrication, and fitting of prosthetic device for, 8; prosthetic care of, 8; "clinic team" concept in management of, 8-9; vocational and economic factors concerning, 15-16; social considerations of, 17-18; behavior of, 18-24, 25-29; psychodynamics, 24; perception of disability of, 24-29; psychological appraisal of, 28-34; rehabilitation of, 35-39
Anderson, M. D., Hospital, *see* University of Texas
Angina pectoris, 88, 108, 112
Ankylosing spondylitis, 54, 55, 57, 60
"Anniversary reaction" in heart disease, 104
Aphasia, in hemiplegia, 141
Aphasia, types of: *global, jargon, pragmatic, semantic, syntactic*, 203; tests for, 219; intellectual capacity of patients with, 222-23
Aphasias, integrative, 201
Apraxias, 204; transmissive, 201
Apoplexy, *see* Hemiplegia
Army Beta Revised Intelligence Test, 316
Arterial hypertension, 102
Arteriosclerosis of the coronary arteries, *see* Coronary heart disease
Arthritic joint, granulation tissue within, 58 (*fig.*)
Arthritis and rheumatism: 51-82; deformity and pains resulting from, 51; antiquity of, 51; historical background of, 51-52; modern medical differentiation between, 52; incidence in the U.S., 52-53; arthritis, due to: infection, 57, rheumatic fever, 57, trauma, 57; of gout, 57; physiotherapy and exercise, in treatment of, 61-62; drugs used in treatment of, 62; psychological implications of, 66-73; special considerations in rehabilitation, 75-82
Arthur Point Scale of Performance Tests, 316
Ataxic type, cerebral palsy, 161
Athetotic (athetoid) type, cerebral palsy, 160-61
Atonic type, cerebral palsy, 161
Audiogram, *see* Hearing, measurement of
Audiometer, *see* Hearing, measurement of
Auditory agnosias, 203-4
Auditory disability: 279-333; definitions and incidence, 280-84; the deaf, 281; the hard of hearing, 282; hypacusic (hard of hearing), 282; anacusic (deaf), 282; dysacusic, 282-83; psychodysacusic, 283; medical-acoustic aspects, 284-93; process of hearing, 284-86, 286 (*fig.*); pathological conditions, 286-90; types, causes, prognosis of hearing impairments, 287-90; measurement of auditory acuity, 290-93, 292 (*fig.*); psychological implications of, 293-307; compensatory communicative measures: language development, speechreading (lipreading), hearing aid, speech therapy, auditory training, finger spelling, the sign language, 305-7; special considerations in psychological appraisal, 307-21: diagnostic team, 308, case history, 310-12, interview, 311-12, observation, 312-14, psychological testing, 314-21, test interpretation, 318-21, recording and reporting, 321; special considerations in rehabilitation, 321-28: goals of compensatory rehabilitation, 322, rehabilitation of children, 323-24, rehabilitation problems and limitations, 325-28; psychological research, 328-33
Auditory projective technique, 360
Auditory training, 307
Axelrod, S., 351-52
Axline, V. M., 368, 369, 371

Bach, F., 71
Backache, diagnosis of, 67-68
Ballantyne, J. C., 284, 323
Ballistocardiograph, 90
"Bamboo spine," 60
Barker, E. C., 64
Barker, R. G., 349
Bauer, W., 71
Bauman, M. K., 345, 356, 358, 396, 397, 398, 399
Bauman's Emotional Factors Inventory, 358, 360

Bauman's Non-language Learning Test, 398
Bellak, L., 111, 112
Bellevue Rehabilitation Service, 152
Belmont, I., 434, 439
Bender, L., 314
Bender Visual Motor Gestalt Test, 316
Benham, F. G., 345
Bennett, R. L., 414
Benton Visual Retention Test, 316
Bergman, M., 406
Berry, G., 297
Best, H., 299, 300
Bettica, L. J., 406
Bice, H. V., 186
Blind Rehabilitation Section, Veterans Administration Hospital, Hines, Ill., 365
Block, W. E., 170
Blum, L. H., 166
Blumberg, E. M., 234, 235
"Body image" and hemiplegia, 141-42
"Bony ankylosis," 60
Bordeaux, J., 289
Bradway, K. P., 354
Braille, 356, 365, 395
Brain damage: in hemiplegia, 132-35; in cerebral palsy, 168; left compared with right, 199-200; in language disorders, 199-201; in quadrantal visual defects, 208-9
Brain-impaired state, psychosometric and projective signs of, 214
Brain injury, behavioral patterns after, 211
Brandow, E. C., Jr., 321
Braverman, S., 360
Breast, loss of, due to cancer, 241-42
British Columbia division of the Canadian Arthritis and Rheumastim Society, 64
Brodie, F. H., 344, 354, 355, 357, 368
Brown, F., 116
Brunschwig, L., 318
Brunschwig Adjustment Inventory, 318
Bryt, A., 270, 271, 272, 273
Burgemeister, B. B., 166
Butazolidin, 62

Campanella, R., 424-28
Canadian Arthritis and Rheumatism Society, British Columbia division of, 64
Cancer: 232-58; psychological resistance to, 232-37; Giant Metabolic Study, 234-35; prostate, 235-36; adjustment counseling in, 237-39; coping with, 239, 248; intimate meaning of, 239-40; thyroid, 241, 250; organ involved, 241-42; prosthesis after breast removal due to, 241, 242; prostatic surgery due to, 242-43; facial disfigurement due to skin, 243-44; reactions of hospitalized patients with, 244-45; counselor's interprative role in, 246-52; hormones and, 249; androgens and, 249; X-ray treatments of, 249; counseling for acceptance of death, 252-58
Canfield, N., 332
Cardiac(s): "personality," 100; report of symptoms: to physician, 106, to psychologist, 107-9; psychotherapy, 111-13; without heart disease, 113; work situation, 113-15; patient classification (*chart*), 118
Cardiac Work Evaluation Clinic, 86
Cardiovascular disability: 85-118; incidence of, 85; survival rate, 85-86; personal and economic cost of, 86-87; major types of, 88; causes of, 88-89; medical diagnostic problems associated with, 89-90; tools and measures available in diagnosis of, 90; psychological implications of, 93-100, 108-9; problem of vocational adjustment, due to, 98-100; psychological evaluation of, 101-9; "team" approach, in treatment of, 116-18; classification of patients with (*chart*), 119
Cardiovascular system, influence of psychic factors on, 86
Cardwell, V. E., 159
Cattell, P., 353, 354, 355
Cattell, R. B., 75, 79
Cattell Infant Intelligence Scale, 175, 176, 183, 353, 354-55, 356
Causes of disability, *see* Etiological factors
Cerebral arteriosclerosis, 85
Cerebral palsy: 159-92; incidence of, 159; etiological factors, 159-60; definitions and classifications, 160-63;

Cerebral palsy (*Continued*)
types of: spastic, 160; atherotic (athetoid), 160-61; dyskinesias (subtypes), 161; rigidity, 161; ataxic, 161; tremor, 161; atonic, 161; medical management of, 163-65; nonmedical specialists and, 163-65; "organic syndrome behavior," 165; psychological aspects and implications, 165-66; psychological findings (*table*), 166; mental retardation and attendant complications, 166-67; psychological behavior, 167-68; motor impairment, 169; perceptual difficulties, 169; coping mechanisms, 169, 170; sensory and motor dysfunction, 170; behavioral manifestations, 170; attitude of society and parents toward patients with, 172; special considerations in psychological appraisal, 172-89; rehabilitation, 189-91; research, 191-92
Cerebrovascular accidents resulting in language disorders, 198-99
Cerebrovascular disease, 85; *see also* Hemiplegia
Cherasky, M., 413, 421
Chevigny, H., 360, 361-62, 363-64
Chicago, University of, Medical Clinics, 354, 357, 368
Chicago Nonverbal Examination, 318
Cholden, L. S., 363, 364, 365-66, 371
Chronic illness, *see* Severe chronic illness
Circulatory deficiencies in the stump after amputation surgery, 8
Circulatory pathology, 87-88
Clark, W. S., 66
Classifications and definitions in: amputation, 4-6; arthritis and rheumatism, 54-57; cardiovascular disability, 88; hemiplegia, 126; cerebral palsy, 160-63; language disorders, 195-204; facial disfigurement, 262-64; auditory disability, 280-83; visual disability, 341-43; deaf-blindness, 377-78; severe chronic illness, 411-16
Cleft palate and/or lip, 262, 265, 266
Cobb, A. B., 246
Cohen, E., 412-13
Cohen, P., 177
Collagen diseases, 54, 56, 65, 67
Collins, M. G., 175
Columbia Mental Maturity Scale, 175, 178-79, 186, 433
Columbia–Presbyterian Medical Center, Department of Otolaryngology, 283
Commission on Chronic Illness, 411
Committee on Nomenclature of La Ligue Internationale contre le Rheumatisme, 57
Committee on Services for the Deaf-Blind of the World Council for the Welfare of the Blind, 405-6
Communication, means of: speechreading (lipreading), 306; finger spelling (manual alphabet), 307, 394; the sign language, 307; interpreter, 312, 394; Tellatouch, 395; printing in the palm, 395; large type, 395; braille, 395
Conference of Executives of American Schools for the Deaf, 281, 282
Congenital amputation, 2-4, 6
Congenital heart disease, 85, 88, 90
Congestive heart failure, 105
Contractures due to amputation surgery and continuous prosthetic wear, 7
Copple, G. E., 397
Copple Sentence Completion Test, 397
Cornell University, 352
Corticosteroids, 62, 69
Coronary artery disease, *see* Coronary heart disease
Coronary heart disease, 85, 88; treatment for, 91-93
Coronary infarct, 85
Coronary occlusion, 85
"Coronary personality," 100
Coronary thrombosis, 85
Cortical damage and language disorders, 205
Courville, C. B., 162
Cousins, R., 161
Cowen, E. L., 345, 371
Cox, C., 64
Crawford, D. M., 397
Crawford, J. E., 397
Crawford Small Parts Dexterity Test, 358, 397
Critchley, M., 371
Cruickshank, W. M., 186, 371

"*Current Research in Work with the Blind*," 369

Dacso, M. M., 421
Dade County Sheltered Workshop, 192
Dallenbach, K. M., 352, 371
Damarin, F., 235, 236
Darling, R. C., 417
David, E. E., 284
Davis, H., 282, 284, 286, 287, 288, 289, 291, 321, 322
De Angelis, G. J., 406
Deaf-Blindness: 376-407; definitions and incidence of, 377-79; medical aspects of, 379; otological investigations, 379-80; opthalmological study, 380; psychological implications, 380-94; intellectual functioning, 383-84; general comprehension of deaf-blind persons, 384-86; reasoning power of deaf-blind persons, 386-87; memory and, 387-88; word power and, 388-89; general personality functioning and, 390-94; special considerations in psychological appraisal, 394-400; rehabilitation team, 401-2; relationships with surrounding realities in patients with, 402-3; education and, 403-4; vocational rehabilitation and, 404-7
Dean, S. I., 360
Death, counseling for acceptance of, 251-58
Decibel, *see* Hearing, measurement of
Degenerative joint disease, 57
Deland, F., 306
Dembo, T., 428
Diarthrosis, normal (*fig.*), 57
Diller, L., 428
DiMichael, S. G., 321, 396
Dodgson, M. C., 101
Doehring, D. G., and R. M. Retan, 212
Doll, E. A., 353, 354
Dorfman, E., 361
Draw-A-Person Test, cerebral palsy, 188
Drever, J., 371
Drugs, in treatment of gout, 63, 64; in treatment of osteoarthritis, 62-63, 64; in treatment of rheumatoid arthritis, 62, 64; in cancer, side effects of, 249
Dunlop, D. M., 283
Dysarthrias, 204, 208, 220
Dyskinesias (cerebral palsy) subtypes, 161

Edgerton, M. T., 269
Edström, G., 67
Educational problems, *see* Psychological implications; Rehabilitation
Electro-Braille Communicator, 406
Electrocardiograph, 90
Ellis, F. W., 233-34
Engel, M., 361
Engle, H. A., 161
Etiological factors in: amputation, 1-6, 3 (*table*); arthritis and rheumatism, 54-55; cardiovascular disability, 88-89; hemiplegia, 127-28; cerebral palsy, 159-60; language disorders, 198, 199, 203; cancer, 232; facial disfigurement, 265; auditory disability, 287-90; visual disability, 343; deaf-blindness, 380; severe chronic illness, 412
Euphoria, 211, 213
Eysenck, H. J., 75, 79

Facial disfigurement: 261-78; incidence and classifications, 262-65; areas or types of, 263-65; medical aspects of, 265-67; psychological implications of, 267-73; emotional disturbances due to, 269-73; special considerations in psychological appraisal of, 273-75; rehabilitation and, 275-78; public education and, 277-78
Factored Aptitude Series (Knieval), 316
Fenichel, O., 294
Fibrositis, 69
Finger spelling, 307, 394
Fink, S. L., 422, 434
Firestone, S., 348
First Institute for Special Workers for the Aural Disabled, 318-21
Fjeld, H. A., 354
Flaccidity, *see* Atonic type, cerebral palsy
Ford, F. R., 289
Fournier, J. E., 292
Fowler, E. P., 282, 284, 286, 291, 302, 314, 321, 379

Fox, M. S., 284
Freedheim, D. K., 165, 167

Gafton, J. P., 64
Gardberg, M., 93
Gardner, R. W., 187
Geist Picture Interest Inventory, 316
Gesell, A., 314
Gesell Preliminary Behavior Intelligence Scale, 175, 176, 182, 186
Gilroy, R. V., 380
Global aphasia, 203, 206
Gold compounds, 62
Goldman, I. B., 270
Goldmann, F., 419, 421
Goldstein, K., 168, 200
Goodhill, V., 321
Goodwill Industries, 192
Gordon, S., 295
Gout, 54-55, 61; drugs used in treatment of, 63, 64; weight reduction and diet, in control of, 63
Grace Arthur Performance Scales, 317
Granulation tissue within arithritic joint (*fig.*), 58
Greenberg, H. M., 368
Groht, M., 306
Guilford, F. R., 292

Hadley Tactaphone, 406
Haeussermann, E., 318
Hall, F. H., 403
Hallenbeck, C. E., 422
Halliday, J. L., 68, 69
Hamburg, D. A., 428
Hammill, J. F., 414
Hamilton, K. W., 416
Hammond, D. R., and M. Allen, 321
Handel, A. F., 377, 378
Harlow, H., 139
Harms, E., 314
Harper, R. A., 326
Haselkorn, F., 111, 112
Haug, C. O., 292
Hayes, S. P., 354, 356, 357, 358, 396, 399
Hayes-Binet, *see* Interim Hayes-Binet Intelligence Tests for the Blind
Head, Henry, 141
Head injuries, externally induced, resulting in language disorders, 198-99
Head noises (tinnitus), 298, 332
Hearing, measurement of, 290-93; audiogram (*fig.*), 292
Hearing, process of, 284-86
Hearing, pathological conditions of, 286-90
Heart, circulatory pathology of, 87
Heart attacks, *see* Heart disease; Cardiovascular disease(s); Coronary infarct; Coronary occlusion; Coronary thrombosis
Heart attacks, "silent," 105
Heart conditions (major) in category of psychosomatic disorders, 86
Heart disease: "nonorganic," 86; rheumatic, 88; hypertensive, 88, 91; coronary, 88; emotional reaction to, 93-97; family attitudes of victims of, 97-98; community attitudes toward, 98; psychotics with, 101; "anniversary reaction" in, 104; "cardiacs" without, 113; classification of patients with (*chart*), 119
Heart murmur, subtleties of, 90
Hebb, D. O., 294
Heider, F., 294, 317
Heider, G. M., 317
Hellerstein, H. K., 99
Hemianopsias, 208-9; homonymous, 210
Hemiparesis, *see* Hemiplegia
Hemiplegia: 125-54; definition of, 125; paresis, hemiparesis and, 125; characteristic stance and symptoms of, 125-26; vasomotor changes due to, 126; incidence of, 126; medical-physical aspects of, 127-30; causes of, 127-28; mortality rate, 128; physical treatment of, 129-30; speech therapy, 130; psychological implications of, 130-44; brain damage in, 132-35; life rhythms, 135-36; organic and nonorganic perceptions, 136; thinking disturbances, 136-37; emotional reactions to, 137-38; depression and anxiety affecting motivation, 139-40; aphasia and, 141; comparative intelligence of right and left hemiplegics, 141, 142; "body image" and, 141-42; family reaction to, 142-43; vocational problems, 143-44; psychological appraisal of the hemiplegic, 144-49; rehabilitation, 141-51; research, 151-53; language disorder and, 205
Hemolytic streptococcal infection, 91

High blood pressure, *see* Hypertensive heart disease
Highland View Hospital, Cleveland, Ohio, 412
Hill, G., 269
Hillman, L., 69
Hirsh, I. J., 284
Hiskey-Nebraska Test of Learning Aptitude for Young Deaf Children, 318
Hoch, P., 314
Hochhauser, E., 322
Hodgson, K. W., 280
Hoerr, N. L., 411
Hohman, L. B., 165, 167
Homonymous hemianopsia, 210
Hoople, G., 284
Hopkins, T. W., 161
Howe, M., 403
Huggins, C. B., 233
Hughes, W., 101
Huizinga, E., 280
Hunt, W. M., 297
Hurlin, R. G., 342
Hypertension, arterial, 102
Hypertensive heart disease, 85, 91
"Hypertensive personality," 100
Hypertrophy of the synovial membrane, 58
Hypotonia, *see* Atonic type, cerebral palsy

Incidence in: amputation, 1-6, 2 (*fig.*), 3 (*table*); arthritis and rheumatism, 52-54; cardiovascular disability, 85-87; hemiplegia, 126; cerebral palsy, 159; language disorders, 198; facial disfigurement, 262; auditory disability, 280, 283-84; visual disability, 342; deaf-blindness, 377; severe chronic illness, 411-12
Industrial Home for the Blind, Brooklyn, N.Y., 401, 405
Input-integrative-output concept of neural function, 201-2, 202 (*fig.*)
Institute for Special Workers for the Aural Disabled, First, 318-21
Institute for the Crippled and Disabled, New York, N.Y., 190
Intelligence testing, *see* Psychological appraisal
Interim Hayes-Binet Intelligence Tests for the Blind, 356, 357, 397
Interpreter in communcation, 312, 394
IQ, *see* Psychological appraisal; Psychological implications; Research
Isakower, O., 279

Jacobson, W. E., 269
Jargon aphasia, 203
Jayne, H. W., 101
Jewish Vocational Service Workshop, 192
Johnson, K. O., 283
Joint, granulation tissue within arthritic (*fig.*), 58
Joint, synovial, 57, 58 (*fig.*)
Joint disease, degenerative, 57
Joints in the spine, rheumatoid changes of, 60
Journal of Chronic Diseases, 412

Kahn, R. L., 428
Kaprio, L. A., 419, 421
Kastein, S., 314
Katz, E., 175, 176, 177, 183, 184, 185
Katz Form survey, 175, 176, 177 (*form*)
Keller, H. A., 403
Keloidal growths, 265
Kephart, N. C., 314
Kersley, G. D., 64
Kessler Institute for Rehabilitation, 151
Kietz, H., 285
King, S. H., 71, 74
Kinney, C. E., 323
Kittleson, S. K., 350
Kleinfeld, L., 279, 287
Knapp, P. H., 279, 296, 302
Knieval, W. R., 316; adaptation of the Factored Aptitude Series, 316
Kolkbrenner, L., 379
Kubzansky, P. E., 294
Kuder Preference Record, 358
Kunze's Musical Reverie Test, 359

La Ligue Internationale contre le Rheumatisme, 57
Laird, C., 323
Lange, J., theory of emotion, 146
Language disorders: 197-228; incidence and classifications of, 198-204; cerebrovascular accidents resulting in, 198-99; externally induced head

Language disorders (*Continued*)
injuries resulting in, 198-99; neurological disease and neurosurgical intervention resulting in, 198-99; hemispheric differences (left/right brain trauma), and 199-200; definitions of: transmissive agnosias, transmissive apraxias, integrative aphasias, 200; central nervous system and, 201-2; input-integrative-output concept of neural function, 201-2, 202 (*fig.*); types of aphasias: global, jargon, pragmatic, semantic, syntactic, 202-3, 222; agnosias and, 203-4; apraxias and, 204; agraphias and, 204; physical concomitants after cortical damage, 205; constriction of the visual field, 209 (*fig.*), 210; behavorial patterns after brain injury, 211; memory loss and euphoria, effect upon, 213; psychometric and projective signs seen on evaluation of brain-impaired patients, 214; psychological appraisal, 215-24; treatment and rehabilitation, 224-28
Lansing, R. W., 235
Large type communication with deaf-blind, 395
Lawrence, M., 284
Leavell, H. R., 441, 442
Lebovits, B. Z., 116
Lehtinen, L., 168, 314
Leiderman, P. H., 294
Leiter's International Performance Scale, 175, 180-81, 186
Lempert, J., 322
Lesion, cerebral palsy, 162
Lesser, M. S., 417
Levine, E. S., 281, 307, 311, 316, 317, 321, 330, 331
Lewin, K. K., 116
Linde, T., 188
Linn, L., 270
Lip reading, *see* Speechreading
Litin, E. M., 430-31, 435
Long, J. S., 307
Longerich, M. C., 289
Lowell, E. L., 306
Lowenfeld, B., 346-47
Lowenthal, M., 434, 439
Lowman, E. W., 57, 81-82
Ludwig, A. D., 70
Lukoff, I. F., 348
McCarthy, D., 173, 184
McCoy, G., 283
MacFarland, D. C., 366-67
Macgregor, F. C., 268
MacIver, J., 86, 113
Mack, R., 377
McKerracher, D. G., 102
Make-A-Picture-Story Test, 318
Manual alphabet, 307, 394
"*Manual for the Psychological Examination of the Adult Blind*," 356, 396
Marie-Strümpell disease, 55
Masland, R. L., 280
Maxfield, K. E., 354
Maxfield-Buchholz Social Maturity Scale for Blind Preschool Children, 353
Maxfield-Fjeld Tentative Adaptation of the Vineland Social Maturity Scale, 354
Mayman, M., 187
M. D. Anderson Hospital, *see* University of Texas
Medical aspects of: amputation, 6-9; arthritis and rheumatism, 57-66; cardiovascular disability, 87-93; cancer, 232; hemiplegia, 127-30; cerebral palsy, 163-65; brain impairment in language disorders, 205-10; facial disfigurement, 265-67; auditory disability, 284-93; visual disability, 342-44; deaf-blindness, 379-80; severe chronic illness, 411-16
Memory loss (aphasia), effects in language disorders, 213
Mendelson, J. H., 294
Ménière's disease, 289, 298
Menninger, K. A., 322
Merrill-Palmer Intelligence Scales, 317
Metabolic Study (cancer), 234-35, 236
Metropolitan Achievement Test, 358
Meyer, E., 269
Meyerson, L., 292, 346, 349, 371
Michal-Smith, H., 167-68
Microtia, 265
Minnesota Multiphasic Personality Inventory, 116, 360
Minnesota Rate of Manipulation Test, 358, 397
Mittelman, B., 371
Montague, H. A., 306
Morris, C., 203
Morris, W. W., 359
Motor agraphia, 204

Motor dysfunction, cerebral palsy, 162, 170
Murphy, G. E. B., 299
Muscular rheumatism, 67
Musculoskeletal system, disturbances of, 68
Musical Reverie Test, Kunze's, 359
Mygind, S. H., 284
Myklebust, H. R., 314, 371, 404

Nadler, E. B., 422
National Conference on Work Evaluation Units, 102
National Council on Psychological Aspects of Disability, 227
National Health Education Committee, 53, 72
National Health Survey, 343
National Institutes of Health, 227
National organizations in speech and hearing, 333-34
National Science Foundation, 227
National Society for Crippled Children and Adults, 227
Nemiah, J. C., 430, 435
Neuroendocrine system, as a factor in arthritis, 69
Neurological disease and neurosurgical intervention, in language disorders, 198-99
Neuromata, in amputation surgery and continuous prosthetic wear, 7-8
New, M. C., 306
New York School of Social Work Research Center, 348
New York State Psychiatric Institute, 331
Nomenclature Committee of the American Academy for Cerebral Palsy, 160
Norris, M., 344, 354, 355, 357, 368
Northwestern University Medical School, 357

O'Connor, C. D., 323
Office of Vocational Rehabilitation, 192, 225, 405
Olin, W. H., 262
Onken, R. E., 377, 378, 379, 400
Ontario School Ability Examination, 318
Organic syndrome behavior, cerebral palsy, 165
Osol, A., 411
Osteoarthritis, 54, 55, 60-61; physiotherapy, drugs, X-ray therapy and vitamins used in treatment of, 62-63, 64
Ostfeld, A. M., 116

Palacios, M. H., 359
Pannus, *see* Granulation tissue within the arthritic joint
Paresis, *see* Hemiplegia
Parnicky, J. J., 377, 378, 379, 400
Patterson, C. H., 188
Pattison, H. A., 322
Penfield, W., 199
Pennsylvania Bi-Manual Worksample, 358, 397
"*Perception and Cerebral Palsy*," 186
Performance Scale for Adult Blind, 397
Perkins Institution, 357
Personality effects of physical disability on, *see* Psychological implications
Personality, premorbid, 94, 130, 212
Personality testing, *see* Psychological appraisal
Petrovich Pain Apperception Test, 35
Phantom limb and pain phenomena, related to prosthetic wear, 32
Phelps, W. M., 161
Phenylbutazone, 62
Pierce, J. R., 284
Pintner, R., 331, 332, 358
Pintner-Paterson Performance Scales, 317
Plastic surgery for facial disfigurement, 263, 265
Pragmatic aphasia, 203
Pregnelone methyl ester, 62
Princeton Rehabilitation Conference, 192
Printing in the palm, 395
Projective Sentence Completions, 397, 398
Prostate, cancer of, 235, 236, 242
Prostheses: ability to wear by amputee, 7, 36-37, 39; fitting of, 8; preprosthetic conditioning, 8-9; chronic medical difficulties, 7-8; pain related to, 13-14; cosmetic problem related to, 14-15; auditory problems con-

Prostheses (*Continued*)
nected with, 15; behavior related to, 21-24; phantom limb and pain phenomena related to, 32; in breast removal, 242; in facial disfigurement, 243-44
Psychic disturbances, *see* Psychological implications
Psychogenic, psychosomatic problems, *see* Psychological implications
Psychological appraisal, special considerations: in amputation, 28-34; in arthritis and rheumatism, 73-75; in cardiovascular disability, 101-9; in hemiplegia, 144-49; in cerebral palsy, 172-89; in language disorders, 215-24; in facial disfigurement, 273-75; in auditory disability, 307-21; in visual disability, 353-61; in deaf-blindness, 394-400; in severe chronic illness, 428-36
Psychological examination, *see* Psychological appraisal
Psychological implications of: amputation, 9-28; arthritis and rheumatism, 66-73; cardiovascular disability, 93-100; hemiplegia, 130-44; cerebral palsy, 165-72; language disorders, 210-15; cancer, 232-45; facial disfigurement, 267-73; auditory disability, 293-307; visual disability, 344-53; deaf-blindness, 380-94; severe chronic illness, 419-28
Psychological research, *see* Research
Psychological testing, *see* Psychological appraisal
"*Psychological Tests for Use with Blind Adults in Vocational Rehabilitation*," 396
Psychological treatment, *see* Rehabilitation; Psychological implications
"Psychoporia," 236
Psychosis, as a result of thyroid deficiency, 102
Psychosomatic Experience Blank, 35
Psychosomatic illness, Halliday's formula and criteria for, 68-69
"Psychosoteria," 236
Psychotherapy, *see* Rehabilitation; Psychological implications
Purdue Pegboard, 397
Purdue Research Foundation of Purdue University, 359

Quadrantial visual defects, 208-9
Quigley, S. P., 30

Radioactive iodine, 250
Rainer, J. D., 302
Randall Island Performance Tests, 317
Raskin, N.J., 368, 369-70
Rauwolfia serpentine, 102
Raven's Progressive Matrices, 175, 179-80, 186
Rehabilitation Center for Crippled Children, 192
Rehabilitation, special considerations in: amputation, 35-39; arthritis and rheumatism, 75-82; cardiovascular disability, 109-14; hemiplegia, 149-51; cerebral palsy, 189-91; language disorders, 224-27; cancer, 246-51; facial disfigurement, 275-78; auditory disability, 321-28; visual disability, 361-69; deaf-blindness, 401-5; severe chronic illness, 436-40
"*Rehabilitation Centers for Blind Persons*," 365
Rehabilitation Record, 418
Reputation Test, 361
Research, psychological in: amputation, 29-30, 33-35; arthritis and rheumatism, 66; cardiovascular disability, 115-18; hemiplegia, 151-53; cerebral palsy, 191-92; language disorders, 226, 227; cancer, 233-37, 240; facial disfigurement, 269-73; auditory disability, 328-33; visual disability, 344-53, 358, 369-71; deaf-blindness, 405-7; severe chronic illness, 440-43
Research Center of the New York School of Social Work, 348
Retinitis pigmentosa, 379, 380
Reynolds, W. E., 71
Rheumatic fever, arthritis due to, 57, 58
Rheumatic heart disease, 85, 88, 91, 105
Rheumatism, nonarticular, 57; psychogenic, 61, 67, 68, 69; muscular, 67; *see also* Arthritis and rheumatism
"Rheumatism and Arthritis," published by American Rheumatism Association, 52
"Rheumatism Review," 56-57
Rheumatoid arthritis, 54, 55, 57, 58, 59 (*fig.*), 61-62, 67; physiotherapy and

exercise, in treatment of, 61-62, 64; drugs used, in treatment of, 62, 64; psychological descriptions of patients with, 68; characteristic individual reaction to, 70
Rheumatoid (ankylosing) spondylitis, 54, 55, 57, 60
Rigidity type, cerebral palsy, 161
Roberts, D. W., 412
Roberts, J. R., 397
Roberts, L., 199
Rocheleau, C., 377
Rochester, University of, 345
Rogers, M., 30
Ronnei, E. C., 283, 305
Rorschach Test, 33; with hypertensives, 115-16; with cerebral palsied, 188; language disorders and, 222-23; auditory disability and, 316, 359
Rosen, S., 322
Rosenfeld, L. S., 419, 421
Rothschild, J., 383, 396
Rotter Incomplete Sentences Test, 361
Ruesch, J., 283
Rullo, F. R., 102
Rusk, H. A., 192, 421
Russ, J. D., 162, 163, 164

St. Joseph's School for the Deaf, 283
Sargent, H., 360, 371
Sargent Insight Test, 360, 361
Scar tissue, in amputation surgery and continuous prosthetic wear, 8
Scheerer, M., 200
Scheinberg, P., 101
Seboloff, H. R., 162, 163, 164
Secord Body Homonym Test, 35
Selective amputation, 2-4
Semantic aphasia, 203
Severe chronic illness: 410-43; general definitions of, 410-11; medical, social, and rehabilitation aspects of, 411-19; incidence of, 411-12; general hospitals compared to "chronic" disease hospitals, 413-14; medical and social definitions of, 415-16; "disability" compared to, 416-17; economic reasons for growth and expansion of rehabilitation in, 417-19; psychological implications of, 419-28; specific psychological reactions to especially severe disability: *negative* reactions, 422-23, *neutralizing* responses, 423, *positive* reactions, 423-24; story of Roy Campanella, illustrative of severe personal problems of, 424-28; special considerations in psychological appraisal of, 428-36; special considerations in psychological treatment and rehabilitation of, 436-40; research and, 440-43
Sherlock, S., 102
Sherwood, K. K., 70
Shontz, F. C., 422, 433, 434
Short, C. L., 71
Shurrager, H., 397
Sigerist, H. E., 51
Sign language, 307
Silver, A. G., 269
Silverman, S. R., 282, 286, 287, 288, 289, 291, 321, 322
Similarities subtests for deaf-blind, 396
Smithdas, R. J., 403
Snellen, H., 342
Solomon, C. J., 69
Solomon, P., 294
Solomon, R. Z., 69
Sommers, V. S., 349, 350, 367-68
Sound Association Technique, 359
Sound Test, 359-60
Spastic type, cerebral palsy, 160
Spaulding, P. J., 344, 354, 355, 357, 368
Speech impairments associated with auditory deficit, 279-333 *passim*, 376-407 *passim*
Speech impairments associated with brain damage, 125-54 *passim*, 159-92 *passim*, 197-228 *passim*
Speechreading, 306
Sphygmomanometer, 90
Stanford Achievement Test, 358
Stanford-Binet Intelligence Scale, Revised, 175, 176, 183-84, 185 (*table*), 354, 358, 397
Stevens, S. S., 284
Strauss, A. A., 168, 314
Streng, A., 323
"Stroke," *see* Cerebrovascular disease; Hemiplegia; Language disorders
Stubbins, J., 429
Sutherland, A. M., 246
Symonds, C., 102
Sympathectomy, 91
Synovial capsule, 57-58, 59 (*fig.*)
Synovial joint, 57-58, 59 (*fig.*)

Synovial membrane, hypertrophy of, 58; osteoarthritis and, 60
Syntactic aphasia, 203

Taaffe, G., 306
"Tautaphone," 359
Taylor, E. M., 318
"Team approach," *see* Psychological appraisal; Rehabilitation
Tellatouch, 395
Terman-Merrill Revised Stanford-Binet Scale, 356
Texas, University of, *see* University of Texas
Thaler, M., 115
Thematic Apperception Test, 33; in connection with: cerebral palsy, 188, language disorders, 222, visual disability, 359
Thomas, C. B., 116
Three-Dimensional Apperception Test, 398
Tiffin, J., 397
Tinnitus (head noises), 298, 332
Tobis, J. S., 413, 434, 439
Tolan, T., 284
Transmissive agnosias, 200
Transmissive apraxias, 200
Transmissive dysarthria, 208
Traumatic amputation, 2-4
Travis, L. E., 306
Tremor type, cerebral palsy, 161
Trumbull, R., 294
Trunnell, J. B., 234, 235, 236
Tuddenham, R. D., 350, 361
Twitchell-Allen, D., 398

Underberg, R. P., 345
United Cerebral Palsy Association, 227
United Cerebral Palsy Rehabilitation Center, Miami, Fla., 190
U.S. Dept. of Health, Education and Welfare, 52, 86, 225, 405
U.S. National Health Survey, 52-53, 86, 87, 341-42
U.S. National Office of Vital Statistics, 86-87
U.S. Office of Vocational Rehabilitation, 53, 365, 367
U.S. Veterans Administration, 104, 343, 346
University of Chicago Medical Clinics, 354, 357, 368
University of Rochester, 345
University of Texas, 352; M.D. Anderson Hospital, 234, 236, 239

Vasomotor changes, due to hemiplegia, 126
Verbal apraxia, 204, 220
Verrillo, R. T., 345
Veterans Administration Hospital, Long Beach, Calif., 233
Vineland Social Maturity Scale, 175, 176, 181-82, 318, 353, 354
Visual agnosias, 203-4, 221
Visual disability: 341-71; incidence and classifications of, 341-44; psychological implications of, 344-53; real limitations, 346-51; attitudes of sighted people toward blindness, 349-57; auditory and tactile abilities, 351-53; obstacle perception, 352-53; psychological appraisal, 353-61; rehabilitation and therapy, 361-69; research, 344-53, 358, 369-71
Vocational adjustment problems: of rheumatic or arthritic individuals, 72-73, 80-82; of cardiacs, 98-100; of hemiplegics, 143-44; of deaf-blind, 402-3
Vocational rehabilitation, *see* Rehabilitation; Psychological implications

Wallace, H. M., 159
Wallen, N. E., 186
Warfield, F., 302
Waterhouse, E. J., 380
Watson, L. A., 284
Watson, S., 397
Wechsler, I. S., 209
Wechsler Intelligence Scales: with cerebral palsied, 184; with hemiplegics, 219-20; in auditory disability, 316; in visual disability, 356; in deaf-blindness, 396, 397
Weinstein, E. A., 428
Weir, D., 418
Weiss, E., 104, 111
Weissman, S., 270, 271
Welling, D. M., 299
Welles, H. H., 332
Wepman, J. M., 225
West, P. M., 233-34
Wever, E. G., 284

Wexler, D., 294
Wheeler, J. I., Jr., 236, 237
White House Conference on Child Health and Protection, 281
Whiteman, M., 348
Whitehurst, M. W., 307
Wilmer, H. A., 359
WISC Verbal Scale, 357-58, 411
Wood, N., 314
Worchel, P., 352, 371
Work and the cardiac, 113-15
Work Evaluation Unit Team, 102, 110-11, 115
Work, W. P., 283
World Council for the Welfare of the Blind, 405, 406
Wright, B. A., 416, 418, 428, 439
Wright, B. C., 312

Zeckel, A., 302, 303
Zimmerman, B., 70
Zubin, J., 314